W9-BYI-316

03-05
ACS

Raymond Colson

ScienceWise

SUCCEEDING IN TODAY'S WORLD

Mirella Agusta-Palmisano
Sarah Barrett
Alan Davis
Deborah Fairchild
Kandis Thompson

IRWIN PUBLISHING
Toronto, Canada

Copyright © 2003 by Irwin Publishing

National Library of Canada Cataloguing in Publication

Main entry under title:
ScienceWise: succeeding in today's world / Mirella Agusta-Palmisano... [et al.].
Includes index.
For use in grade 11.
ISBN 0-7725-2926-4

1. Science. I. Agusta-Palmisano, Mirella II. Title: ScienceWise

Q161.2.S39 2003 500 C2003-901838-2

This book is protected by copyright. No part of it may be reproduced or transmitted in any form or by any means, electronic or mechanical, including photocopy, recording or any information storage and retrieval system now known or to be invented, without the prior written permission of the publisher, except by a reviewer who wishes to quote brief passages in connection with a review written for inclusion in a magazine, newspaper, or broadcast.

Any request for photocopying, recording, taping, or for storing of informational and retrieval systems, of any parts of this book should be directed in writing to CANCOPY (Canadian Reprography Collective), One Yonge Street, Suite 1900, Toronto, ON M5E 1E5.

We acknowledge for their financial support of our publishing program, the Canada Council, the Ontario Arts Council, and the Government of Canada through the Book Publishing Industry Development Program (BPIDP).

Project Developer: Doug Panasis
Senior Developmental Editors: Jackie Dulson, Lee Geller
Editorial: Naomi Pascoe, Andrea Byrne, Simone Heck
Production Editor: Patricia Ciardullo
Cover and Text Design: Dave Murphy/ArtPlus Ltd.
Page Layout: ArtPlus Ltd.
Illustration: ArtPlus Ltd., Renné Benoit
ArtPlus Ltd. Production Co-ordinator: Dana Lloyd
Photo Research: Lisa Brant
Photo Shoot Co-ordinators: Trent Photographics, Jackie Dulson, Joe Nizio
Indexer: May Look

Published by
Nelson
1120 Birchmount Road,
Scarborough, Ontario
M1K 5G4

Printed and bound in Canada
2 3 4 5 06 05 04 03

Acknowledgements

The authors and publisher would like to thank the following reviewers for their insights and suggestions:

Dave Arthur, former Teacher,
Waterloo Region District School Board

Kyn Barker, Consultant,
York Region District School Board

John Bottos, Teacher,
Toronto Catholic District School Board

Robert Brown, Teacher,
Toronto Catholic District School Board

Robert Callott, former Head of Science,
York Region District School Board

Pat Durst, Bias Reviewer, formerly
York Region District School Board

Ann Harrison, Teacher,
Niagara Catholic District School Board

Elizabeth Jarman, Teacher,
Simcoe County District School Board

Domenica Leone, Teacher,
Hamilton-Wentworth Catholic District School Board

Igor Nowikow, Teacher,
York Region District School Board

The authors and publisher would like to thank the staff and students at Pickering High School, and Loyola Catholic Secondary School, for use of their facilities and resources in the production of this book.

Table of Contents

UNIT 2 *Electric Circuits* 69

CHAPTER 3: *Electricity – What Is It?* 70

CHAPTER 4: *Practical Electricity* 102

UNIT 3 *Micro-organisms* 141

CHAPTER 5: *Characteristics of Micro-organisms* 142

CHAPTER 6: *Micro-organisms and Human Life* 182

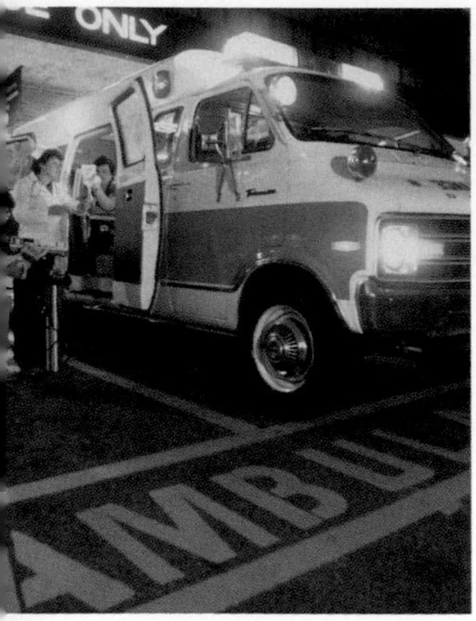

UNIT 4 *The Immune System and Human Health* 217

UNIT 5 *Human Impact on the Environment* 281

UNIT 1

Materials and Safety

CHAPTER 1

Safety and You

This chapter will look at safety symbols, the hazards associated with using certain substances, and the laws in Canada that apply to the safe use of chemical substances. You will also learn how to handle, store, and dispose of different chemicals. Look at Figure 1.1. What safety labels are on a can of hairspray? Why do you think they are there? Why should you not walk on the lawn for 72 hours? Do you think this boy is wearing enough safety protection? Why or why not?

FIGURE 1.1

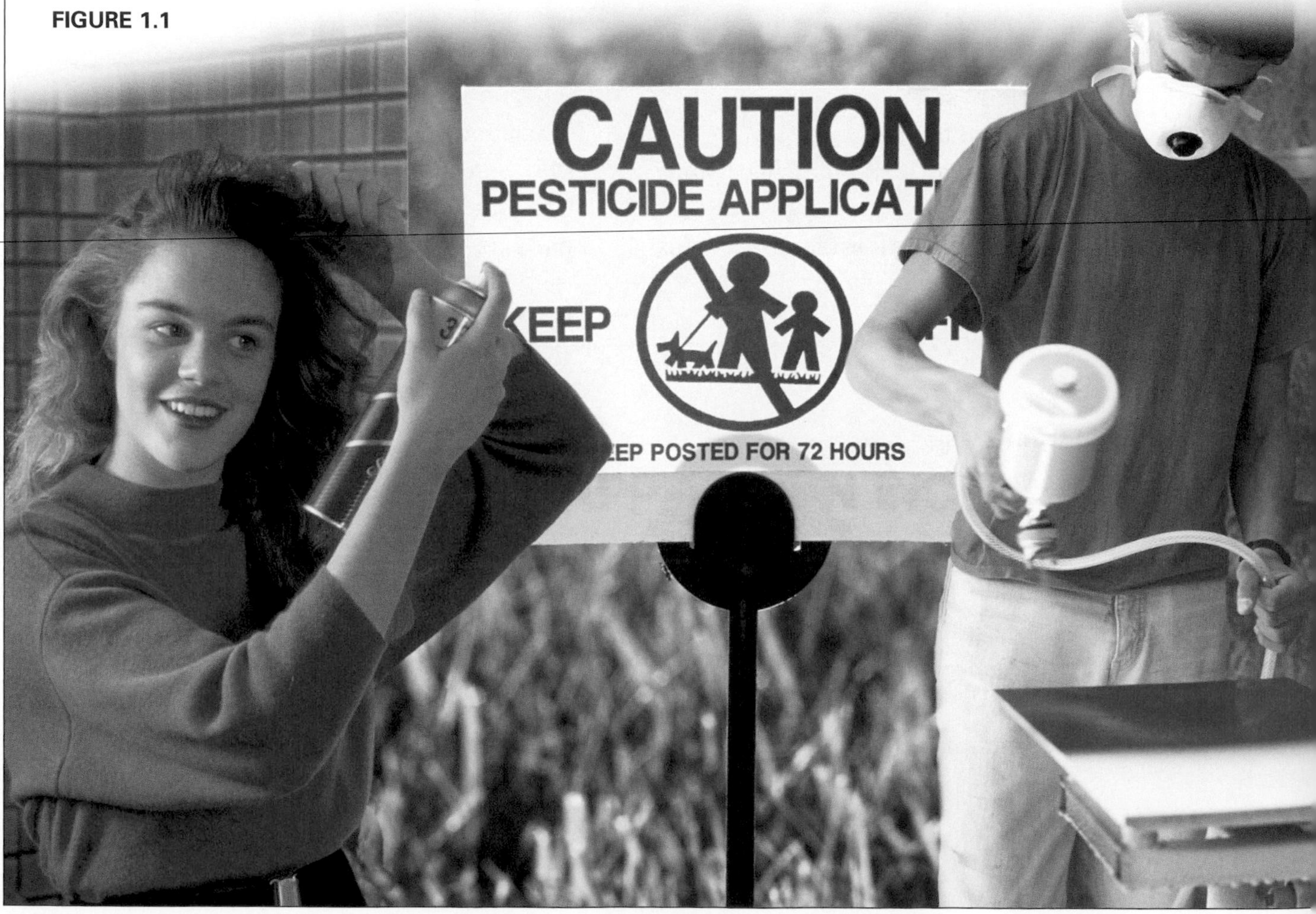

What You Will Learn

After completing this chapter, you will be able to:

- Identify and explain the WHMIS and the HHPS symbols (1.1)
- Identify and explain how to safely store chemical substances (1.2)
- Describe factors that can increase the dangers of chemicals that burn easily (1.2)
- Identify safe handling, storage, and disposal methods of various hazardous materials (1.2)
- Identify and analyze the different aspects of fire safety (1.1, Case Study, 1.2)
- Describe how chemical substances enter the human body (1.3)
- Apply general safety procedures to the workplace and the home (1.1, 1.2, 1.3)
- Explain the terms learned in this chapter (1.1, 1.2, 1.3)
- Explain why there are safety procedures to follow at school, at home, and in the workplace (1.3)

What You Will Do

- Categorize hazardous chemicals (1.1)
- Prepare WHMIS safety cards (Activity 1A)
- Investigate safe handling, storage, and disposal of chemical substances (1.2)
- Locate, select, and analyze information on the disposal of chemicals (1.2)
- Use graphic organizers to classify ideas (1.1, 1.2, 1.3)
- Identify jobs related to this chapter (1.1, 1.2, 1.3)

Words to Know

absorption
acid cabinet
acute
aqueous solution
auto-ignition temperature
Building Code
Canadian Hazardous Products Act
chronic
dry chemicals
exposure
Fire Code
flammable cabinet
flashpoint
fume hood
HHPS (Household Hazardous Product Symbols)
ingestion
inhalation
MSDS (Material Safety Data Sheets)
Occupational Health and Safety Act
parts per million (ppm)
toxicity
WHMIS (Workplace Hazardous Materials Information System)

A puzzle piece indicates knowledge or a skill that you will need for your project, Designing a Safety Board Game, at the end of Unit 1.

1.1 Safety at Work and at Home

In Canada, there are laws, or legislation, to keep Canadians safe at work and at home. Being able to identify safety symbols and understand labels can help you create a better and safer environment. In this section, you will learn about the Workplace Hazardous Materials Information System (WHMIS) and Household Hazardous Product Symbols (HHPS).

Safety Laws

It is important to be aware that there are safety laws that must be followed in every workplace.

Occupational Health and Safety Act: These laws allow you to be safe in the workplace. This is where you would find WHMIS.

Fire Code: These laws contain fire safety standards for equipment, systems, buildings, structures, and lands. These codes are developed to reduce the risk of fires.

Building Code: These laws allow for the safe construction of buildings.

Canadian Hazardous Products Act: Another important safety law. It requires that all consumer products containing hazardous chemicals are properly identified. They are identified by the shape and colour of the symbol and the picture inside the symbol. These symbols, as shown in Figure 1.2, are known as **Household Hazardous Product Symbols (HHPS)**.

Household Hazardous Product Symbols

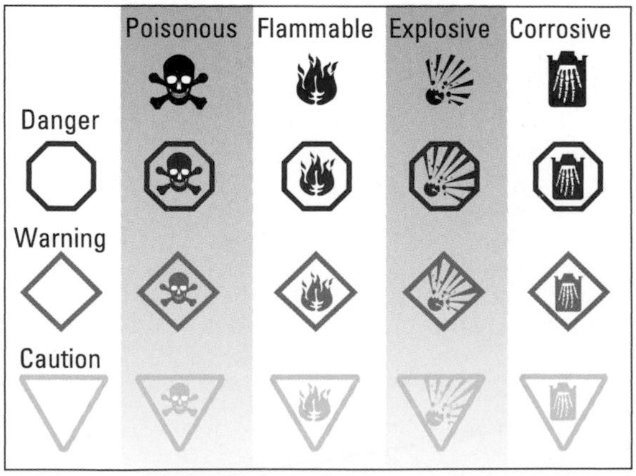

FIGURE 1.2 Identify 2 consumer products that have any of these symbols.

WHMIS Legislation

WHMIS is Canada's standard method of communicating information about hazardous materials. It was developed to deal with hazardous, or potentially harmful, chemicals. It is the law. WHMIS legislates a standard way of labelling chemicals for all Canadian workplaces. It is important for people working with chemicals to read and understand the labels of the chemicals they use to help prevent injuries, fires, or explosions caused by the unsafe use of chemicals. Also, workers must know which chemicals require special handling and disposal procedures.

WHMIS informs workers about the chemicals they may use in 3 ways:

- Worker education
- Labels, in both English and French
- Material Safety Data Sheets (MSDS)

How WHMIS Works

FIGURE 1.3 Information travelling from the supplier to the worker.

WHMIS Education

Workers who handle chemicals must complete an education program. This program provides information and instruction on the use of chemicals and the procedure to follow in case of an emergency.

All workers, part- or full-time, have the right to receive WHMIS training. If you are unsure about something, ask!

WHMIS Labels

Look at Figure 1.4 on page 6. It identifies the information that must appear on WHMIS labels.

WHMIS labels also have hazard symbols. Hazard symbols are standardized pictures used to identify any risks involved with using the chemical. Figure 1.5 on page 7 identifies 8 WHMIS symbols and explains the proper method of handling chemicals labelled with each symbol.

A WHMIS Supplier Label

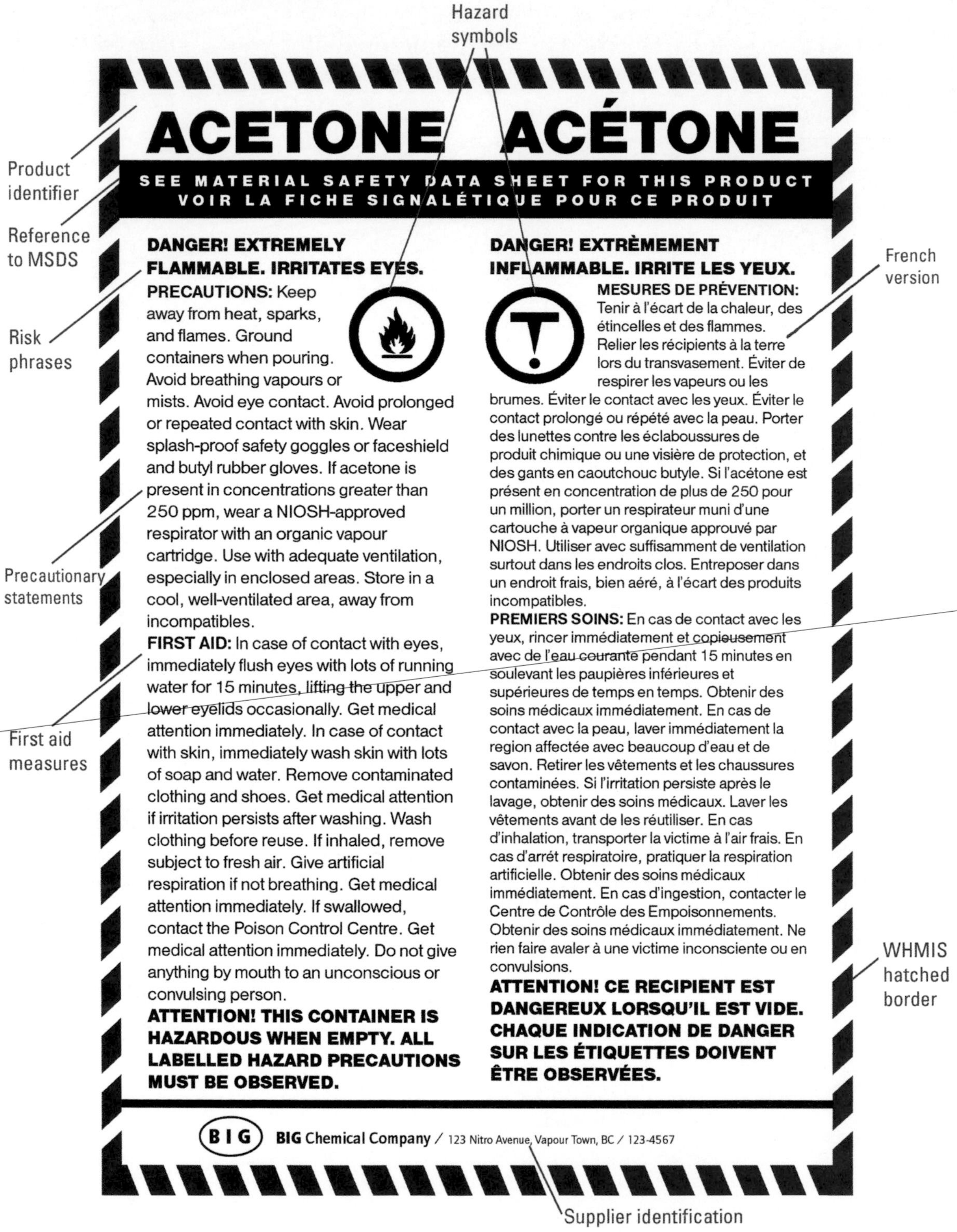

Hazard symbols
ACETONE ACÉTONE
SEE MATERIAL SAFETY DATA SHEET FOR THIS PRODUCT
VOIR LA FICHE SIGNALÉTIQUE POUR CE PRODUIT
DANGER! EXTREMELY FLAMMABLE. IRRITATES EYES.
PRECAUTIONS: Keep away from heat, sparks, and flames. Ground containers when pouring. Avoid breathing vapours or mists. Avoid eye contact. Avoid prolonged or repeated contact with skin. Wear splash-proof safety goggles or faceshield and butyl rubber gloves. If acetone is present in concentrations greater than 250 ppm, wear a NIOSH-approved respirator with an organic vapour cartridge. Use with adequate ventilation, especially in enclosed areas. Store in a cool, well-ventilated area, away from incompatibles.
FIRST AID: In case of contact with eyes, immediately flush eyes with lots of running water for 15 minutes, lifting the upper and lower eyelids occasionally. Get medical attention immediately. In case of contact with skin, immediately wash skin with lots of soap and water. Remove contaminated clothing and shoes. Get medical attention if irritation persists after washing. Wash clothing before reuse. If inhaled, remove subject to fresh air. Give artificial respiration if not breathing. Get medical attention immediately. If swallowed, contact the Poison Control Centre. Get medical attention immediately. Do not give anything by mouth to an unconscious or convulsing person.
ATTENTION! THIS CONTAINER IS HAZARDOUS WHEN EMPTY. ALL LABELLED HAZARD PRECAUTIONS MUST BE OBSERVED.
DANGER! EXTRÈMEMENT INFLAMMABLE. IRRITE LES YEUX.
MESURES DE PRÉVENTION: Tenir à l'écart de la chaleur, des étincelles et des flammes. Relier les récipients à la terre lors du transvasement. Éviter de respirer les vapeurs ou les brumes. Éviter le contact avec les yeux. Éviter le contact prolongé ou répété avec la peau. Porter des lunettes contre les éclaboussures de produit chimique ou une visière de protection, et des gants en caoutchouc butyle. Si l'acétone est présent en concentration de plus de 250 pour un million, porter un respirateur muni d'une cartouche à vapeur organique approuvé par NIOSH. Utiliser avec suffisamment de ventilation surtout dans les endroits clos. Entreposer dans un endroit frais, bien aéré, à l'écart des produits incompatibles.
PREMIERS SOINS: En cas de contact avec les yeux, rincer immédiatement et copieusement avec de l'eau courante pendant 15 minutes en soulevant les paupières inférieures et supérieures de temps en temps. Obtenir des soins médicaux immédiatement. En cas de contact avec la peau, laver immédiatement la region affectée avec beaucoup d'eau et de savon. Retirer les vêtements et les chaussures contaminées. Si l'irritation persiste après le lavage, obtenir des soins médicaux. Laver les vêtements avant de les réutiliser. En cas d'inhalation, transporter la victime à l'air frais. En cas d'arrêt respiratoire, pratiquer la respiration artificielle. Obtenir des soins médicaux immédiatement. En cas d'ingestion, contacter le Centre de Contrôle des Empoisonnements. Obtenir des soins médicaux immédiatement. Ne rien faire avaler à une victime inconsciente ou en convulsions.
ATTENTION! CE RECIPIENT EST DANGEREUX LORSQU'IL EST VIDE. CHAQUE INDICATION DE DANGER SUR LES ÉTIQUETTES DOIVENT ÊTRE OBSERVÉES.
BIG
BIG Chemical Company / 123 Nitro Avenue, Vapour Town, BC / 123-4567
Product identifier
Reference to MSDS
Risk phrases
Precautionary statements
First aid measures
French version
WHMIS hatched border
Supplier identification

FIGURE 1.4 WHMIS labels are required to have the information shown above.

Table of Workplace Hazardous Materials Information System (WHMIS)

The symbol represents:	It means that the material...	And that you should...	Example
Class A Compressed Gas 	May explode near heat or fire.	Handle with care by keeping away from fires; store in a safe area.	Some aerosol spray cans
Class B Flammable and Combustible Materials 	May burst into flames.	Keep material away from heat source and other combustible material.	Gasoline
Class C Oxidizing Materials 	May react violently or cause an explosion when it comes into contact with combustibles like gasoline.	Store away from combustibles.	Bleach
Class D, Division 1 Poisonous and Infectious Materials Causing Immediate and Serious Toxic Effects 	May cause death if taken orally (for example, eaten or drunk) or inhaled, and can be absorbed through skin.	Work in a well-ventilated area and wear breathing protection.	Cyanide
Class D, Division 2 Toxic Materials Causing Other Toxic Effects 	May cause death, birth defects, cancer, or sterility.	Work in a well-ventilated area and wear protection for hands, body, face, and eyes.	Lead
Class D, Division 3 Biohazardous Infectious Material 	May cause an infectious disease or other reaction.	Work in special biological areas with people who are trained in handling this material.	HIV (AIDS)
Class E Corrosive Materials 	May cause eye and skin irritation; causes burns if exposed for long periods.	Work in a well-ventilated area and wear protection for hands, body, face, and eyes.	Battery acid
Class F Dangerously Reactive Materials 	May cause unexpected reactions when exposed to water, electric shock, or heat.	Store in proper containers and handle with care.	Nitroglycerine (used in dynamite)

FIGURE 1.5 Where might you find these types of symbols?

You may use WHMIS symbols and MSDS in your board game.

WHMIS Material Safety Data Sheets

Looking only at WHMIS labels is not enough to know all the information about chemical products. Therefore, all products in the workplace come with WHMIS labels and **Material Safety Data Sheets (MSDS)**. The MSDS provide detailed information about the chemical product.

MSDS Tips

1. *MSDS must be readily available to the worker at the work site. (MSDS are usually found in a clearly labelled binder.)*
2. *MSDS must be read before you work with any chemical product.*
3. *MSDS must be updated at least every 3 years.*

Example of a Material Safety Data Sheet

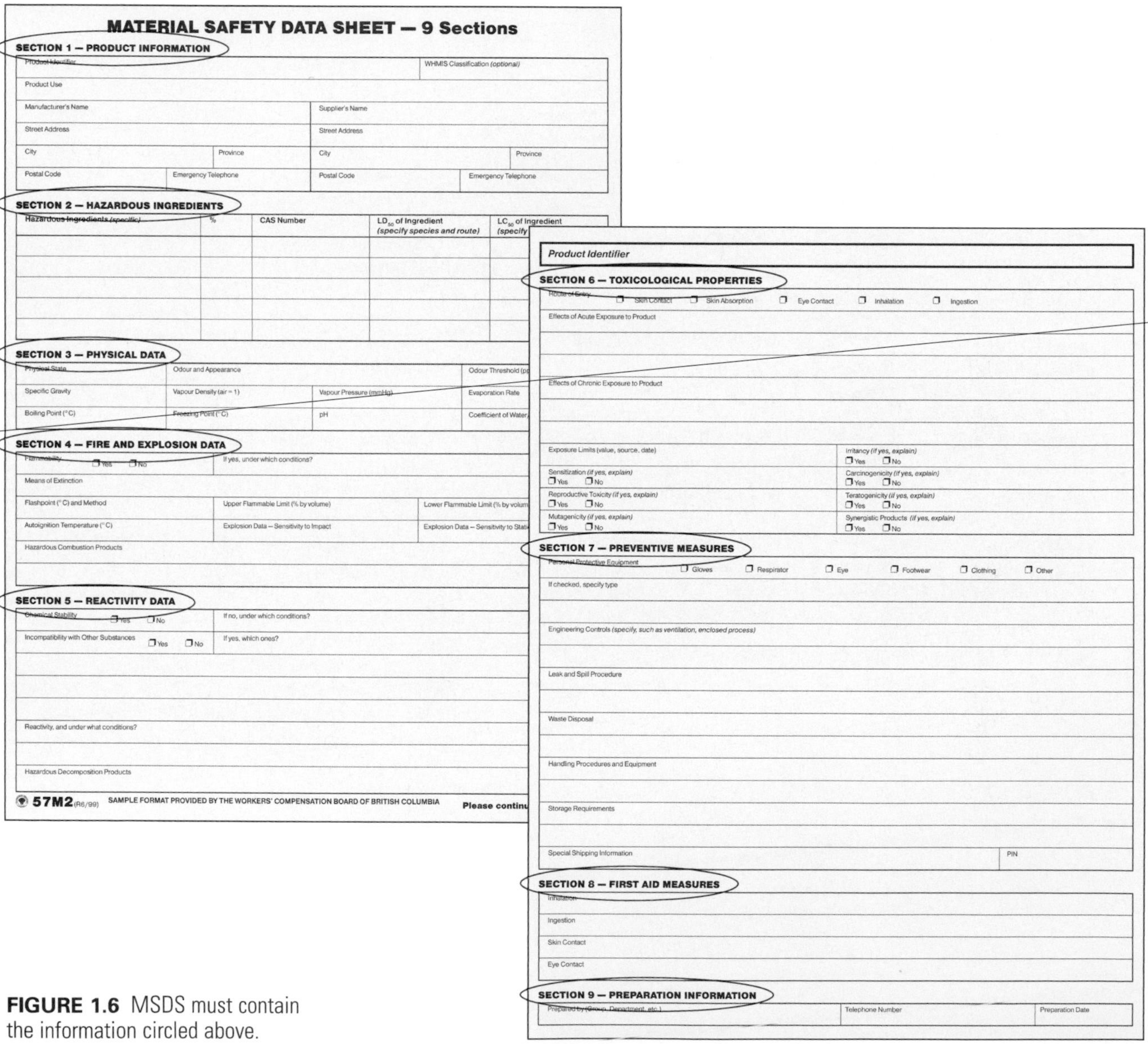

MATERIAL SAFETY DATA SHEET — 9 Sections

SECTION 1 — PRODUCT INFORMATION
Product Identifier | WHMIS Classification (optional)
Product Use
Manufacturer's Name | Supplier's Name
Street Address | Street Address
City | Province | City | Province
Postal Code | Emergency Telephone | Postal Code | Emergency Telephone

SECTION 2 — HAZARDOUS INGREDIENTS
Hazardous Ingredients (specific) | % | CAS Number | LD_{50} of Ingredient (specify species and route) | LC_{50} of Ingredient (specify

SECTION 3 — PHYSICAL DATA
Physical State | Odour and Appearance | Odour Threshold (pp
Specific Gravity | Vapour Density (air = 1) | Vapour Pressure (mmHg) | Evaporation Rate
Boiling Point (°C) | Freezing Point (°C) | pH | Coefficient of Water/

SECTION 4 — FIRE AND EXPLOSION DATA
Flammability ❐ Yes ❐ No | If yes, under which conditions?
Means of Extinction
Flashpoint (°C) and Method | Upper Flammable Limit (% by volume) | Lower Flammable Limit (% by volum
Autoignition Temperature (°C) | Explosion Data — Sensitivity to Impact | Explosion Data — Sensitivity to Stati
Hazardous Combustion Products

SECTION 5 — REACTIVITY DATA
Chemical Stability ❐ Yes ❐ No | If no, under which conditions?
Incompatibility with Other Substances ❐ Yes ❐ No | If yes, which ones?
Reactivity, and under what conditions?
Hazardous Decomposition Products

57M2 (R6/99) SAMPLE FORMAT PROVIDED BY THE WORKERS' COMPENSATION BOARD OF BRITISH COLUMBIA — Please continu

Product Identifier

SECTION 6 — TOXICOLOGICAL PROPERTIES
Route of Entry ❐ Skin Contact ❐ Skin Absorption ❐ Eye Contact ❐ Inhalation ❐ Ingestion
Effects of Acute Exposure to Product
Effects of Chronic Exposure to Product
Exposure Limits (value, source, date) | Irritancy (if yes, explain) ❐ Yes ❐ No
Sensitization (if yes, explain) ❐ Yes ❐ No | Carcinogenicity (if yes, explain) ❐ Yes ❐ No
Reproductive Toxicity (if yes, explain) ❐ Yes ❐ No | Teratogenicity (if yes, explain) ❐ Yes ❐ No
Mutagenicity (if yes, explain) ❐ Yes ❐ No | Synergistic Products (if yes, explain) ❐ Yes ❐ No

SECTION 7 — PREVENTIVE MEASURES
Personal Protective Equipment ❐ Gloves ❐ Respirator ❐ Eye ❐ Footwear ❐ Clothing ❐ Other
If checked, specify type
Engineering Controls (specify, such as ventilation, enclosed process)
Leak and Spill Procedure
Waste Disposal
Handling Procedures and Equipment
Storage Requirements
Special Shipping Information | PIN

SECTION 8 — FIRST AID MEASURES
Inhalation
Ingestion
Skin Contact
Eye Contact

SECTION 9 — PREPARATION INFORMATION
Prepared by (Group, Department, etc.) | Telephone Number | Preparation Date

FIGURE 1.6 MSDS must contain the information circled above.

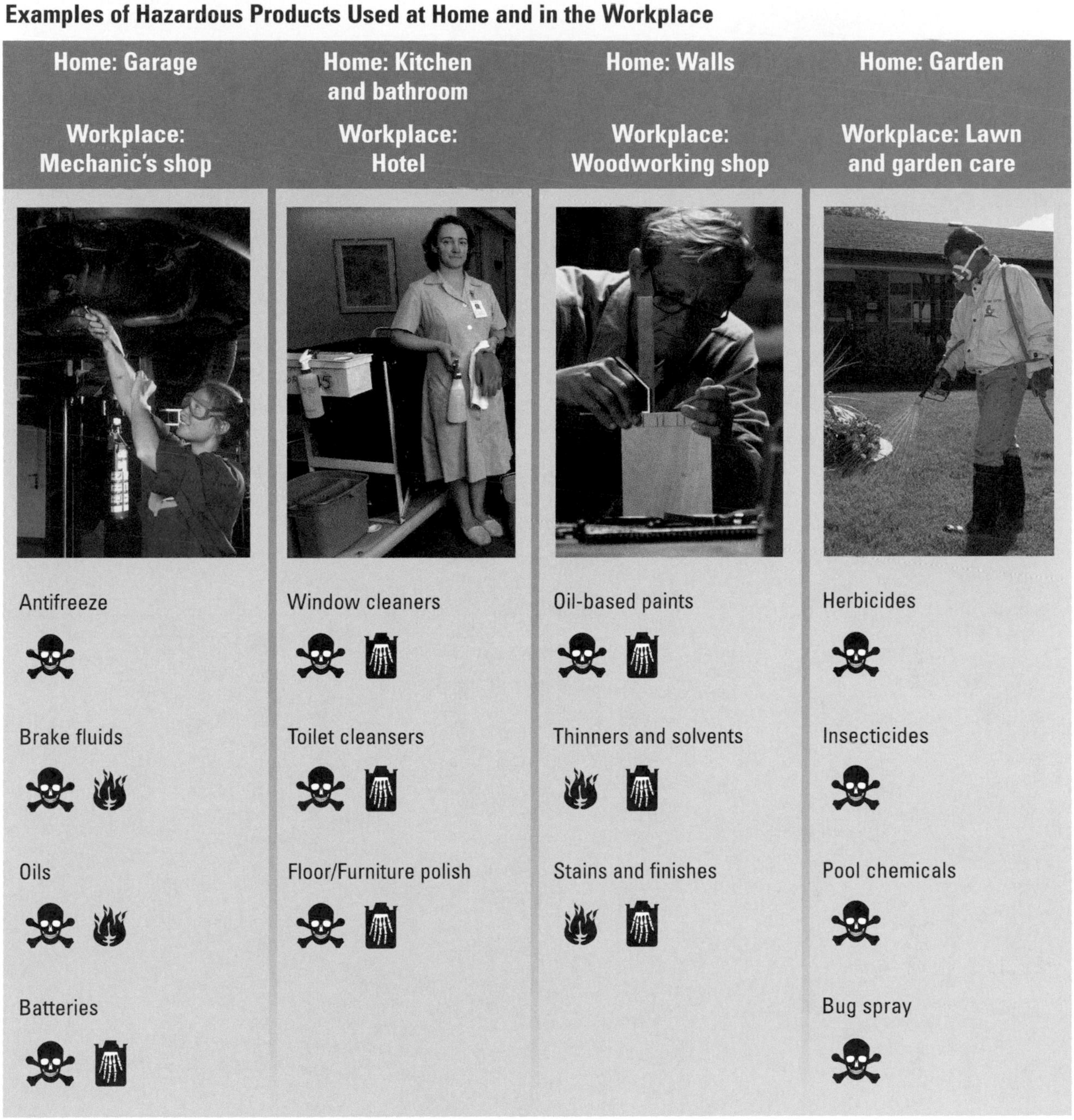
Examples of Hazardous Products Used at Home and in the Workplace
Home: Garage
Workplace: Mechanic's shop
Home: Kitchen and bathroom
Workplace: Hotel
Home: Walls
Workplace: Woodworking shop
Home: Garden
Workplace: Lawn and garden care
Antifreeze
Brake fluids
Oils
Batteries
Window cleaners
Toilet cleansers
Floor/Furniture polish
Oil-based paints
Thinners and solvents
Stains and finishes
Herbicides
Insecticides
Pool chemicals
Bug spray

FIGURE 1.7 Can you identify WHMIS symbols that correspond to each of the products mentioned?

Review and Apply

1. Use Figure 1.8 to answer the following:
   a) Identify and explain each hazardous product symbol.
   b) What is the product name?
2. Use Figure 1.9 to answer the following:
   a) What personal protective equipment is required to use this product?
   b) What material should you avoid when using this product?
   c) How should you store this product?

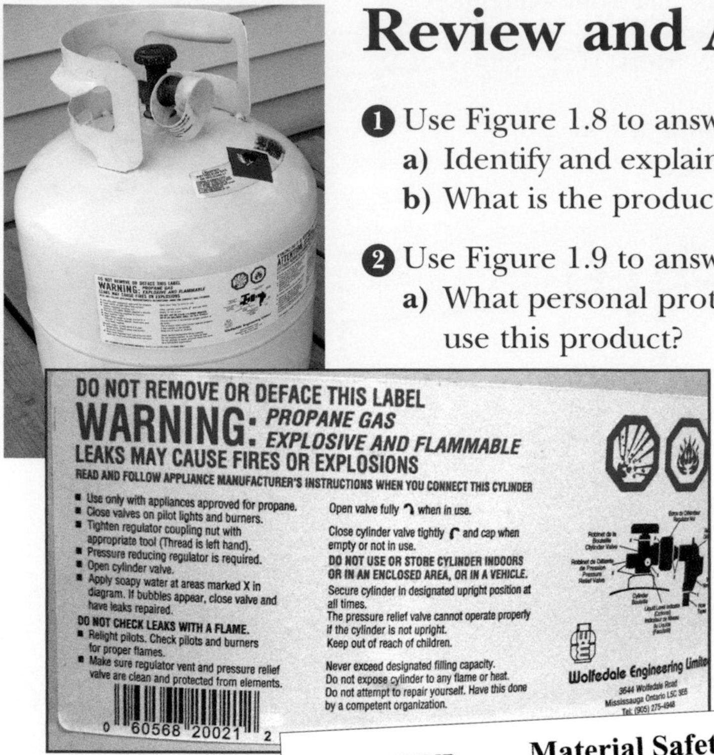

FIGURE 1.8

PRAXAIR — **Material Safety Data Sheet** — E-4646-E

I. PRODUCT INFORMATION

PRODUCT IDENTIFIER:	Propane	SUPPLIER/ MANUFACTURER NAME & ADDRESS:	Praxair Canada Inc. 1 City Centre Drive Suite 1200 Mississauga, Ontario L5B 1M2
TRADE NAME:	Liquefied Petroleum Gas	PHONE NO:	(905) 803-1600
		FAX NO:	(905) 803-1690
CHEMICAL IDENTITY:	Propane	EMERGENCY PHONE NO:	1-800-363-0042
SYNONYMS:	Dimethylmethane, PropylHydride, Propyldihydride		
FORMULA:	C3H8	PRODUCT USE:	Many
CHEMICAL FAMILY:	Alkane	WHMIS CLASS:	A, B1
SHIPPING NAME:	Liquefied Petroleum Gas,‡ or Propane	PRODUCT IDENTIFICATION NUMBER: UN 1075 UN 1978	TDG CLASSIFICATION: 2.1

V. REACTIVITY DATA

STABILITY: UNSTABLE ( ) STABLE (x)

CONDITIONS OF CHEMICAL INSTABILITY:
See Section VII.

INCOMPATIBLE PRODUCTS:
Oxidizing agents, chlorine dioxide.

HAZARDOUS DECOMPOSITION PRODUCTS:
Thermal decomposition or burning may produce CO/CO2.

HAZARDOUS POLYMERIZATION:
MAY OCCUR ( ) WILL NOT OCCUR (x)

CONDITIONS OF REACTIVITY:
None

VII. PREVENTIVE MEASURES

PERSONAL PROTECTION:

RESPIRATORY PROTECTION:
Select in accordance with the provincial regulations or guidelines. Selection should also be based on the current CSA standards Z94.4, "Selection, care and use of respirators". Respirators should be approved by NIOSH and MSHA.

PROTECTIVE GLOVES: Preferred for cylinder handling and to prevent liquid exposure.

EYE PROTECTION: Select in accordance with the current CSA Standard Z94.3, "Industrial eye and face protection", and any provincial regulations or guidelines.

OTHERS: Metatarsal shoes for cylinder handling. Protective clothing where needed. Select in accordance with the current CSA standard Z195, "Protective foot wear", and any provincial regulations or guidelines.

SPECIAL HANDLING AND STORAGE REQUIREMENTS:
DANGER: Flammable, liquefied gas under pressure. Use piping and equipment adequately designed to withstand pressures to be encountered. May form explosive mixtures with air. Ground all equipment. Only use spark proof tools and explosion-proof equipment. Keep away from heat, sparks and open flames. Store and use with adequate ventilation at all times. Use only in a closed system. Close valve when not in use and when empty. Keep away from oxidizing agents.

FIGURE 1.9 Part of MSDS for propane.

3. Join with another student and brainstorm. In the workplace, WHMIS is used. At home, HHPS are used. Why do you think there are 2 systems to identify safety hazards?

4. Look at Figure 1.10.
   a) Identify each safety symbol.
   b) List 5 household products that display the safety symbols shown here. Make sure to include products that have at least 2 or 3 safety symbols on them.
   c) How do you think these warnings affect the use of products?

FIGURE 1.10

5. Safety laws are made to protect both workers and employers. State 3 ways that safety laws are applied in the workplace. Compare your answers with other classmates. What would you change, if anything?

6. In a graphic organizer, organize the concepts you have learned about in this section.

7. **Identifying WHMIS labels**

Working in pairs, obtain from your teacher 2 or 3 chemical bottles that display WHMIS labels. Brainstorm the answers to the following questions:

a) What does each chemical bottle have in common?
b) What is the importance of chemicals having these types of labels?
c) Why have hazard symbols on each bottle?

Safety on the Job

In 1999, 16 young workers died in Ontario workplaces. Every day, more than 40 young workers are injured or hurt on the job.

Working in Ontario

You may have a job in a fast-food restaurant or a store. You may be working as a cleaner or on a factory assembly line. Every job has its share of hazards. Some hazards can cause immediate injury. You could slip and fall on a wet or greasy floor. You could be burned by a hot grill or from cleaning products that contain sulphuric acid or ammonia. Other injuries are not so immediate. You may develop an allergic reaction or a rash from working with certain products.

What Can You Do?

You have 3 basic health and safety rights:

1. You have the right to know if your workplace uses unsafe materials, dangerous machinery, or anything else that can make you sick or cause injury while you are working.
2. You have the right to get involved in health and safety inspections of your workplace, and to receive proper training.
3. You have the right to refuse to work if you think what you are doing is unsafe.

Use Figure 1.11 to choose 2 jobs in which the workers may encounter hazards. List 3 hazards.

FIGURE 1.11

Surf the Web

You now know what your rights are. But what are your responsibilities as a worker? Visit **www.science.nelson.com** and follow the links for ScienceWise Grade 11, Chapter 1, Section 1.1 to find out.

Making WHMIS Safety Cards

ACTIVITY 1A

In this activity, you will prepare WHMIS Safety Cards using WHMIS labels and MSDS.

What You Will Need

- index cards
- small box or container in which to keep index cards
- pen or pencil
- MSDS for copper, aluminum, zinc, nickel, magnesium, iron filings, and hydrochloric acid

What You Will Do

1. At the top centre of each index card, write the name of the chemical.
2. Place the following headings on each index card: Hazardous Product Symbols, Physical Data, Personal Protective Equipment, First Aid, and Safety Diagram.

Name of Chemical
Hazardous Product Symbols:
Physical Data:
Personal Protective Equipment:
First Aid:
Safety Diagram:

FIGURE 1.12 An example of a safety card.

3. Look up the MSDS for copper. Under the heading Hazardous Product Symbols, draw the WHMIS hazardous symbols for the chemical.
4. Under the heading Physical Data, list the appearance of the chemical.
5. Under the heading Personal Protective Equipment, list all the safety equipment needed when using the chemical.
6. Under the heading First Aid, list the treatment.
7. Under the heading Safety Diagram, draw a picture of yourself using this chemical safely.
8. Repeat steps 1 through 7 with the remaining chemicals: aluminum, zinc, nickel, magnesium, iron filings, and hydrochloric acid.
9. Visit the custodian's office at school. Ask to look at 2 consumer products and their MSDS. Make safety cards for these products.
10. Place all safety cards in alphabetical order in a small box or container.

What Did You Find Out?

1. How does a safety card differ from both a WHMIS label and MSDS?

Making Connections

2. How could you use your safety cards at home or at school?
3. Interview the custodian to find out how hazardous materials are stored and handled. What safety precautions are taken?

1.2 Using Chemicals Wisely

You have just taken a new job as a chemical technician. Your first assignment is to clean out the chemical storage area and reshelve all the chemicals in a safe way. What do you need to know about each chemical to do your job properly? If needed, how will you dispose of chemicals safely?

Storage of Chemicals

It is important to plan and maintain chemical storage areas to avoid losses, accidents, or disasters. You must be careful to store chemicals that could react to one another in separate areas. Also, you want to make sure that chemicals are stored at the correct temperature.

In a chemical storage area there are 2 special cabinets: an acid cabinet and a flammable cabinet. An **acid cabinet** is a well-ventilated sealed cabinet where acids, such as hydrochloric acid, are stored. Acids release fumes that can be very dangerous, so a well-ventilated cabinet is very important. The **flammable cabinet** is a sealed cabinet where chemicals that are easily set on fire, such as acetone, are stored. This cabinet prevents any heat or electrical source from reaching the chemicals stored in it.

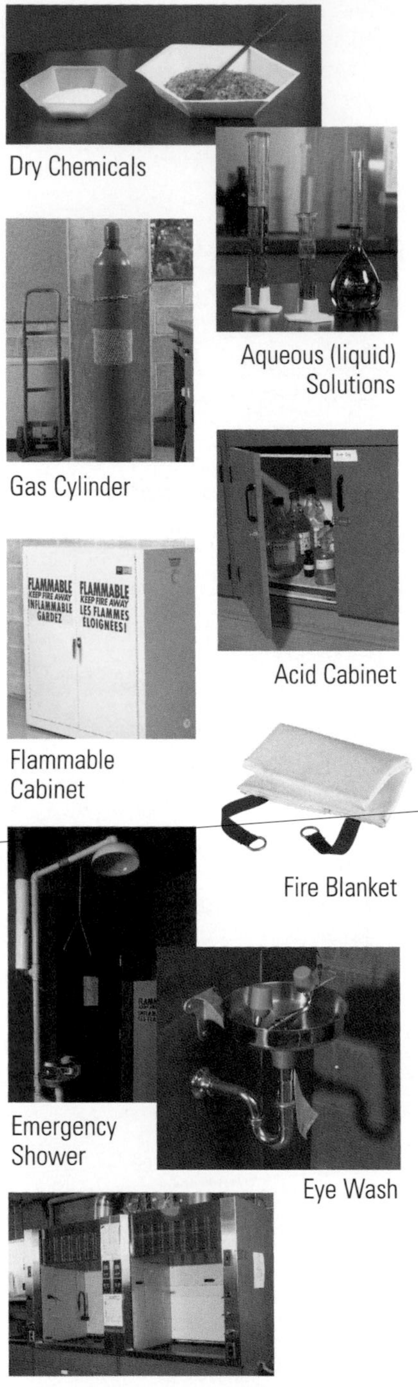

FIGURE 1.13 Chemicals and safety equipment found in a lab.

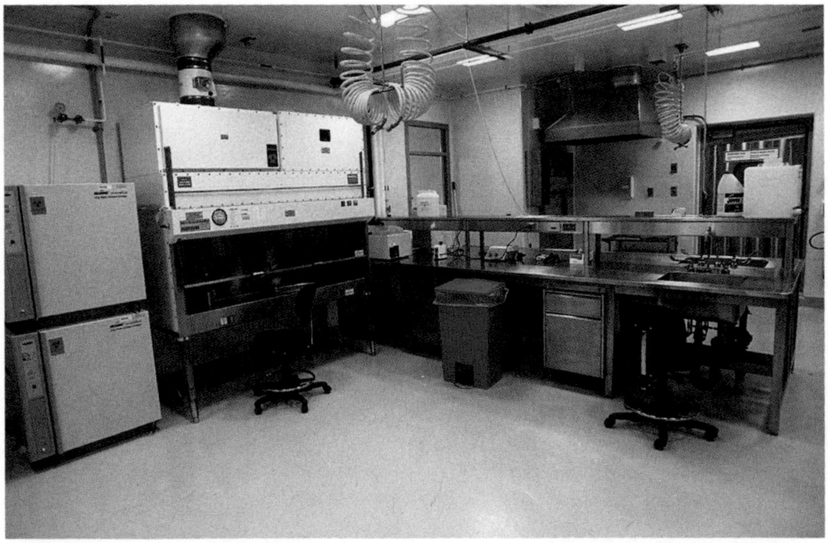

FIGURE 1.14 A workplace lab.

Dry chemicals are chemicals that are found in crystal or powder form and are stored on shelves according to their group name. For example, sodium carbonate, lithium carbonate, and potassium carbonate would be stored on the same shelf because their group name is carbonate.

Aqueous solutions are dry chemicals that have been dissolved in water. They are stored in closed containers on shelves.

The **fume hood** is a well-ventilated, closed area that allows you to work or do experiments without breathing in excess fumes.

It is important to realize that each chemical must be stored in its correct location. When storing chemicals there are a few rules to remember, at school or in the workplace.

Safety Rules

1. *All chemicals should be stored in their original containers with the WHMIS labels clearly visible.*
2. *The MSDS for each chemical should be filed alphabetically in a convenient binder.*
3. *Acids should be stored in a vented acid cabinet, as they may release toxic fumes.*
4. *Bases should be stored separately from acids, as bases may react with acids.*
5. *Flammable substances should be stored in a flammable cabinet away from sources of heat or electrical sparks.*
6. *All other chemicals should be stored according to the storage instructions on their MSDS.*

Flammable Substances

When looking at the MSDS of a chemical, there is a section entitled Fire or Explosion Data. This section has important information related to the proper storage temperature for the chemical. The temperature of the storage area or any heat source found in the room must be regulated so that it will be compatible with the chemicals. Therefore, it is important to watch both the chemicals and the temperature. The **flashpoint** is the minimum temperature that can cause the chemical to give off a vapour that will combine with the air and burst into flames. The **auto-ignition temperature** of a substance is the temperature at or above which a material will spontaneously ignite (catch fire) without an external spark or flame. For example, gasoline has a flashpoint of –46°C and an auto-ignition temperature of 471°C. This means that gasoline will form vapours at –46°C and will burn if exposed to a flame. If the temperature reaches 471°C, the gasoline will self-explode.

If the flashpoint or auto-ignition temperature is reached, then this could cause an explosion. An explosion occurs when the chemical bursts or blows up violently.

Exposure to a Chemical

Over time chemicals will change state from liquid to gas or solid to gas. Humans can be in danger if exposed to chemical gases. Therefore, on WHMIS or MSDS you can find the exposure time and concentration at which your safety is at risk. See Figure 1.15 for a list of acronyms found in MSDS.

Important MSDS Acronyms for Exposure to Chemicals

Acronym	Which stands for...	Which means...
LD50	Lethal Dose 50%	Kills 50% of the time for a certain dose.
LC50	Lethal Concentration 50%	Kills 50% of the time when you inhale that concentration (usually within 4 h).
TWAEV	Time Weighted Average Exposure Value	The concentration of a chemical that you can be exposed to in a working day (in 8 h).
STEV	Short Term Exposure Value	The concentration of a chemical present in the air that you can be exposed to in any 15 min period, provided the TWAEV is not exceeded.
CEV	Ceiling Exposure Value	The concentration that should never be exceeded for any length of time.

FIGURE 1.15

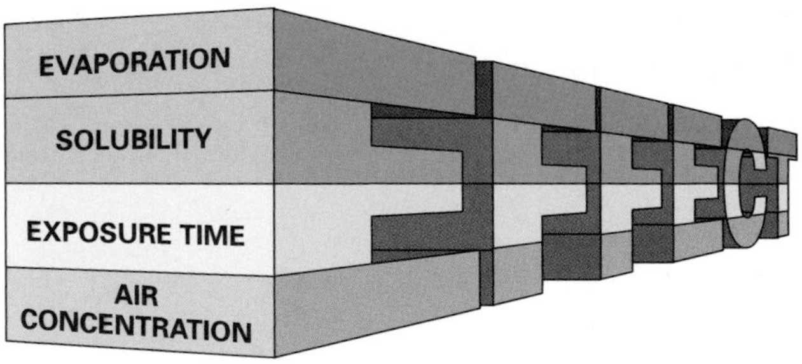

FIGURE 1.16 Each of these affects your safety when dealing with chemicals.

Exposure concentration is the amount of a chemical in grams in a million grams of air or water. The exposure concentrations are calculated in **ppm (parts per million)**. This is one gram of solute in a million grams of solution. For example, the acceptable amount of chlorine ion in drinking water is 200 ppm or, in other words, 200 g of chlorine ions for every million grams of water. What would LC50 = 250 000 ppm mean?

Disposal of Chemical Waste

Do all wastes go down the sink? The answer to this question is no. The issue of waste disposal at school, at home, or at work is an important social and environmental issue. At school or in the workplace, read the MSDS. All lab storage rooms need to have areas for safe disposal.

Many household hazardous wastes contain the same chemicals found in industrial hazardous wastes. Therefore, the hazards are the same. Here are some examples of products that should be disposed of properly after use:

- pool chemicals
- bleach
- paints
- antifreeze
- fire extinguishers
- pesticides
- drain cleaner
- fire starter
- batteries
- mosquito repellant
- used motor oil
- brake fluid
- nail polish remover
- prescription medication

How would you properly dispose of one of the chemicals listed above?

Any product that has a label like the following:

should be disposed of only at a special hazardous waste disposal facility. Keep in mind that some hazardous products do not have warning labels but are still considered hazardous. Not disposing of hazardous products properly may cause serious problems. Hazardous products that are buried in the ground can get into the soil and contaminate the groundwater. Disposing of corrosive chemicals down the sink can damage plumbing. Burning hazardous products only spreads them over a wider area. Improper disposal of hazardous products may pose risks to people handling waste and landfill operators. Workers have suffered eye injuries, chemical burns, and other medical problems as the result of hazardous products in regular garbage. Chemicals have also reacted in garbage trucks, leading to fires that have destroyed equipment.

Knowing about proper storage and disposal of chemical products in the home, lab, or workplace will be useful in designing your board game.

ScienceWise Fact

One litre of motor oil can contaminate 2 000 000 litres of drinking water.

Review and Apply

1. Make a list of how to prevent an explosion or fire from occurring at home or in the workplace. Share your answers with your classmates.
2. What important information must you look at on MSDS when dealing with flammable substances?
3. You have just received a shipment of hydrochloric acid, sulphuric acid, ammonia and acetone. As a chemical technician one of your responsibilities is to put each chemical away. Identify each chemical and explain where it would be stored and why.
4. Dina has just finished changing the oil in her car. What should she do with the used oil? Why? Draw a diagram or write a paragraph to explain your answer.
5. Make a pamphlet that shows the importance of safety in the lab, home, or workplace. Include the consequences when safe practices are not followed.
6. Add the new concepts from this section to the graphic organizer you started in Section 1.1.
7. **Hazardous Waste Disposal**

   In groups, research the hazardous waste disposal of a chemical of your choice and its danger to the environment. Can alternative chemicals be used? Role-play a scene where your researched chemical has been disposed of inappropriately. Show the danger this causes to the environment. In your group, show the proper method for disposal and suggest an alternative, safer chemical that could be used.

Job Link

Gas Fitter

Gas fitters install natural gas lines in residences and in commercial or industrial places.

Responsibilities of a Gas Fitter

- install related equipment such as gas meters, regulators, valves, and burners
- maintain and repair equipment
- install underground gas mains

Where do they work?

- public utilities
- plumbing and heating contractors
- building maintenance companies
- plumbing/gas fitting service companies

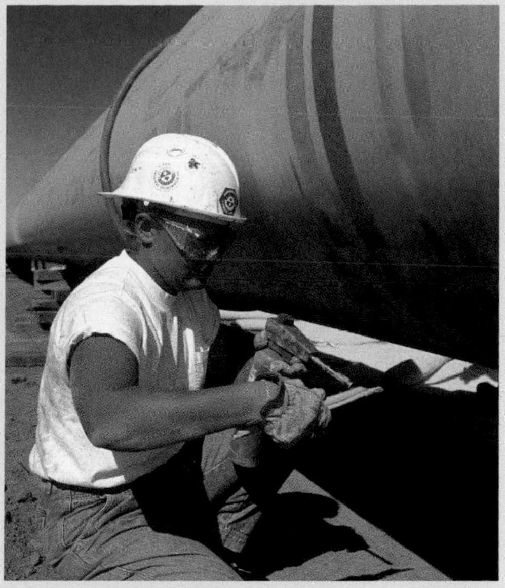

FIGURE 1.17 A career as a gas fitter.

Skills for the Job

- a perfectionist; because of the hazards involved, there is no room for error
- alert, efficient, precise, and reliable
- punctual, and shows good judgement and common sense
- good problem solver to analyze a situation, spot difficulties, and quickly decide on what needs to be done
- independent worker
- good written and verbal communicator

Education

- a secondary school diploma may be required
- a valid driver's licence
- licences or a certificate by completing a 3- to 4-year provincially regulated apprenticeship program, available from technical institutes or community colleges

Surf the Web

To find 3 related careers, look at **www.science.nelson.com** and follow the links for ScienceWise Grade 11, Chapter 1, Section 1.2.

CASE STUDY

Disasters in the Workplace

FIGURE 1.18 A thick cloud of poisonous gas was released into the atmosphere.

What happened in Hamilton?

On Wednesday July 9, 1997, at approximately 7:50 P.M., a massive fire occurred at the Plastimet recycling plant in Hamilton, Ontario. The plant mainly recycled plastics, including polyvinyl chloride (PVC), from the auto industry. When the plant caught on fire, 400 tonnes of plastics burned, releasing toxic, or poisonous, gases into the atmosphere.

Who came to help?

During the fire, provincial agencies were called to the scene, including police, fire, and ambulance; provincial ministries of the environment, health, and labour; and private organizations that specialize in dealing with hazardous material.

The fire burned for 77 hours. An estimated 210 million litres of water was poured on the site. The emergency teams were still on site 144 hours after the disaster, trying to recover contaminated water. A major concern was the potential thunderstorm 5 days later. The storm-water runoff could cause contamination in the sewer systems of the surrounding areas.

a) Suggest reasons why 3 provincial agencies were called to the scene of the fire.

Health and Safety

Initially, no residents were evacuated from their houses as the smoke from the fire went straight into the upper atmosphere. However, as the winds changed direction, the City of Hamilton evacuated 650 residents from their homes as a precaution. Other people were told to stay in their homes and keep their windows shut because of the toxic smoke cloud over the city. The firefighters needed to be well protected at all times to limit their exposure to the chemicals.

b) Why do you think the City of Hamilton evacuated some residents?

The Environment

When evacuated residents returned to their homes, they found their plants had been killed. Health officials told them not to eat garden fruits and vegetables. Residents were told that their exposure to dioxin (a by-product of burnt PVC that may cause cancer and interfere with hormones) was within acceptable levels. However, they were also told not to let their children play on black carbon (soot) filled lawns.

c) What safety precautions could residents take against dioxin?

The Investigation

After the fire, many questions were left unanswered, especially who was responsible for this disaster. In the fall before the fire, Plastimet had 20 Fire Code violations. They had not yet installed fire sprinklers, emergency lights, a fire safety plan, or additional exits. Fire officials have demanded tougher fines and jail sentences for businesses that ignore fire codes. Plastimet was given the responsibility of cleaning up the site.

Analysis and Communication

1. How do you think this disaster could have been prevented?

Making Connections

2. At school, why do you think you have fire drills? Do you always exit the school the same way? Explain why it is important to have a planned evacuation route at home, at school, and in the workplace.

3. On a sheet of paper, design an evacuation plan for your home in the event of a fire. List all the steps you would need to follow so that everyone in your home could get out safely.

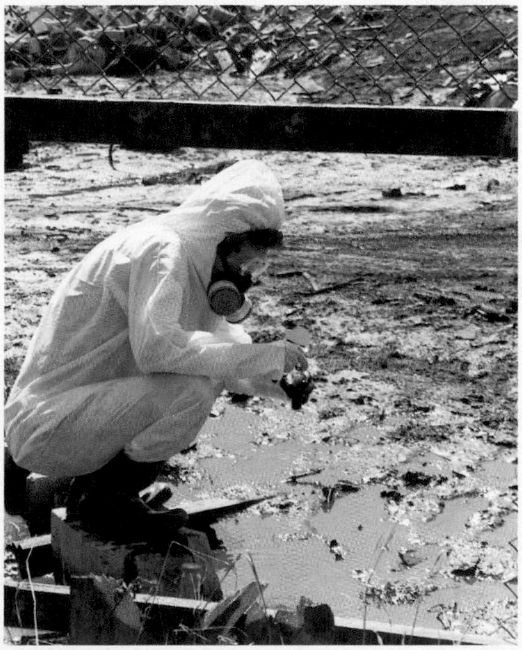

FIGURE 1.19 Near the scene of the fire, a soil sample is taken to test. Why do you think the soil is being tested?

1.3 The Effects of Hazardous Materials on the Body

Chemical products have become part of all of our lives. They are involved in daily activities. For example, many farmers use chemical pesticides to prevent and control insects from destroying their crops. You may use a chemical product to clean your kitchen sink. However, many chemicals, especially if not used properly, may endanger your health and poison the environment. The workplace is not the only place where you are exposed to chemicals. In what other places do you encounter chemicals? How do chemicals affect you?

How Chemicals Enter the Body

A chemical does not affect you until it enters your body or you come into contact with it. There are 3 main ways that chemical substances can enter the body.

1. **Inhalation** (breathing in)
2. **Absorption** (through the skin and eyes)
3. **Ingestion** (eating, swallowing)

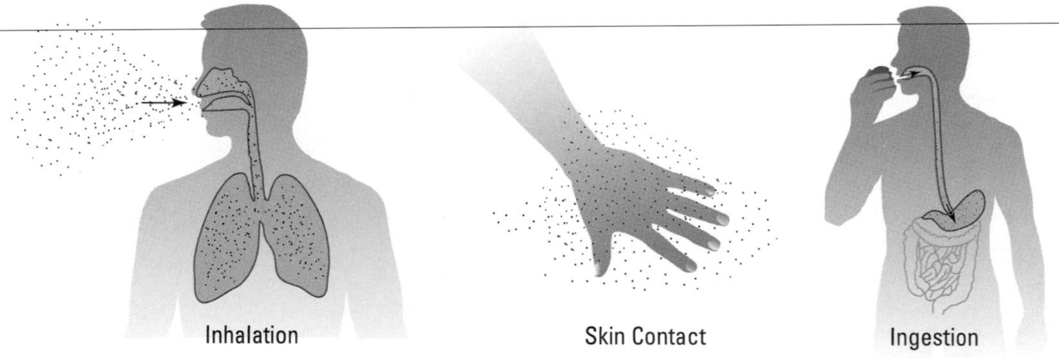

FIGURE 1.20 Three ways that chemicals enter the body.

Most Common Ways That Chemicals Enter the Body

1. Most chemicals may go into the air in the form of dust, mist, fumes, gas, or vapour and then may be inhaled. Therefore, even if you are not directly handling chemicals, you are still exposed to danger.

2. Handling chemicals in liquid form without the proper protection can cause absorption through the skin. Dust may also be absorbed through the skin by sweat. Eyes may also absorb chemical substances, either from splashes or from vapours.
3. Gases, dusts, vapours, fumes, liquids, or solids may be ingested by swallowing particles in the air. Food or cigarettes may be contaminated by dirty hands.
4. Chemicals can transfer across the placenta of a pregnant woman to her unborn baby.

Be Safe!

Do not eat, drink, or smoke at a place of work where dangerous chemicals are being used—it can be hazardous to your health.

Toxicity and Hazards of Chemicals

Chemicals can be grouped into categories that cause health risks. Refer to Figure 1.21.

Health Risks Caused by Chemicals

Chemical categories	Explanation/ Toxicity	Hazard (health risks)	Examples of chemicals
Dry chemicals	These are small particles that can penetrate into the lungs very easily.	Destroy lung tissue and cause lung cancer.	Asbestos Substances containing crystalline silica, such as sand, concrete, ceramics
Solvents— Organic chemicals that are used to dissolve fats and grease	These evaporate and ignite very easily. They can enter through the skin or by inhaling fumes when burned.	Cause irritation of the skin. Dangers to the liver, kidneys, bone marrow, or nervous system.	Benzene Carbon tetrachloride Carbon disulphide
Metals	Metals may enter the body in the form of dust and fumes (in grinding or welding) or through the skin.	May cause damage to the nervous system. May cause cancer, allergies, or birth defects.	Lead Mercury Nickel Chromium Arsenic
Acids and Bases	These are used as water solutions when treating or cleaning metals, and can splash the skin.	Acids corrode human tissues. Bases are caustic.	Sulphuric acid Phosphoric acid Ammonia Potassium hydroxide
Pesticides	Pesticides are used to destroy or control pests, and can enter the body in a variety of ways.	Can accumulate and poison humans and the environment.	DDT Insecticides

FIGURE 1.21 Dangers of using certain chemicals.

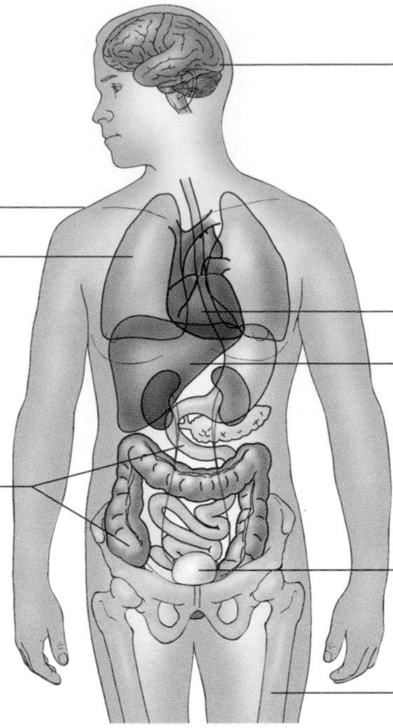

FIGURE 1.22 Parts of the body affected by toxicity.

Exposure to Chemical Substances

Chemical toxicity and protection are important concepts to know when designing your board game.

The harmful effects of chemical substances depend on toxicity and exposure. **Toxicity** is the ability of a substance to cause harmful effects. Figure 1.22 shows body parts that can be affected by toxicity. The **exposure** will depend on the concentration of the hazardous chemical and on the amount of contact time. Often, people may not know how long they have been exposed to certain chemicals, as many hazardous chemicals do not release an odour even if they are present in the air.

The effect of chemicals may be **acute**. This means that a rapid or quick effect may be experienced after a short exposure. An example is a burn. A **chronic** effect requires repeated exposure and involves a delay between the time of exposure and any health symptoms. An example is the development of liver cancer from inhaling low levels of benzene at a workplace over several years. Both acute and chronic exposure can cause permanent injury.

Protection

To protect against hazardous chemicals, special equipment must be worn at school, at home, or at the workplace (Figure 1.23).

Proper Protection

Protection for the...	Examples at school	Examples at home	Examples at work
Eyes	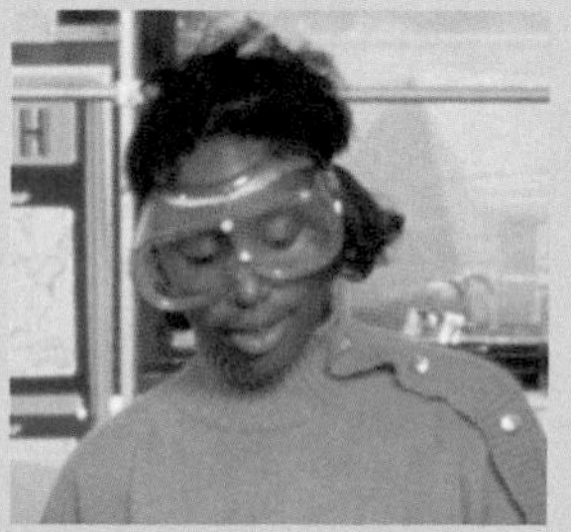		
Skin			
Lungs	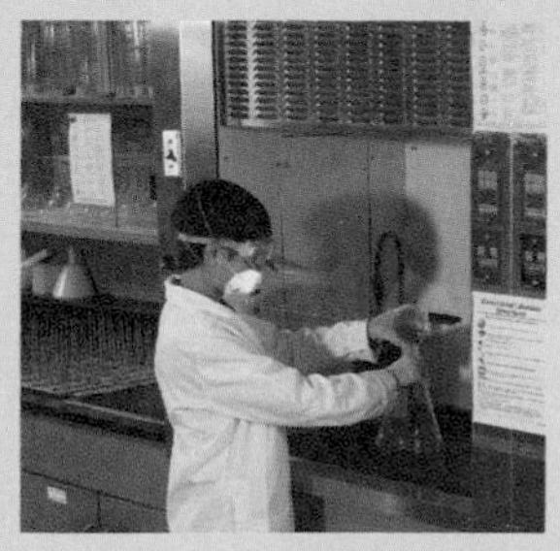	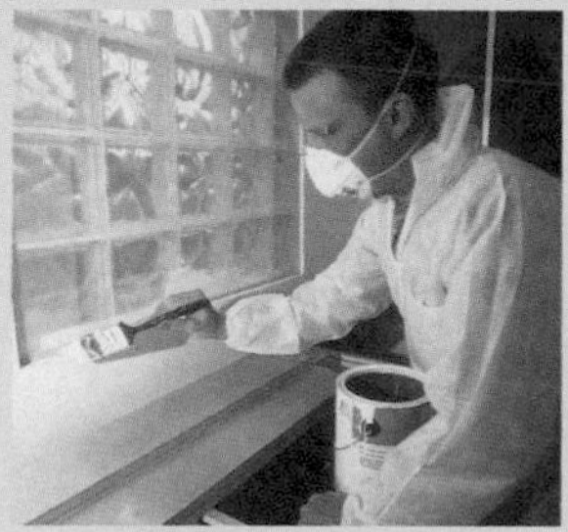	
Body			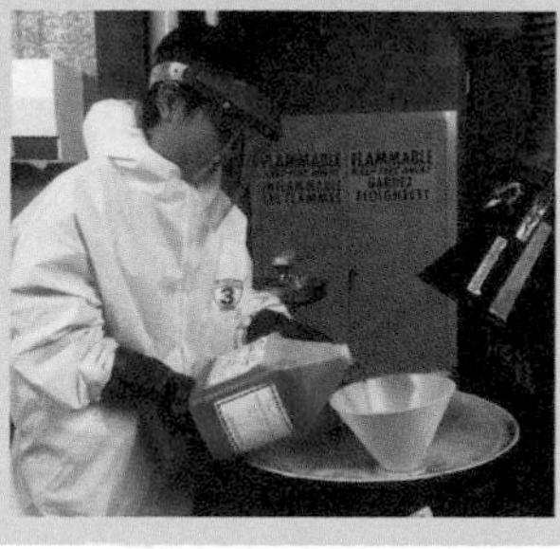

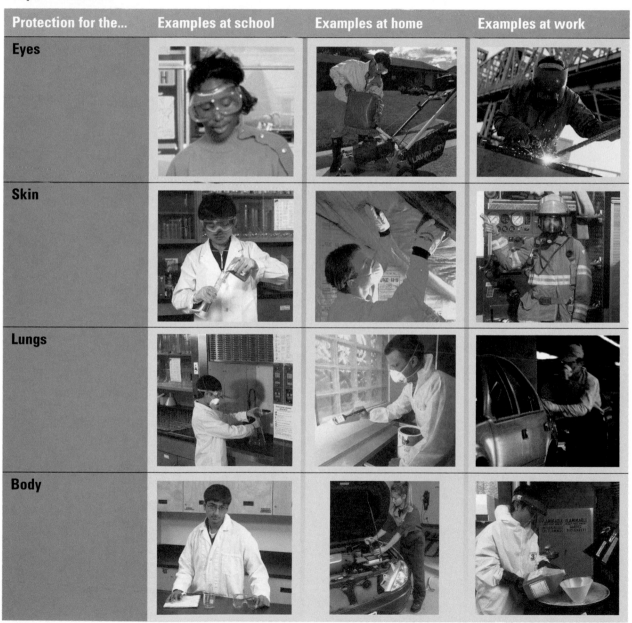

FIGURE 1.23 Wearing proper protection can help prevent exposure to chemical substances.

Review and Apply

1. Copy and complete Figure 1.24 in your notebook.

Chemical category	Route of entry into the human body	Hazard	Job	Prevention
Dry and liquid chemicals			Painter	
Solvents			Sheet metal operator	
	Inhalation			Dust mask
Acids and bases	Absorption	Bleach, detergent		
Pesticides			Lawn care technician	

FIGURE 1.24

2. You have a summer job as a gardener. You have been asked to make a presentation to the Health and Safety Committee about safe work environments. In your presentation, you must include:
   a) A poster illustrating the safety and personal protection equipment used.
   b) A concept map showing the hazards of disposing chemicals such as pesticides in the water system.

3. Warren works as a cook in a fast-food restaurant. He got a burn from hot grease splashing on him. ~~Is it an acute or chronic effect?~~ How could the burn have been prevented?

4. Add the new concepts in this section to the graphic organizer you started in Section 1.1.

Try This at Home

Handling and Disposing of Hazardous Chemicals

Mr. and Mrs. Jackson have hired you to help them sort and dispose of some chemical products. Mrs. Jackson cleaned out the garage and found used car oil, an empty container of paint thinner, and old antifreeze. Mr. Jackson cleaned out the bathroom and found an empty bottle of nail polish remover (acetone), expired prescription medicine, and some old cleaning products.

Your job is to provide them with the following information:

- class of hazardous material (reactive, poisonous)
- route of entry (inhalation, ingestion, absorption)
- proper protection (if needed) while using each product
- action plan for proper disposal.

1.4 Chapter Summary

Now You Can...

- Explain why there are safety procedures to follow at school, at home, and in the workplace (1.1)
- Categorize hazardous chemicals using WHMIS and HHPS (1.1, 1.3)
- Identify and explain how to safely store chemical substances (1.2)
- Describe how chemical substances enter the human body (1.3)
- Apply general safety procedures in the workplace and the home (Activity 1A, 1.3)
- Identify and analyze the different aspects of fire safety (Case Study)
- Identify safe handling, storage, and disposal of various hazardous materials (1.1, 1.2, Case Study, 1.3)
- Explain the terms acute and chronic as related to this chapter (1.3)
- Describe factors that can increase the dangers of chemicals that burn easily (1.2)
- Identify and explain WHMIS and HHPS (1.1, 1.2)

Concept Connections

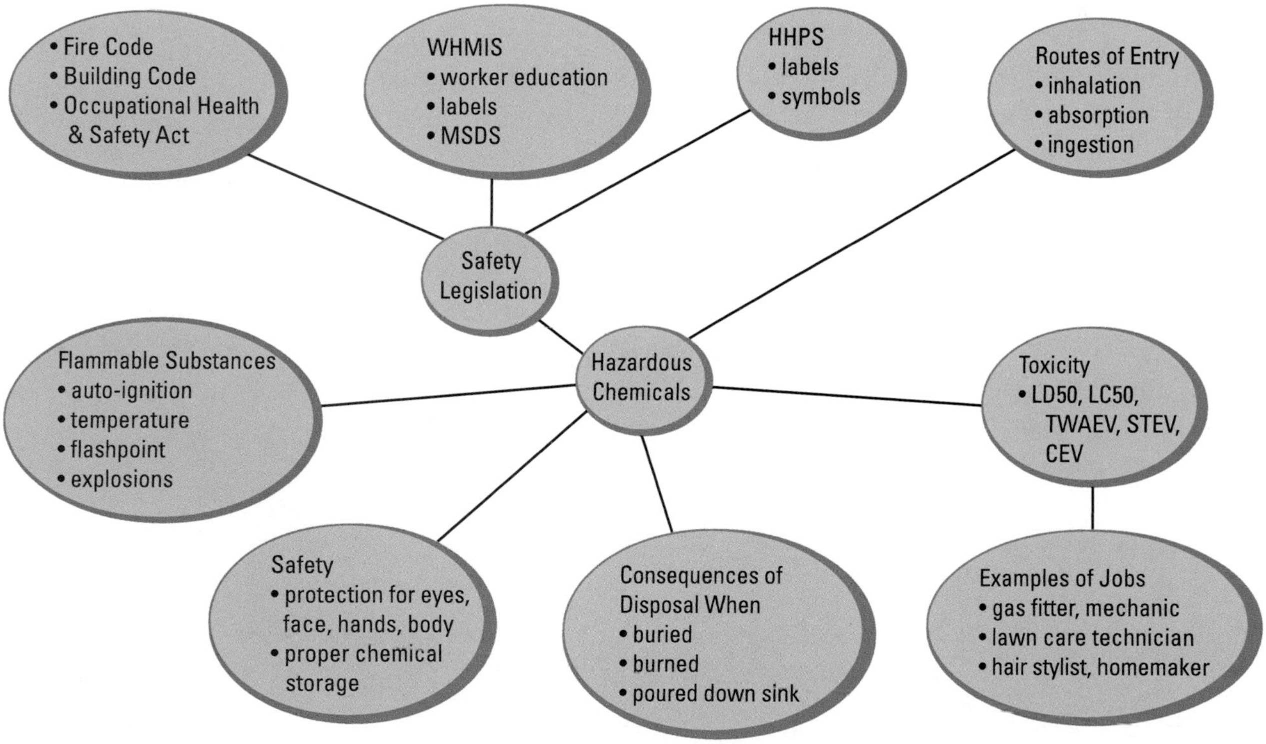

FIGURE 1.25 Compare your completed graphic organizer to the one on this page. How did you do? Can you add any new links to your organizer?

CHAPTER 1 *review*

Knowledge and Understanding

1. For each of the following statements indicate True or False. If False, rewrite the statement to make it true.
   - **a)** It is important to read the MSDS for chemicals that you use in the workplace.
   - **b)** Looking at a WHMIS label gives enough information about the hazardous material.
   - **c)** Household consumer products use HHPS.
   - **d)** The safety laws can be followed if you feel like it.
   - **e)** All chemicals can be stored together.
   - **f)** If you wear protective equipment, you do not have to worry about the exposure time of chemicals.
   - **g)** All chemical wastes can go down the sink.

2. As a part- or full-time worker, what are some of your rights concerning safety? What responsibilities do you also have?

3. Match each WHMIS symbol in Column B with its correct explanation from Column A.

Column A	Column B
a) Compressed Gas	**i)** 
b) Flammable and Combustible Material	**ii)** 
c) Oxidizing Material	**iii)** 
d) Poisonous Materials Causing Serious and Immediate Toxic Effects	**iv)** 
e) Toxic Material Causing Other Toxic Effects	**v)** 
f) Biohazardous Infectious Material	**vi)** 
g) Corrosive Material	**vii)** 
h) Dangerously Reactive Material	**viii)** 

4. Draw 3 ways that toxic materials may enter the body, and give an example of each that you might encounter.

Inquiry

5. You are preparing a lab that needs a dilute solution of concentrated sulphuric acid. Explain how you would handle this chemical, store the concentrated sulphuric acid, and dispose of excess sulphuric acid. (Hint: MSDS may be useful)

6. Today is a lab day and a new student has joined your class. Your teacher has paired you with this student. This student has never studied any of the material you have just learned in this chapter. Your task is to explain to the new student the safety precautions, including proper personal equipment, and proper handling and storage that must be taken when dealing with the following chemicals: copper (II) nitrate, iron (II) nitrate, and tin (IV) chloride. What would you teach this new student?

Making Connections

7. Many pesticide companies use synthetic chemicals instead of organic chemicals as pesticides for your lawn.

   Research each kind of chemical. List the advantages and disadvantages of using synthetic chemical and organic chemicals. Which chemical would you prefer to use? Why?

8. Obtain an MSDS from your teacher. Use the sheet to answer the following:
   a) Write the product name and trade name of the chemical.
   b) What is the LD50, LC50, TWAEV, STEV, and CEV?
   c) What is the flashpoint and auto-ignition temperature?
   d) Explain the routes of entry.
   e) How would you store this chemical?

9. Many toxic chemicals are by-products of agriculture, industry, or home use. How is hazardous chemical waste disposed of in your area? Write a report to describe local methods. Can you suggest any improvements? Why or why not?

Communication

10. Write a letter to your local fire department or prepare a script for a television interview asking questions about the importance of fire codes and examples of accidents that have occurred as a result of companies attempting to cut costs.

11. Discuss why it is important to have a system like WHMIS in the workplace. How does this benefit the worker and employer?

12. Choose 2 lab safety rules that you have in your science classroom and explain their importance when doing a lab.

CHAPTER 2

Rates of Chemical Reactions

This chapter looks at chemical reactions and the factors that can affect the speed, or rate, of chemical reactions. These factors can have positive or negative effects. Following proper safety procedures is very important in preventing accidents. As well, you will learn about the reactivity of metals and fuels with oxygen and other substances. Look at Figure 2.1. What do you think causes rust? What do gasoline and propane need in order to burn? What materials do you think were used to start the campfire? Why?

FIGURE 2.1

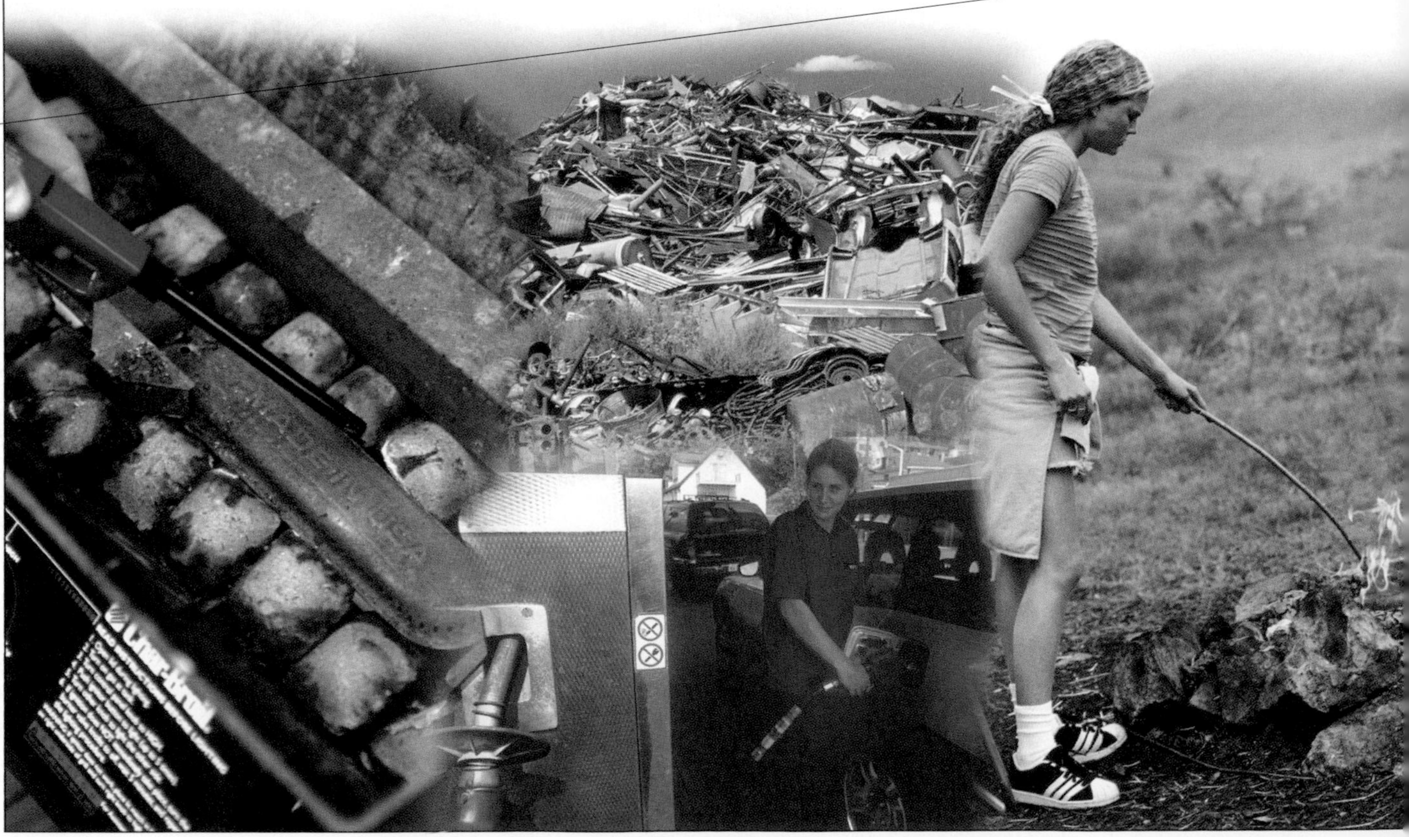

What You Will Learn

After completing this chapter, you will be able to:

- Describe the factors that affect the rate of chemical reactions, paying attention to what makes the reactions dangerous (2.1)
- Describe chemical tests for gases (2.1)
- Identify oxidizing agents and describe their reactivity with fuels and other oxidizable materials (2.2, 2.3, Lab 2D, Activity 2E)
- Predict the reactivity of metals with acids and oxygen using the activity series of metals (2.2; Labs 2A, 2B, 2C)

What You Will Do

- Prepare questions that describe the rates of chemical reactions (2.1, 2.3, Lab 2C)
- Use lab equipment to safely and accurately compare the corrosive action of acids on different metals (Labs 2A, 2B)
- Investigate the combustion of different flammable liquids (Lab 2D)
- Identify and collect information on science-technology careers (Job Link)
- Communicate ideas and results of laboratory experiments (Labs 2A, 2B, 2C, 2D; Activity 2E)
- Demonstrate an understanding of safe laboratory practices (Labs 2A, 2B, 2C, 2D; Activity 2E)
- Make and use a fire extinguisher and prepare an evacuation route (Activity 2E)
- Create a table to present information (Labs 2A, 2B, 2C, 2D; Activity 2E)

Words to Know

activity series
atom
chemical change
chemical reaction
combustion reaction
corrosion
electron
galvanizing
global warming
hydrocarbons
incomplete combustion
ion
oxidation
oxidizing agent
products
rate of reaction
reactants
redox reaction
reduction
reducing agent

A puzzle piece indicates knowledge or a skill that you will need for your project, Designing a Safety Board Game, at the end of Unit 1.

2.1 Chemical Reactions

Can you imagine a firework that would take a year to react, or a cake that needs 2 days to bake? In this section, you will learn about the factors that affect the rate of chemical reactions.

Chemical Change

A **chemical reaction** occurs when the properties of the **products**—what you end up with—are different from the **reactants**—the starting substances. The following is an example of a chemical reaction:

$$\text{hydrogen gas} + \text{oxygen gas} \longrightarrow \text{water} + \text{heat}$$
$$\{\text{reactants}\} \longrightarrow \{\text{products}\}$$

This type of change is called a **chemical change**. A chemical change always involves forming a new substance. A chemical change may be observed during a chemical reaction when the following happens:

FIGURE 2.2A Bubbles of gas form.

FIGURE 2.2B Heat or light is given off.

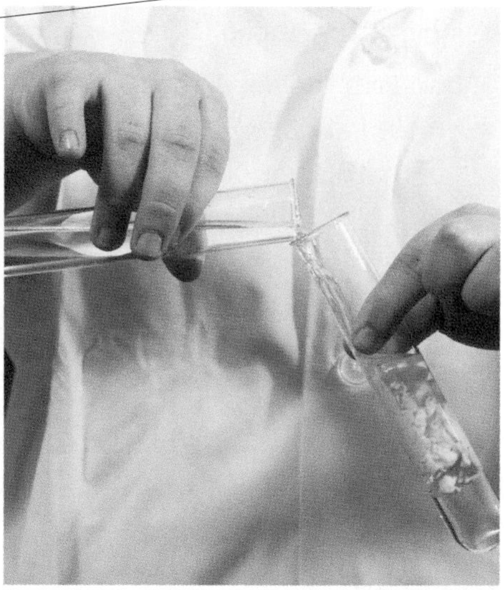

FIGURE 2.2C A solid material (called a precipitate) is formed.

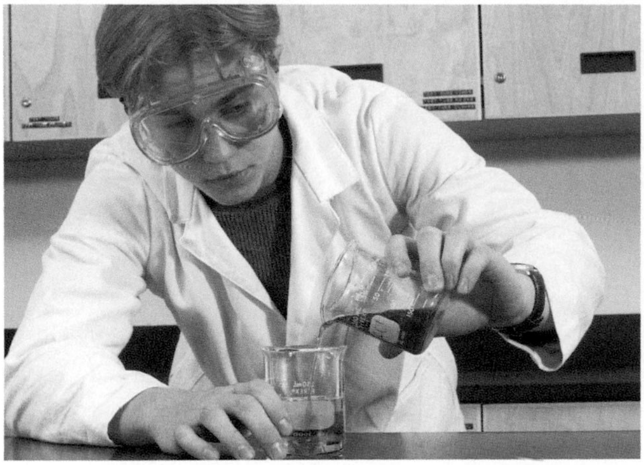

FIGURE 2.2D A new colour is observed.

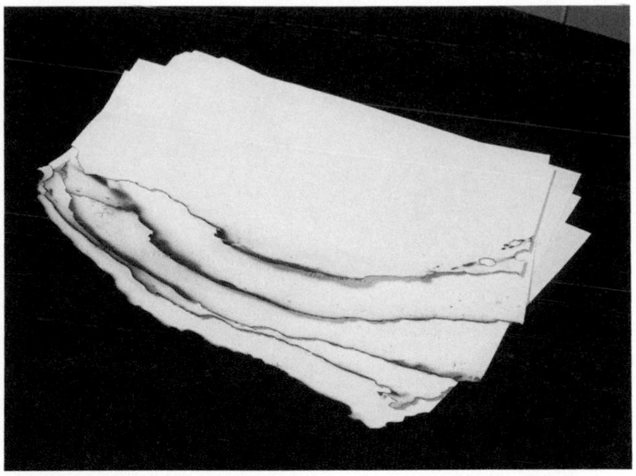

FIGURE 2.2E If this paper had kept burning, it would have ended up a pile of ashes. How would you describe this change?

Chemical Test

Chemical changes are not only used to make new substances. They are also useful in identifying unknown substances. The tests that are used to determine unknown substances are called chemical tests (see Figure 2.3).

Testing to Determine Unknown Substances

Chemical test for	What to do	Result
Oxygen gas	Place glowing splint into test tube with collected gas.	Glowing splint bursts into flames.
Hydrogen gas	Place a burning splint into the test tube with collected gas.	A "pop" sound will be heard.
Carbon dioxide gas	Bubble the gas through limewater. (Limewater is a clear, colourless solution of calcium hydroxide and water.)	Limewater will turn milky white.
Water vapour	Touch the water vapour with a piece of cobalt chloride paper.	Blue cobalt chloride paper will turn pink.

FIGURE 2.3

Chemical Rates of Reaction

The rate at which a new substance forms is called the **rate of reaction.** Different chemical substances will produce products at different rates. Look at Figure 2.4 for factors that affect the rate of reactions.

Factors that Affect the Rate of Reaction

Factors that affect rate of reaction	What is the effect?	Examples
Temperature	Generally reactions occur faster at a higher temperature.	 Putting food in a refrigerator slows down the chemical reaction between the micro-organisms that react with the food.
Surface area	The greater the surface area that is exposed, the faster the reaction.	 Wood chips have more surface area exposed than a log of wood, so they burn faster.
Concentration	The higher the concentration of reactant, the faster the reaction.	 Zinc reacting in concentrated hydrochloric acid. How do you think zinc would react in less concentrated, or dilute hydrochloric acid?
Catalyst	A substance that increases the rate of the chemical reaction without being used up by the reaction, so there is just as much of the catalyst at the end of the reaction as there was at the beginning. Catalysts work so quickly (and can be reused) that only a small amount is needed to make a reaction happen faster.	 Enzymes are specialized proteins found in your body that act as catalysts by speeding up the breakdown of food.

FIGURE 2.4

Rates of Reaction and Their Consequences

The factors that increase the rate of reaction can be either positive or negative. Many industries use chemical reactions to produce new products or to change existing products. For example, ammonia is a very important chemical in today's society. It is used in the production of fertilizers, plastics, nylon and household cleaners. Ammonia, made industrially, uses the Haber process. This process uses 2 factors that increase the rate of reaction: high temperatures (around 500°C), and an iron catalyst.

FIGURE 2.5 Why are there signs for no smoking, no matches and no open flames outside of grain elevators?

When working with chemical reactions there are dangers involved in increasing the rate of reaction. Grain elevators are used to store wheat and other grains. If an open flame came into contact with particles of wheat dust and the particles reacted with the oxygen in the air an explosion could occur. How does this happen? Remember that the surface area of the particle of wheat dust is larger (more particles are exposed to the air) than that of each bundle of wheat so it would catch fire more easily.

One of Canada's worst mine disasters occurred in Plymouth, Nova Scotia, in 1992. The Westray coal dust explosion claimed the lives of 26 miners. Figure 2.6 shows an overhead view of the entrance to the Westray mine 2 days after the explosion.

FIGURE 2.6 How does the surface area of coal dust particles in coal mines create a dangerous situation?

You may need to know about the factors that affect the rate of a chemical reaction when designing your board game.

Review and Apply

1. Complete Figure 2.7.

Factors affecting the rate of a chemical reaction	What does it do?	Example

FIGURE 2.7

2. Burning leaves is considered what type of change? Explain your answer.

3. When zinc is placed in hydrochloric acid, zinc chloride and hydrogen gas are produced. How would you test for hydrogen gas?

4. Why do photographers store film and batteries in a refrigerator?

5. Create a poster warning of potential explosion dangers that could be placed outside a grain elevator or coal mine. Include the reasons and effects of the rate of reactions.

6. In a graphic organizer, arrange the concepts you have learned in this section.

7. **Food Preservation**

What did the pioneers do to preserve their food and prevent it from reacting with oxygen and spoiling?

They used various methods, such as salting, curing, canning, pickling, drying and sugar-coating to preserve food. Choose 2 of these methods. Find out how they worked and if they are still used today. Use the factors that affect the rates of reaction to help explain how each method works. Present your findings as either a written report, web page, or pamphlet.

FIGURE 2.8

Air Bags and Safety

Did you know that air bags involve a chemical explosion? The chemical NaN_3 (sodium azide) is used in air bags in the form of pellets. If a car containing air bags hits something, or is hit, the high impact allows the pellets of NaN_3 along with a suitable catalyst to react, producing sodium, nitrogen gas and heat. This reaction produces very high temperatures and releases a large amount of nitrogen gas that fills the air bags in a fraction of a second.

FIGURE 2.9 Chemistry in action.

ScienceWise Fact

An automobile air bag fills up with about 65 L of nitrogen gas in approximately 27 ms. Note: A ms (millisecond) is one-thousandth of a second.

LAB
2A Chemical Reactions: Effects of Acids on Metals

When metals and acid solutions are mixed together a chemical reaction occurs. The result is a new substance, usually a gas. In this activity, the following general equation will be used:

metal + acid → metal compound [salt] + hydrogen gas

Be Safe!

• Hydrochloric acid is corrosive. Any spills on the skin, in the eyes, or on clothing, should be washed immediately with plenty of water. Report any spills to your teacher.

• When lighting the wooden splint, be very careful around the flame. Tie back long hair and remove any hanging jewellery.

Purpose

In this lab, you will determine the effects of acids on metals and a test for the presence of hydrogen gas.

Materials

- hydrochloric acid
- iron filings
- aluminum
- nickel
- 7 test tubes
- wooden splint, or toothpick
- safety goggles
- dropper-bottle
- magnesium ribbon
- copper wire
- tin
- zinc
- test tube rack
- lighter
- lab coat
- tongs

Procedure

1. Put on your safety goggles and lab coat.
2. Obtain dropper-bottles of hydrochloric acid from your teacher.
3. Obtain, and keep separately, small samples of each of the metals (magnesium ribbon, iron filings, copper wire, aluminum, tin, nickel and zinc).
4. Place your 7 test tubes in the test tube rack.
5. Label each test tube with the name of one of the metals from step 3. See Figure 2.10.

FIGURE 2.10 Step 5.

6 Create a data table in your notebook using the headings in Figure 2.11.

Metal	Observations	
	Metal and hydrochloric acid	Lit splint near test tube

FIGURE 2.11

7 Add 10 drops of hydrochloric acid to each test tube.

8 Using tongs, add 1 piece of metal to its labelled test tube.

9 While observing the reaction in step 8, light a wooden splint and bring it toward the test tube (Figure 2.12).

10 Record your observations in your data table.

11 Repeat steps 8 to 11 for the remaining metals.

12 Dispose of all chemical wastes as indicated by your teacher. Clean up your work area.

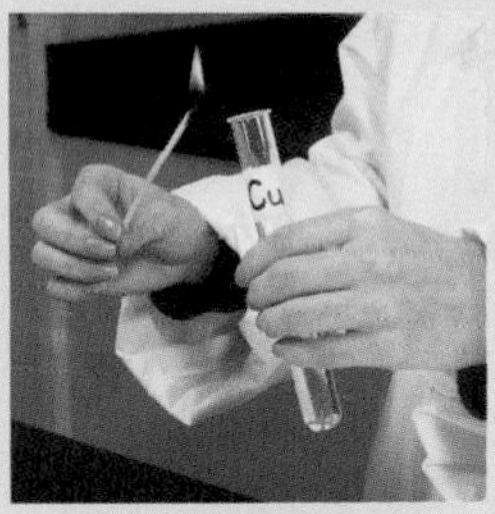

FIGURE 2.12 Step 10.

Be Safe!

Use care around an open flame.

Analysis and Conclusion

1 What happened to each metal in the acid?

2 **a)** Which metal was the most reactive in the acid?
b) Which metal was the least reactive in the acid?

3 **a)** Why was the chemical waste not poured down the sink?
b) What other safety precautions were followed in this activity?

4 **a)** What evidence indicated that a gas was produced?
b) How do you know that hydrogen gas was produced?

5 List the metals in order of most reactive to least reactive.

Extension and Connection

6 Have you ever noticed how the features on outdoor metal structures become damaged over time? Explain the effects of acid rain on these structures.

2.2 Oxidation of Metals

FIGURE 2.13 Why do cars rust? Why are cars painted?

Have you ever seen a car that looks like the rust is what is holding it together? Refer to Figure 2.13. Rust on a car is the result of the oxygen in the air and the metal of the car (iron) reacting with one another. But what chemical reaction is responsible for the rust?

During a Chemical Reaction

Everything on Earth is made up of **atoms.** Atoms are made up of neutrons, protons and **electrons.** An atom that has gained or lost electrons is called an **ion.**

When an atom loses an electron, the atom becomes positively charged (see Figure 2.14).

For example: sodium → sodium ion + 1 electron

$$Na \rightarrow Na^{+} + 1e-$$

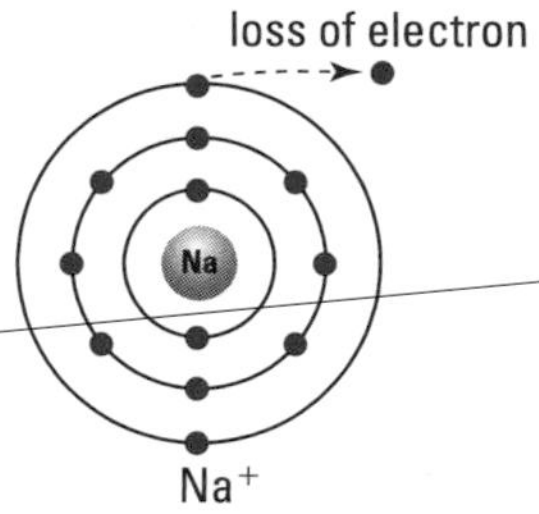

FIGURE 2.14 A sodium atom losing an electron.

When an atom gains an electron, the atom becomes negatively charged (see Figure 2.15).

For example: chlorine + 1 electron → chloride ion

$$Cl + 1e^{-} \rightarrow Cl^{-}$$

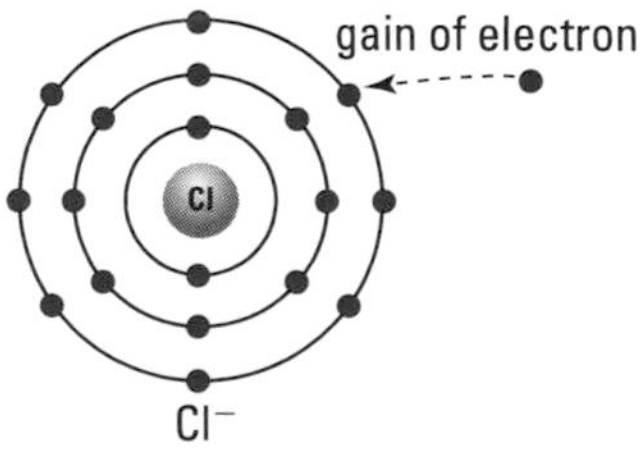

FIGURE 2.15 A chlorine atom gaining an electron.

Atoms become ions at different times. When certain solid crystals are dissolved in water, they break apart into their ions. This happens with sodium chloride (NaCl)—commonly called table salt. It breaks apart in water into sodium ions and chloride ions.

In a chemical reaction, like rust appearing on a car, electrons are transferred from one substance to another. One of the substances loses electrons and the other substance gains electrons. In the case of the car, iron loses electrons and oxygen gains electrons. The loss of one or more electrons from a substance is called **oxidation.** The gain of electrons is called **reduction.** When iron loses electrons and combines with oxygen in the air it becomes oxidized and the result is rust. The substance losing electrons is called the **reducing agent**. The substance gaining one or more electrons is called the **oxidizing agent** (oxidizer).

Oxidation and reduction always occur together in a chemical reaction involving electron transfer. The reaction is called a **redox reaction.** Figure 2.16 shows how oxygen reacts with iron.

iron (Fe) + oxygen (O_2) → iron oxide (Fe_2O_3)
loses electrons + gains electrons
oxidization + reduction → redox reaction
reducing agent + oxidizing agent → redox reaction

FIGURE 2.16 The chemical reaction of iron and oxygen.

Think back to Section 1.2 on storage and handling of chemicals. Where do you think you would store substances that are oxidizing agents? Oxidation reactions usually give off a lot of heat. This means that they can cause other materials to combust easily, or make fires burn more intensely. For these reasons, always store oxidizing agents away from flammable or combustible materials. As well, these substances should not be near sources of heat, flames, or sparks.

How Oxidizing Agents React with Metals

Do all metals oxidize, or lose electrons? Look at Figure 2.17. The ones that tend to oxidize are:

Iron (Fe)

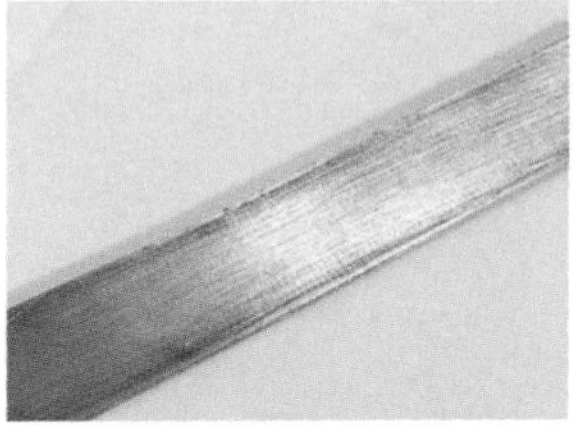
Copper (Cu)

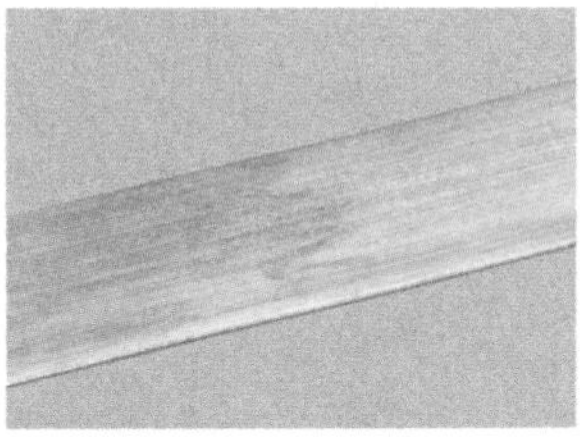
Zinc (Zn)

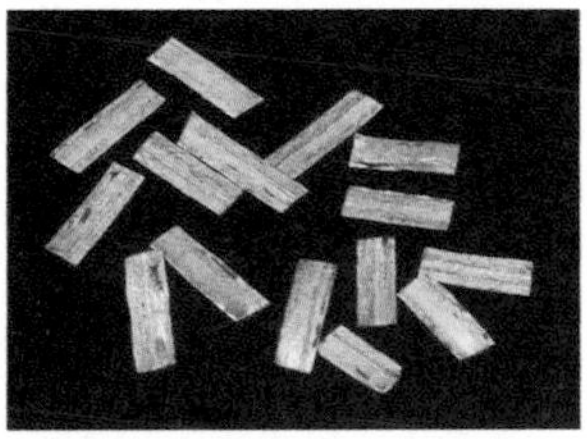
Magnesium (Mg)

Silver (Ag)

Aluminum (Al)

Tin (Sn)

FIGURE 2.17 Metals that may lose electrons.

There are other oxidizing agents besides oxygen, as shown in Figure 2.18.

Oxidizing Agents

Oxidizing agent	Examples in the home, school and workplace
Chlorinated hydrocarbons	Bleach, caulking compounds, adhesives, sealants
Peroxides	Hydrogen peroxide
Borax	Washing detergent

FIGURE 2.18 Examples of oxidizing agents.

The Activity Series

Remember that most metals lose electrons in redox reactions. Metals have different attractions for electrons. Some metals lose electrons easily and others do not. By testing different combinations of metals and ions, you can order metals from most reactive (easily gives up electrons) to least reactive (does not like to give up electrons). This list of how well a metal gives up electrons is called the **activity series.**

Figure 2.19 lists the activity series of some metals and their ions, from the most reactive to the least reactive. Hydrogen, which is not a metal, is included in the activity series because the metals above it in the series can give up electrons to it.

You can use the information in the activity series to predict which metal elements will react in solution. Any element higher in the activity series (near the top) has a weaker hold on electrons than an element below it and so will react in solution.

Example 1: Will copper react with a solution containing silver ions?
Solution: Copper is above the silver ion, so it will react.

Example 2: Will gold react with a solution containing silver ions?
Solution: Gold is below the silver ion, so it will not react.

Activity Series

	Metal
Most Reactive	Lithium
	Potassium
	Calcium
	Sodium
	Magnesium
	Aluminum
	Zinc
	Iron
	Nickel
	Tin
	Lead
	Hydrogen
	Copper
	Silver
Least Reactive	Gold

FIGURE 2.19

Application of Activity Series

When metal is chemically eaten away the process is called **corrosion.** Corrosion begins at the surface of the materials and it is often a surface layer that protects the rest of the material.

How do we protect materials from corrosion? Rusting is the most common form of corrosion. The activity series plays an important role in the protection of metals from corrosion. There are 3 main methods used to protect materials against corrosion.

1. Painting the object (for example: a car). See Figure 2.20.
2. a) Coating a more reactive material with a less reactive material. This coating forms a barrier between the metal and the air (for example: a thin layer of copper welded onto a piece of iron).
   b) Coating a less reactive material with a more reactive material. This process is called **galvanizing** (for example: coating iron nails with zinc).
3. Placing another more reactive material close to the material, the more reactive material competes for electrons (for example: zinc pieces placed on a steel boat motor helps prevent the motor from rusting).

Knowing how to protect materials against corrosion may be useful when designing your board game.

FIGURE 2.20 Can you think of other consumer products that use these methods of protection from corrosion?

Review and Apply

1. Why do you think it is important to choose galvanized nails for an outdoor project, but not for an indoor project?
2. Why are steel bridges repainted every few years?
3. Why is the roofing on the Parliament Buildings now green?
4. Choose a career that uses the activity series of metals. Draw a cartoon strip that shows a person of that career using the activity series in the workplace.
5. Using the activity series from Figure 2.19 on page 42, which of the following reactions would occur? Explain your answers.
   a) Zinc metal in a solution containing sodium ions.
   b) Magnesium metal in a solution containing potassium ions.
   c) Gold metal in a solution containing aluminum ions.
   d) Copper metal in a solution containing silver ions.
6. Add the new concepts from this section to the graphic organizer you started in Section 2.1.

Preventing Ships from Corroding

The corrosion of the hulls—the body or frame—of ships in seawater is a major problem. One way to prevent the rusting of iron ships is to attach small bars of magnesium to the hull. Magnesium is more active than iron so the magnesium bars will corrode in seawater before the iron hull will.

FIGURE 2.21 Why do ships not rust quickly in seawater?

Job Link

Tool and Die Makers

Tool and die makers use many types of machine tools and must be familiar with machining properties, such as hardness and heat tolerance, of a variety of common metals.

FIGURE 2.22 A career as a tool and die maker.

What do they do?

They make, repair and modify custom-made prototype or special tools, dies (metal forms), jigs (wooden templates used to cut things out), fixtures (devices that hold metal while it is shaved, stamped, or drilled) and gauges that require precise dimensions.

Where do they work?

- manufacturing industries
- tool and die, mould making and machine shops

Responsibilities

- read and interpret drawings and specifications of tools, dies, prototypes and models
- operate a variety of machine tools to cut, turn, mill, plane, bore, grind and otherwise shape work pieces to prescribed dimensions
- machine, fit and assemble castings and other parts to make metal patterns
- machine, fit and assemble parts to make metal moulds for plastic injection moulding

Education

- must have a secondary school education
- must have a certificate in tool and die making that may be obtained by completing an apprenticeship program or 5 years work experience and college courses in tool and die making

Surf the Web

Go to **www.science.nelson.com** and follow the links for ScienceWise Grade 11, Chapter 2, Section 2.2. Research 3 industries that hire tool and die makers and what they are hired to do.

LAB 2B

Reactivity of Metals with Oxygen

Be Safe!

Magnesium metal produces an extremely hot, white flame when lit. Do not look directly at the white glow when it reacts. Use care around an open flame. Tie back long hair and remove any hanging jewellery.

Why are cars painted? Why are metals painted and/or oiled? Active metals oxidize (lose electrons) readily. In this lab, you will compare the reactivity of various metals in the presence of oxygen.

Purpose

In this lab, you will rank the metals zinc, iron, copper, silver, tin, nickel, magnesium and aluminum in order of reactivity with oxygen.

Prediction

How would you rank the above metals from most reactive to least reactive with oxygen? Write your prediction.

Materials

- safety goggles
- lab coats
- tongs
- steel wool
- deflagrating spoon (optional)
- approximately 5-cm piece of each metal: zinc, iron, copper, silver, tin, nickel, magnesium, and aluminum
- Bunsen burner

Procedure

Part One: Teacher Demonstration

Magnesium metal will be tested by your teacher using a safety shield or in a fume hood.

1. Create a data table using the headings in Figure 2.23 to record your observations.

Metal	Initial appearance of metal	Appearance of metal during burning (combining with oxygen)	Appearance of metal once burning is over

FIGURE 2.23

2. A 5-cm piece of magnesium is polished with a small piece of steel wool.
3. Your teacher will hold one end of the magnesium with tongs and place it in the hottest part of the Bunsen burner flame. Record your observations.
4. As soon as a reaction starts, your teacher will remove the magnesium from the flame. Record your observations.

Part Two: Testing the Metals

1. Put on your lab coat and safety goggles.
2. Polish a 5-cm piece of iron with a small piece of steel wool.
3. Hold one end of the iron with tongs. Carefully place the iron in the hottest part of the Bunsen burner flame (Figure 2.24).
4. After 20 seconds, remove the iron from the Bunsen burner flame. Record your observations in your data table.
5. Repeat steps 2 to 4 with zinc, copper, silver, tin, nickel and aluminum. Record your observations after each metal is observed in the flame.
6. If a piece of zinc is used, you may place it in the deflagrating spoon. Place the spoon in the hottest part of the Bunsen burner flame. Remove after 20 seconds and record what changes you observed in your data table (optional).

FIGURE 2.24 Part 2, step 3.

Analysis and Conclusion

1. For each reaction, what evidence did you have that the metal was being oxidized?
2. Rank the metals from the most reactive to the least reactive in the presence of oxygen.
3. How does your answer to question 2 relate to the ability of each metal to give electrons?
4. What safety precautions did you follow in the activity? Why?

Extension and Connection

5. Compare the reactivity of metals with an acid (Lab 2A) to the reactivity of metals with oxygen (Lab 2B).

LAB

2C

Ranking Metals in Activity Series

Metals can react with other oxidizing agents (ions). In this lab, you will perform a number of reactions to make an activity series for some metals. Knowing how metals will react is important when choosing specific situations. Welders, carpenters and sheet metal workers are just a few of the jobs that need to know about the reactivity of metals. Why do you think this is?

Purpose

In this lab, you will rank the reactivity of different metals.

Prediction

How would you rank the following metals in order of most reactive to least reactive: magnesium, zinc, iron, copper, lead and aluminum?

Be Safe!

The chemicals used are toxic and irritants. Handle them carefully and rinse thoroughly if you get any on your skin. Report any spills to your teacher immediately.

Materials

- dropper-bottles containing aqueous solutions of the following (note: aq is the short form of aqueous):
  - copper (II) nitrate, $Cu(NO_3)_{2(aq)}$
  - iron (II) nitrate, $Fe(NO_3)_{2(aq)}$
  - magnesium nitrate, $Mg(NO_3)_{2(aq)}$
  - lead (II) nitrate, $Pb(NO_3)_{2(aq)}$
  - zinc nitrate, $Zn(NO_3)_{2(aq)}$
  - aluminum nitrate, $Al(NO_3)_{3(aq)}$
- 6 small pieces of each of the following: copper, iron, magnesium, lead, zinc and aluminum
- 6 well plates, or 6 small test tubes and a test tube rack
- 6 labels
- safety goggles
- lab coats

Procedure

1. Put on your safety goggles and lab coat.
2. Label the wells (or test tubes) with symbols for the metal ions in solution: Cu^{2+}, Fe^{2+}, Mg^{2+}, Pb^{2+}, Zn^{2+}, Al^{3+}
3. Half fill each well (or test tube) with the solution that matches each label (Figure 2.25).
4. Add a small amount of copper metal to each well (or test tube), except the one containing copper (Figure 2.26).
5. Allow 30 to 60 seconds for the reaction. Observe the reactions and record your observations in a data table like Figure 2.27 . (If there is no reaction write NR.)

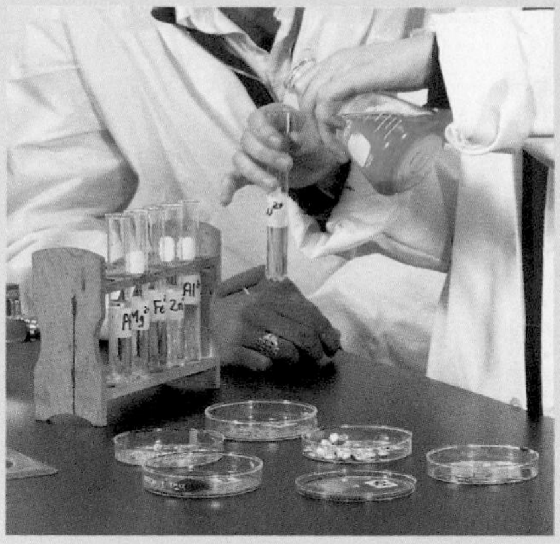

FIGURE 2.25 Step 3.

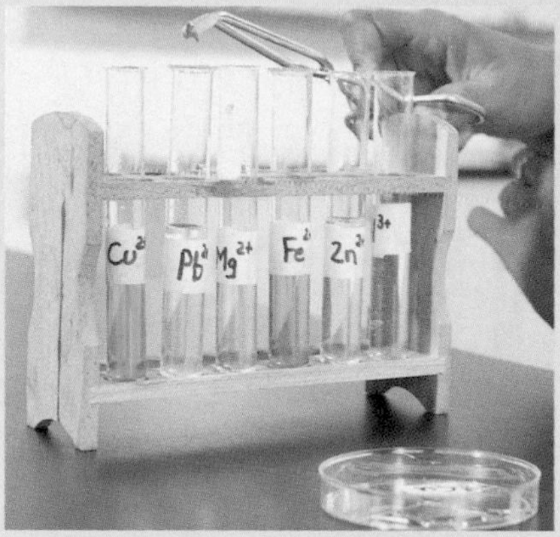

FIGURE 2.26 Step 4.

	Metals					
Metal ion	**Copper**	**Iron**	**Magnesium**	**Tin**	**Zinc**	**Aluminum**
Cu^{2+}						
Fe^{2+}						
Mg^{2+}						
Pb^{2+}						
Zn^{2+}						
Al^{3+}						

FIGURE 2.27

6. Empty the solutions into a container supplied by your teacher. Thoroughly rinse the well plates or test tubes.
7. Repeat steps 3 to 6. Test a small amount of each metal, until the data table is complete.
8. Dispose of all chemicals as instructed by your teacher. Clean your work area.

CONTINUED

Analysis and Conclusion

1. Which metal had the most reactions?
2. Which metal had the least reactions?
3. Rank the metals from the most reactive to the least reactive.
4. Which solution (ion) had the most reactions?
5. Which solution (ion) had the least reactions?
6. Rank the solutions from the most reactive to the least reactive.
7. How do the lists in questions 3 and 6 compare?
8. In a chart, summarize your results of metal and metal ion reactivity.
9. Compare your observations table (Figure 2.27) with at least 2 other groups in the class. Explain reasons for any differences.

Extension and Connection

10. With your knowledge of metal reactivity, explain why cars are not made of magnesium.
11. Why are iron nails galvanized (zinc-coated)?
12. Give examples of other products that use the activity series.

2.3 Combustion

What do jet engines, the space shuttle and a match have in common? They all have a burning reaction, where a substance combines with oxygen to produce heat and light. This chemical reaction is called a **combustion reaction.**

Complete Combustion

During complete combustion there is enough oxygen to combine with a fuel to produce carbon dioxide, water vapour and energy. Look at Figure 2.28. The fuels usually used are **hydrocarbons**—a compound of hydrogen and carbon atoms.

Hydrocarbons Around Us

Example of hydrocarbon	Chemical formula	Consumer use
Methane	CH_4	Natural gas in furnace
Propane	C_3H_8	Barbeque tanks, camp stove
Butane	C_4H_{10}	Lighter fluid
Octane	C_8H_{18}	Gasoline for cars
Tetradecane	$C_{14}H_{30}$	Jet fuel

FIGURE 2.28

The general word equation for a combustion reaction is:

hydrocarbon + oxygen → carbon dioxide + water vapour + energy (heat and light)

In Section 1.2 you learned about flashpoints and auto-ignition temperatures. Fuels are combustible, which means they could explode if they reach their flashpoints or auto-ignition temperatures. What is needed for a fire to start? Look at Figure 2.30; it is commonly called the fire triangle. It shows the 3 factors needed for a combustion reaction to happen. Removing the fuel or oxygen, or reducing the fuel's temperature can extinguish fires.

A negative effect of combustion is its contribution to global warming. **Global warming** is the increase in the average temperature of Earth's atmosphere. A major contributor to global warming is the increase of carbon dioxide in the atmosphere. From 1850 to 1990, the concentration of carbon dioxide from the combustion of hydrocarbons increased about 500 times!

FIGURE 2.29 How are these things related?

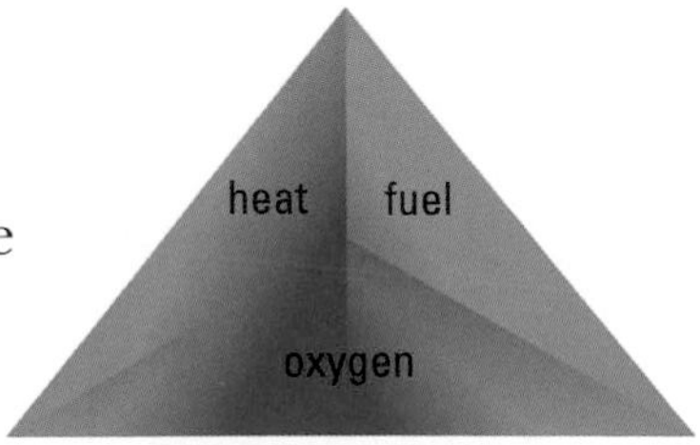

FIGURE 2.30 For combustion to occur, all 3 factors must be present.

Incomplete Combustion

When there is not enough oxygen available to combine with hydrocarbons, then other products such as carbon monoxide and carbon are produced. This is known as **incomplete combustion.** The larger the hydrocarbon molecule, the more likely that incomplete combustion will occur. Look at Figure 2.32. Between octane (gasoline used in cars) and methane (natural gas), which is most likely to produce incomplete combustion? Why?

In incomplete combustion, the release of carbon monoxide (a poisonous, colourless, odourless gas) can cause many health problems such as difficulty breathing and headaches. Leaving a car idling (the motor running while stopped) can increase the level of carbon monoxide in the air.

Surf the Web

Should every home have a carbon monoxide detector? Go to **www.science.nelson.com** and follow the links for ScienceWise Grade 11, Chapter 2, Section 2.3 to learn about them. Create a poster explaining your viewpoint.

FIGURE 2.31 A carbon monoxide detector.

FIGURE. 2.32 What is the danger presented by this gas?

ScienceWise Fact

During the ice storm of Eastern Canada in 1998, at least 6 people died due to carbon monoxide poisoning. The causes? Lighting fires in blocked chimneys and using kerosene heaters and charcoal briquette barbecues indoors instead of outdoors.

Rate of Chemical Reaction and Combustion

Knowing about combustion will be helpful in designing your board game.

The rate of combustion depends not only on the type of hydrocarbon and the amount of oxygen being used, but also the temperature. Larger molecules of hydrocarbons will burn using large amounts of oxygen at high temperatures. Smaller molecules of hydrocarbons will burn using smaller amounts of oxygen at lower temperatures. For example, jet fuel needs large amounts of oxygen, high temperatures and the power of a starter engine to burn. Butane in a lighter needs only the oxygen found in the air, low temperatures and the spark of the lighter to burn. Why do you think this is?

Three, two, one, BLAST OFF! Once launched, how does a space shuttle keep firing once it has passed beyond Earth's oxygen-rich atmosphere and entered the vacuum of space?

The shuttle generates a thrust or push by igniting a mixture of fuel and an oxidizer. The fuel in this case is liquid hydrogen and the oxidizer is liquid oxygen. In order to keep them in a liquid state rather than boiling into a gas, they are kept in separate chambers of the engine at very low temperatures. Upon take-off, the 2 liquids are combined in a combustion chamber.

In order to provide the shuttle with enough thrust to launch into space, it also employs fuel in a solid state contained in 2 solid rocket boosters (SRBs). Along with the solid rocket fuel, the SRBs include an oxidizer and a catalyst. Think back to the rates of reaction. Why do you think a catalyst is necessary? The solid fuel provides more than 70 percent of the thrust during take-off, but the SRBs do not actually accompany the shuttle into space. Approximately 45 km above Earth, the spent SRBs separate from the shuttle assembly to splash down in the ocean, where they will be recovered and reused for future missions.

Since the solid fuel is so powerful, could the shuttle only use solid fuel? Why is there the need for liquid fuel and oxidizer as well? Once the solid fuel is ignited, its consumption cannot be

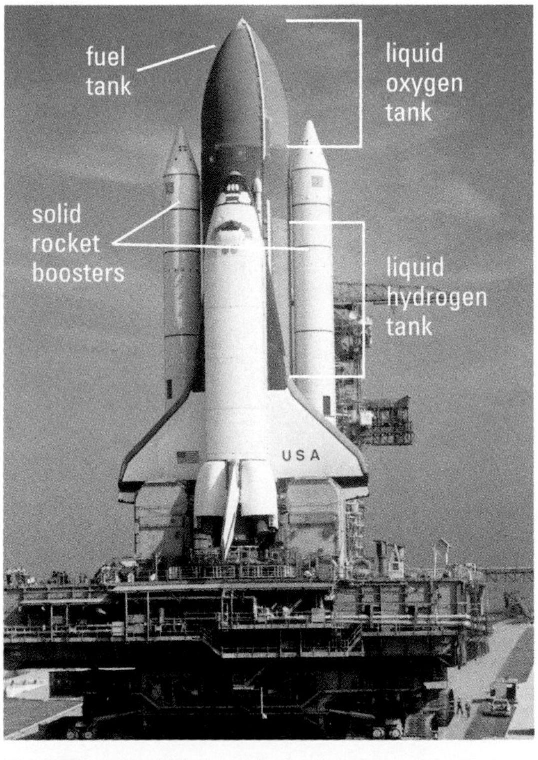

FIGURE 2.33 Why are the hydrogen and oxygen tanks kept apart?

regulated so it will burn until it is completely used up. The rate of consumption of the liquid fuel and oxidizer, on the other hand, can be regulated through the use of valves. For this reason the solid fuel is exhausted while generating the immense initial thrust necessary to reach orbit, while the liquid fuel is mainly employed to maneuver the shuttle once it has reached orbit.

Fireworks (Figure 2.34) are another example of the combustion of fuels with oxygen and solid oxidants. The solid oxidants allow for the glitter effects, various colours and smoke. During the initial combustion the fuels react with oxygen.

FIGURE 2.34 What safety precautions must be followed when viewing a fireworks display? Explain how the rates of reaction affect fireworks.

Review and Apply

1. Why is combustion a hazard to the environment?

2. Why should you never light a barbeque in your home or a closed space?

3. In a hospital area where pure oxygen is being used there are "no smoking" or "no igniting any spark" signs. Why do you think this is?

4. Make a chart comparing corrosion and combustion. How are they different? How are they the same? Include examples of each.

5. Add the new concepts you learned in this section to the graphic organizer you started in Section 2.1.

6. **Dangerous Explosion**

On December 6, 1917, 2 ships collided in the Halifax harbour. One ship was carrying 2766 tonnes of explosive picric acid, which was ignited by the collision of the 2 ships. This explosion resulted in the death of over 1600 people and injured about 9000. Much of the northend of Halifax was destroyed.

a) With a partner, brainstorm the dangers of transporting combustible materials and how accidents can be prevented.

b) Create a pamphlet that would give information about the transportation of combustible material and the safety precautions that should be taken.

FIGURE 2.35 The scene in the northend of Halifax after the explosion. About 6000 people were left homeless and property damage was estimated at $50 million.

LAB 2D

Combustion of Fuels

Be Safe!

The fuels being used are very flammable. Make sure they are all stored in closed containers so their vapours do not ignite. Use care around an open flame. Tie back long hair and remove any hanging jewellery.

Many workplaces contain flammable products. Grocery stores have shelves full of vegetable oil, and hardware stores have varsol and other products for removing paint. How easily do you think fuels combust? In this activity, you will test different fuel samples to determine how they combust.

Purpose

In this lab, you will test the combustion of some flammable liquids.

Materials

- lab coats and safety goggles
- 1 test tube rack
- 4 cloth wicks or floating wicks
- 1 Bunsen burner
- 1 stopwatch
- limewater (calcium hydroxide solution)
- baking soda
- 8 small test tubes
- 4 rubber stoppers that fit in test tube
- 4 wooden splints
- small sample (1 mL) of alcohol, varsol, mineral oil and vegetable oil, each in a closed container

Procedure

1. Put on your lab coat and safety goggles.
2. Place 1 mL of alcohol in a test tube and carefully insert 1 cloth wick. Make sure the wick is at least 2 cm inside the test tube as per Figure 2.36. Allow a few seconds for the wick to absorb the fuel.
3. Place the test tube in the test tube rack.
4. Light 1 wooden splint using a Bunsen burner. Use the splint to light the wick.
5. Start the stopwatch and record the amount of time the wick remains lit.

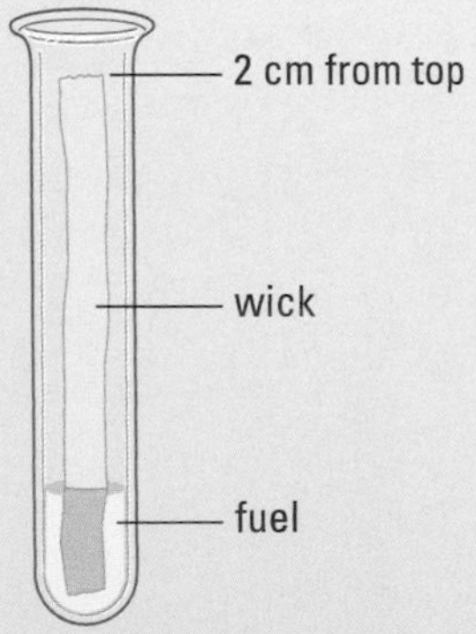

FIGURE 2.36

6 Record your observations in a data table like Figure 2.37.

Combustion of Fuels

Type of fuel	Time to burn (s)	Observation of burning wick	Observation with limewater
Alcohol			
Varsol			
Mineral oil			
Vegetable oil			

FIGURE 2.37

7 Half fill a test tube with limewater.

8 As the wick is burning, place the test tube containing limewater near the opening of the test tube with the burning wick. Collect the gas. After 30 seconds, remove the test tube of limewater and place a rubber stopper in it. Shake the test tube (Figure 2.38) and record your observations.

9 Repeat steps 3 to 8 with the remaining samples of fuel.

10 Dispose of all chemicals as instructed by your teacher. Clean your work area.

Be Safe!

- Make sure to test each sample of fuel one at a time and to keep the fuels in separate closed containers when not in use.
- In the event of a fire, alert your teacher immediately.

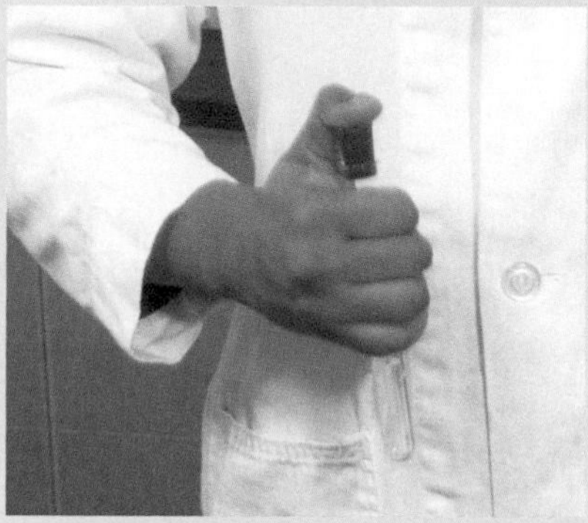

FIGURE 2.38 Step 8.

Analysis and Conclusion

1 List the fuels from the most combustible to the least combustible.

2 What common observation was seen for each fuel burned?

3 What gas is produced? How do you know?

4 Write a word equation for the complete combustion of each fuel.

5 Compare your results with those of other students in your class. Were they the same? Different? Why do you think so?

6 Explain how the factors that affect rates of reaction played a role in the combustion of each fuel.

CONTINUED

Extension and Connection

When a match burns there are a series of connected reactions that occur. The process starts at the outside of the match and works its way in.

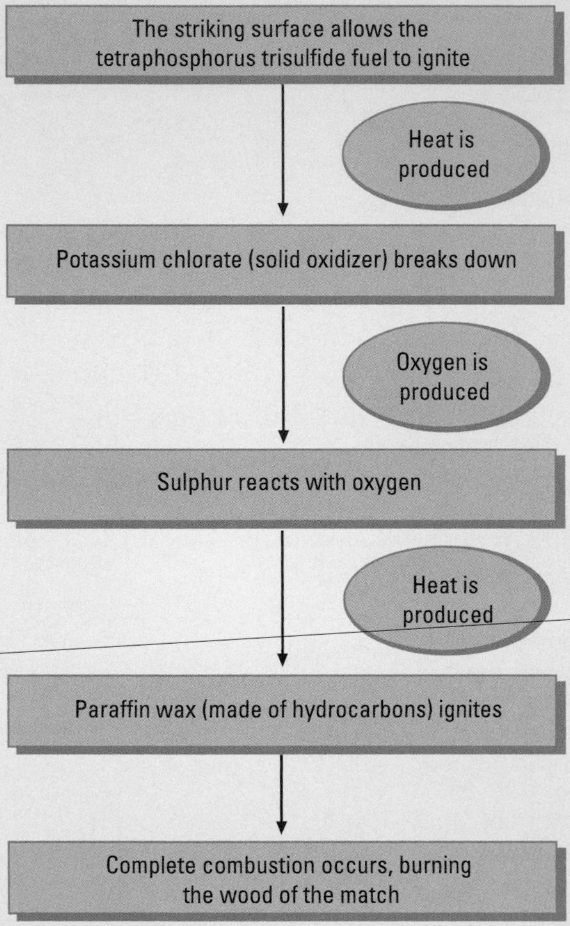
The striking surface allows the tetraphosphorus trisulfide fuel to ignite
Heat is produced
Potassium chlorate (solid oxidizer) breaks down
Oxygen is produced
Sulphur reacts with oxygen
Heat is produced
Paraffin wax (made of hydrocarbons) ignites
Complete combustion occurs, burning the wood of the match

FIGURE 2.39

7. Research the differences between "strike anywhere" and safety matches. Should strike-anywhere matches be illegal? Justify your position.

8. Find out how diving "torches" work underwater.

ACTIVITY 2E

Making a Fire Extinguisher

Did you know that smoke alarms are the most effective early-warning devices available? Smoke alarms should be installed on every level of your home, preferably near sleeping areas. According to the Office of the Fire Marshall, having an operating smoke alarm can help lower your chance of dying in a home fire by 50 percent!

Fire safety and prevention are very important. Before you begin this activity, brainstorm with your class ways you can help prevent a fire at home, school and in the workplace and outline what fire safety precautions you should always follow. Prepare a fire safety and prevention checklist that you can use at home.

Fire extinguishers are used to put out fires. Depending on the type of fire, a different type of fire extinguisher is needed. Newer fire extinguishers use a picture and label to identify the type of fires for which they should be used. Older fire extinguishers have different coloured shapes with a letter in the middle that identifies the type of fire they will extinguish. Both of these types of labels are shown in Figure 2.40, along with a description of the different classes of extinguishers. In this activity, you will make a fire extinguisher.

Types of Fire Extinguishers

Class of fire extinguisher	What is the major ingredient?	Type of fire it puts out	What it looks like
Class A  Ordinary combustibles 	Water and foam	Burning paper, wood, cloth, rubber and many plastics	
Class B  Flammable liquids 	Foam, carbon dioxide, dry chemicals	Flammable liquids such as kitchen greases, oils, paints and solvents	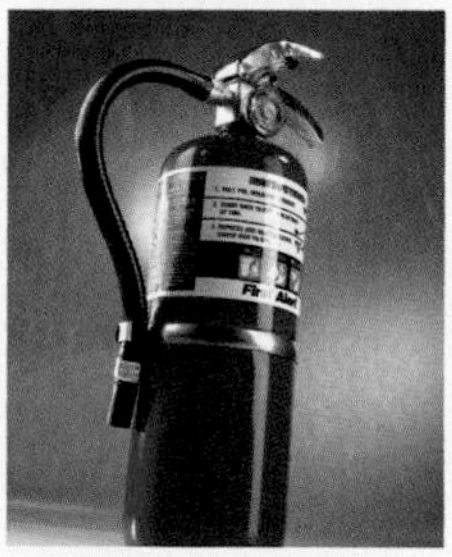

CONTINUED

Class of fire extinguisher	What is the major ingredient?	Type of fire it puts out	What it looks like
Class C  Electrical equipment 	Carbon dioxide and dry chemicals	Electrical fires	
Class A-B-C  Ordinary combustibles Flammable liquids Electrical equipment 	Carbon dioxide and multi-purpose dry chemicals	All types of fires	
Class D  Combustible metals	Dry powders	Combustible metals such as potassium, magnesium and sodium that typically burn at very high temperatures. (This type of fire occurs in a laboratory or in an industry that uses these materials; it is not a common type of fire.)	

FIGURE 2.40

What You Will Need

- 1 250-mL Erlenmeyer flask
- 1 one-hole rubber stopper for the flask
- 1 no-hole rubber stopper for test tube
- 1 straw with a flexible end
- 2 small test tubes
- 1 test tube holder
- 1 graduated cylinder
- 20 g sodium hydrogen carbonate (baking soda)
- 20 mL acetic acid (vinegar)
- limewater (calcium hydroxide solution)
- safety goggles and lab coat
- 250 mL of water
- stirring rod

What You Will Do

Part One: Making and Using a Fire Extinguisher

1. Put on your safety goggles and lab coat.
2. Fill the Erlenmeyer flask with 125 mL of water.
3. Add 10 g of sodium hydrogen carbonate and mix until it is dissolved.
4. Pour 10 mL of acetic acid into one of the small test tubes. Place it inside the Erlenmeyer flask. Be careful not to mix the 2 liquids. Refer to Figure 2.41.

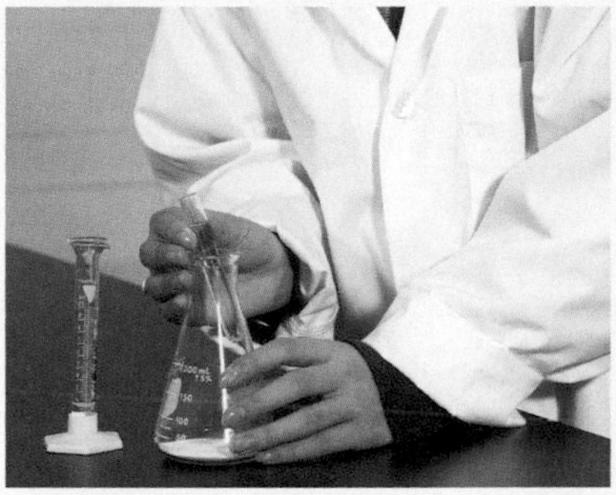

FIGURE 2.41 Step 4.

5. Insert the straw into the rubber stopper, making sure the flexible end is on top.
6. Insert the rubber stopper and straw into the flask.
7. Your teacher will start a small fire inside a beaker with a piece of paper.
8. Place your finger on the open end of the straw. Refer to Figure 2.42. Carefully turn the Erlenmeyer flask upside down so that the 2 solutions mix. Remove your finger from the straw and point the nozzle of the straw towards the fire. Record your observation.

FIGURE 2.42 Step 8.

9. Dispose of the mixture in the flask as instructed by your teacher. Clean your flask and test tube.

Part Two: Testing the Gas Released

1. Repeat steps 2 to 6 from Part One.
2. Fill your second test tube with limewater. Place it in a test tube holder.

Be Safe!

Use care around an open flame. Tie back long hair and remove any hanging jewellery.

CONTINUED

3. Place your finger on the open end of the straw. Carefully turn the Erlenmeyer flask upside down so that the 2 solutions mix. Remove your finger from the straw and point the nozzle of the straw towards the test tube containing limewater.

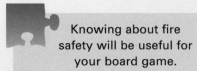

FIGURE 2.43 Step 3.

4. Do not allow any of the liquid to pour from your fire extinguisher to the test tube containing limewater.
5. After 30 seconds, insert a rubber stopper into the test tube and gently shake the tube to mix the gas. Record your observations.
6. Dispose of the mixture in the flask and test tube as instructed by your teacher. Clean your work area.

What Did You Find Out?

1. What gas is released when the 2 solutions are mixed? How do you know? Why did it put out the fire?
2. Consider Lab 2D. If something caught fire, what type of fire extinguisher would you use? Explain your answer.

Making Connections

3. Explain the importance of having a working fire extinguisher at home, at school or in the workplace.
4. Make a presentation to another Grade 11 class, explaining why it is important to have an evacuation plan at home, school and work. In your presentation you must include:
   a) diagrams of effective, safe and quick evacuation plans for home, school and a sample workplace
   b) reasons why evacuation plans should be practised at least 4 times a year
   c) what happens when evacuation plans are not in place.
5. Inspect your home using the fire safety and prevention checklist you created before beginning this activity.

Knowing about fire safety will be useful for your board game.

2.4 Chapter Summary

Now You Can...

- Describe factors that affect the rate of chemical reaction (2.1)
- Describe tests for gases (2.1)
- Identify some oxidizing agents and describe their chemical reactivity (Labs 2A, 2C; 2.2, 2.3)
- Predict the reactivity of metal elements using the activity series of metals (2.2, Lab 2C)
- Predict the reactivity of metals with acids and oxygen (Lab 2B)
- Write word equations for complete and incomplete combustion (2.3)
- Use rates of reactions to answer questions on combustion (2.3, Activity 2D)
- Compare the corrosive action of acids on various metals and collect and test for hydrogen gas (Lab 2A, 2.1)
- Compare the ease of combustion of various flammable liquids (Activity 2D)
- Prepare and use a fire extinguisher and determine proper fire precautions in the home, school and workplace (Lab 2E)

Concept Connections

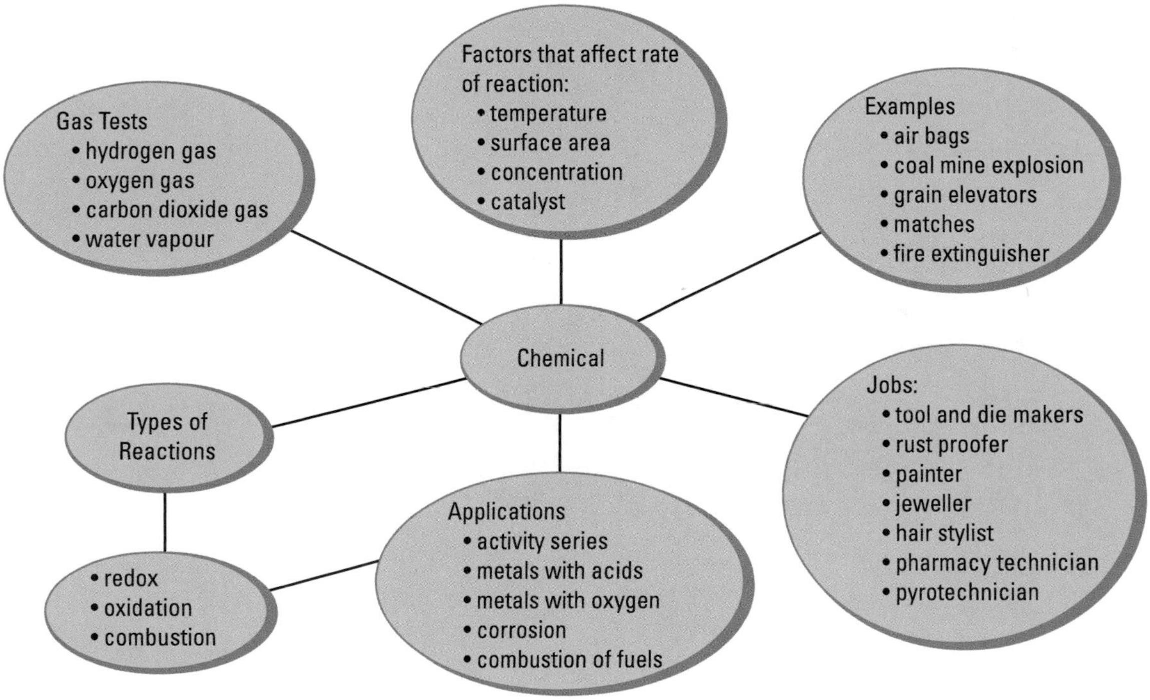

FIGURE 2.44 Compare your completed graphic organizer to the one on this page. How did you do? Can you add any new links to your organizer?

CHAPTER 2 *review*

Knowledge and Understanding

1. For each of the following statements indicate True or False. If False, rewrite the statement to make it true.
   - **a)** In a chemical reaction the properties of the products are different from those of the reactants.
   - **b)** For the chemical test of oxygen gas a burning splint is used.
   - **c)** The rate of chemical reaction is not affected by temperature.
   - **d)** When acids react with metals, they produce hydrogen gas and a metal compound.
   - **e)** An atom that has lost or gained electrons is called a proton.
   - **f)** A redox reaction involves the transfer of electrons.
   - **g)** Combustion reactions do not produce carbon dioxide gas.
2. Provide an example of each of the 4 factors that affect the rate of reaction and explain how each works.
3. Use the activity series found in Figure 2.19 on page 42, to arrange the following metals from least reactive to most reactive: aluminum, copper, calcium, lead, gold and zinc.
4. Write the formula for the complete combustion of the hydrocarbon octane.
5. Identify the different classes of fire and the type of fire extinguisher that should be used in each case.
6. Create a poster about fire safety and fire prevention.
7. A well-known oxidizing agent is oxygen. It will react with metals and fuels. Give 2 examples of other oxidizing agents.

Inquiry

8. Wally has been given 2 pieces of metal: zinc and stainless steel. He must identify which piece of metal is more reactive. Explain the procedure he should use and identify the type of gas that would be released. How could he test for this gas?
9. List the factors that affect the rates of reaction. Choose one and create a lab explaining how you could test it. Make sure to include what your result would be if you performed the lab.

Making Connections

10 You work at a grocery store and your manager has asked you to cut some apples and serve them to the customers as they enter the store. As you begin to serve the pieces of apple you notice some of the pieces are turning brown. A little boy coming into the store says he does not like brown apples. Explain to him why the apple pieces have changed colour. How could you stop the apple pieces from turning brown?

FIGURE 2.45

11 Beth works for a machine shop. She is asked to coat a piece of iron with magnesium to protect it from corroding. Will this procedure work? Why or why not?

12 Su-Lee works as a cook in a restaurant on weekends. As she was cooking, the oil in the pan caught fire. Su-Lee threw water on the fire to try to put it out. What should Su-Lee have done instead? Why?

13 If you take flour dust and sprinkle it on an open flame it will catch on fire. However, if you take a piece of dough and place it on an open flame it will not catch on fire. Explain why both these statements are true.

Communication

14 Give an example of how the combustion of octane is influenced by the factors that affect the rate of a chemical reaction.

15 Write an example of an important application for preventing corrosion. (Hint: Use the activity series.) Explain how it applies in the workplace.

16 As you are leaving school, you notice one of your teachers sitting in the car reading a book with the motor idling. Outline to your teacher the consequences that leaving the car running may have on the environment. What gases are released? What should the teacher do instead? Why?

PUTTING IT ALL TOGETHER

Designing a Safety Board Game

WHMIS, HHPS, Material Safety Data Sheets (MSDS), proper storage of chemicals, safe handling, storage and disposal of materials, safety procedures to follow at home, school and in the workplace and practices that promote fire safety! How do these things all fit together? In this activity, you will work in groups of 4 to design a board game about materials and safety.

The Project

In your group, you will create a game board, game pieces and scenario-type questions relating to the information you have learned in Chapters 1 and 2. Your questions may involve drawing, writing, or acting. Be as creative as possible! Do not forget to include questions about the importance of safety at home, school and in the workplace.

What You May Need

- MSDS
- access to Internet and/or library resources
- coloured pens, markers and/or pencils
- cardboard, or a computer, to make the questions
- any material to make the game board and game pieces
- die, spinner, or number wheel

FIGURE 1A Some of the materials you may use when designing your board game.

What You Will Do

1. Based on the information researched and learned in Unit 1, each member of your group will create 10 questions with answers, for a total of 40 questions. Look through Chapters 1 and 2 as well as through your notes to get ideas for your questions. Make sure you share your questions with your group members so you do not have the same question twice.

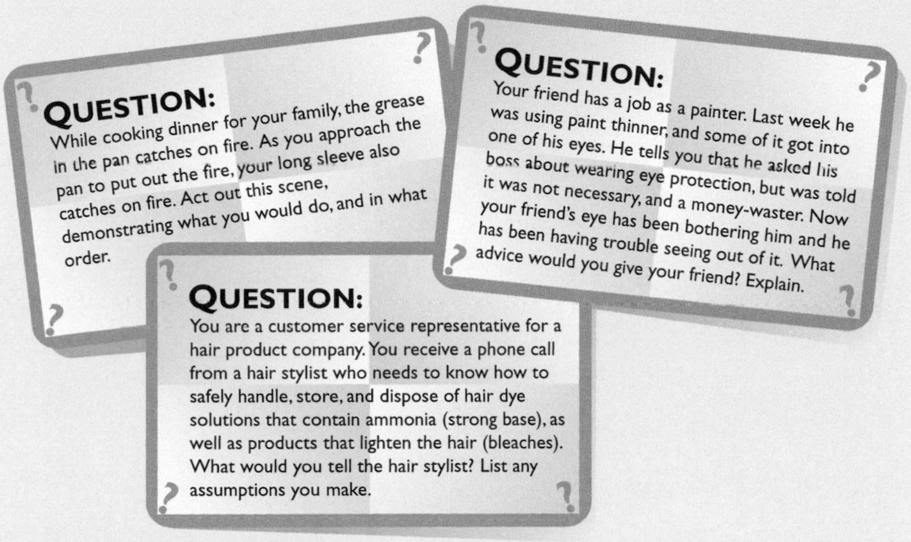

QUESTION:
While cooking dinner for your family, the grease in the pan catches on fire. As you approach the pan to put out the fire, your long sleeve also catches on fire. Act out this scene, demonstrating what you would do, and in what order.
QUESTION:
Your friend has a job as a painter. Last week he was using paint thinner, and some of it got into one of his eyes. He tells you that he asked his boss about wearing eye protection, but was told it was not necessary, and a money-waster. Now your friend's eye has been bothering him and he has been having trouble seeing out of it. What advice would you give your friend? Explain.
QUESTION:
You are a customer service representative for a hair product company. You receive a phone call from a hair stylist who needs to know how to safely handle, store, and dispose of hair dye solutions that contain ammonia (strong base), as well as products that lighten the hair (bleaches). What would you tell the hair stylist? List any assumptions you make.

FIGURE 2A Sample questions for your board game.

2. As a group, brainstorm what you want your game board and game pieces to look like. Once you have agreed on a design, begin making it. Your group will also decide how you will play your game. You will need to create a list of rules. The game should be played within 30 minutes and all the researched information should be included in the game, such as questions, photos, artwork, or diagrams.

CONTINUED

Assessment

3 Present your board game and how it works to the class. Compare your board game with the other groups in your class. What did you think they did well? What did you like best about your group's board game? If you were to do this activity again, what changes would you make to your board game? Why?

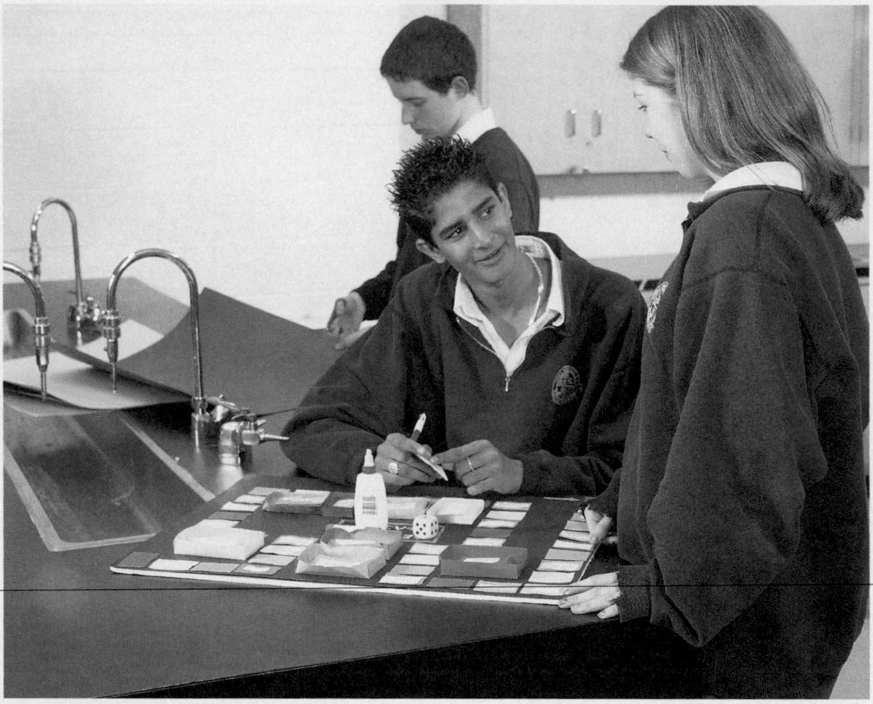

FIGURE 3A A sample board game.

UNIT 2

Electric Circuits

CHAPTER 3: Electricity—What Is It?
CHAPTER 4: Practical Electricity
PUTTING IT ALL TOGETHER: Wiring a New Office

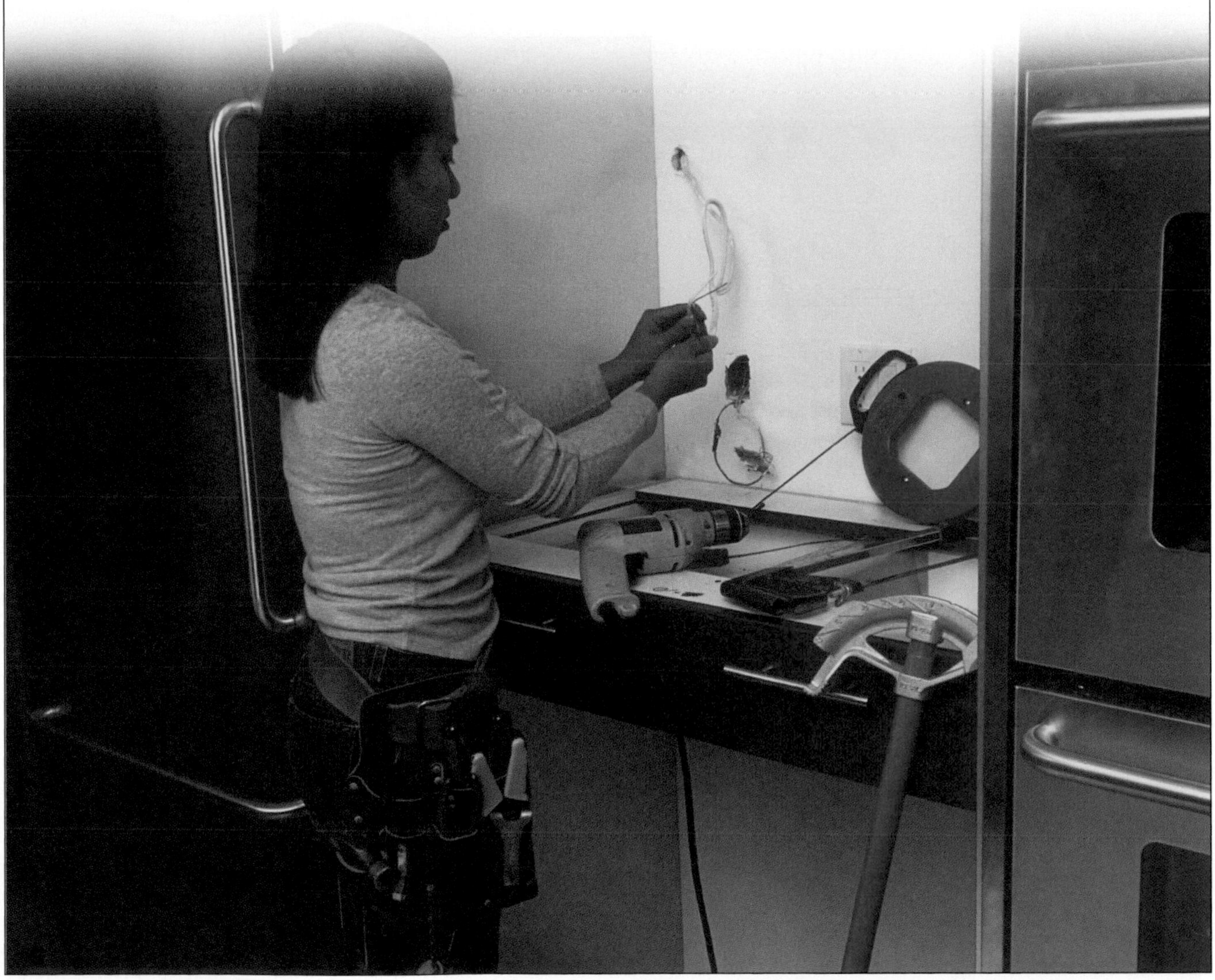

CHAPTER 3

Electricity— What Is It?

You use electricity every day, when you switch on a light, use a hair dryer, watch television, or listen to the radio. But what makes electricity work? In this chapter, you will learn how electric circuits work and how to safely construct, design, and analyze common electric circuits. Look at Figure 3.1. Why do you think the trees are being trimmed around the electric wires? Why do cars sometimes need a boost?

FIGURE 3.1

What You Will Learn

After completing this chapter, you will be able to:

- Describe the components of common electric circuits (3.1; Labs 3A, 3B, 3C, 3D)
- Explain the difference between direct and alternating current (3.2)
- Describe the functions of components that regulate the flow of electricity in electric circuits (3.3)
- Identify the SI units for potential difference, current and resistance (3.1)
- Use and describe proper safety procedures for working with electricity at home and at work (3.1, 3.3; Labs 3A, 3B, 3C, 3D)
- Analyze the relationship among potential difference, electric current and resistance in a complete electric circuit (3.1, Lab 3A, 3.3)
- Describe and identify situations in which electric circuits can be fire hazards or dangerous to human life (3.1, 3.3)

What You Will Do

- Construct and inspect simple electric circuits (Labs 3A, 3B, 3C, 3D)
- Identify and correctly use equipment to measure potential difference, electric current and resistance (3.1, 3.3)
- Use safe practices while working with electric circuits (Labs 3A, 3B, 3C, 3D)
- Draw and interpret schematic diagrams of electric circuits (3.1, 3.3)
- Build a circuit using the appropriate tools (Lab 3D)
- Analyze electric circuits, identify any faults and make corrections (3.3; Labs 3A, 3B, 3C, 3D)
- Use lab equipment safely, effectively and accurately (Labs 3A, 3B, 3C, 3D)

Words to Know

alternating current (AC)
ammeter
ampere
circuit breaker
closed circuit
conductor
coulomb
current
direct current (DC)
electric circuit
energy source
fuse
load
ohm
ohmmeter
open circuit
parallel circuit
potential difference
potential energy
resistance
resistor
schematic diagram
series circuit
short circuit
turbine
volt
voltmeter

A puzzle piece indicates knowledge or a skill that you will need for your project, Wiring a New Office, at the end of Unit 2.

3.1 Learning about Electricity

Electricity is a form of energy. It is produced by the movement of electrons. But do you know what actually happens when you flip a switch to turn on the light, or the computer, or the television set? Why do all the lights not go out in your home when 1 light bulb burns out? Electricity is very useful, but if people do the wrong thing, electricity can also hurt. In some cases it can even kill. Safety is key when it comes to electricity.

Electric Circuits

How does electricity flow? Electricity flows through paths, or **electric circuits**. Electrons travel through these paths, but only if they can move around the path and get back to where they started. If the path is broken, the electrons will not move.

A **closed circuit** allows electrons to travel through an unbroken path and back to where they started. An **open circuit** has a break in the path. Electrons will not move through an open circuit.

All circuits must contain 3 things: connecting conductors, an energy source, and a load. A **conductor** is a device, such as a wire, that allows electricity to pass easily through it. An **energy source**, such as a battery, is what gives the circuit its energy. A **load** is a device or appliance that uses the energy, such as a light bulb. Figure 3.2 shows the circuit symbols used when drawing a circuit.

You will use circuit symbols for your project, Wiring a New Office.

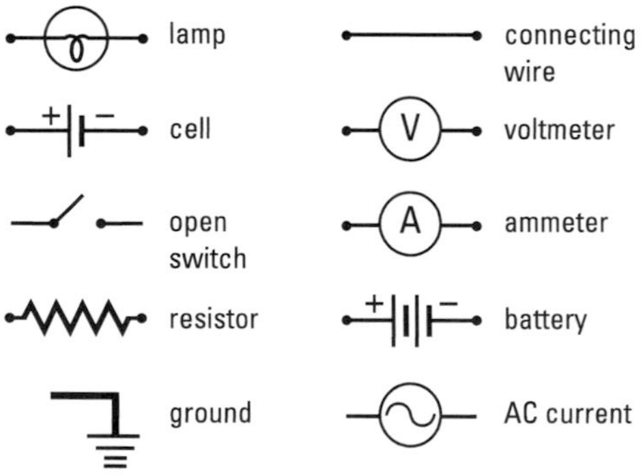

FIGURE 3.2 These are the symbols for the basic parts of a circuit.

Electric Current

The flow of electrons around an electric circuit is measured by the **current**. Imagine that each electron is a drop of water. The current would be like a river. In a river, there are too many drops of water to count. In a similar way, there are too many electrons in a current to count! To count them easily, we "package" electrons into groups of charge called **coulombs**.

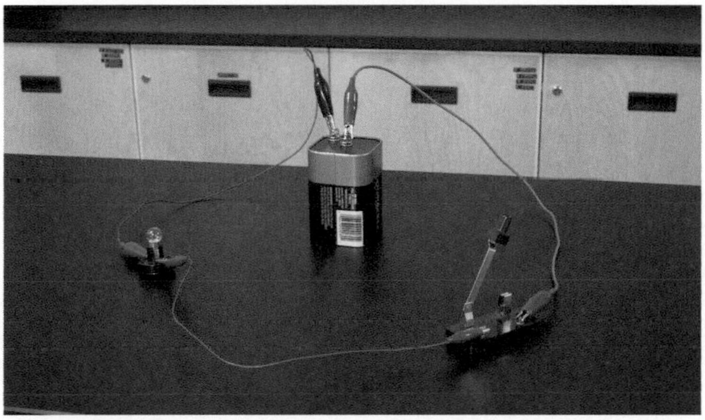

FIGURE 3.3A An electric circuit will work without a switch. Why are switches included in electric circuits?

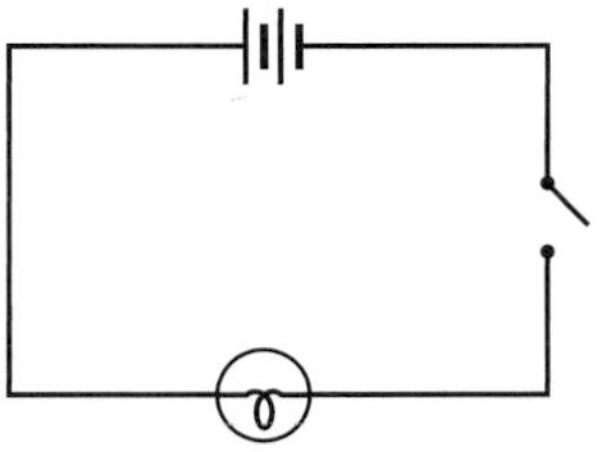

FIGURE 3.3B We use symbols to represent circuits. The symbols above represent the circuit at the left. This diagram is called a **schematic diagram.**

Electric current is measured in **amperes** (A).

A device called an **ammeter** is used to measure how many coulombs of charge pass a certain point in a circuit every second. To measure current, the ammeter must be in the circuit as shown in Figure 3.4A. Current is a measure of how many electrons are flowing through a circuit at any given time.

FIGURE 3.4A Proper arrangement of an ammeter in a circuit.

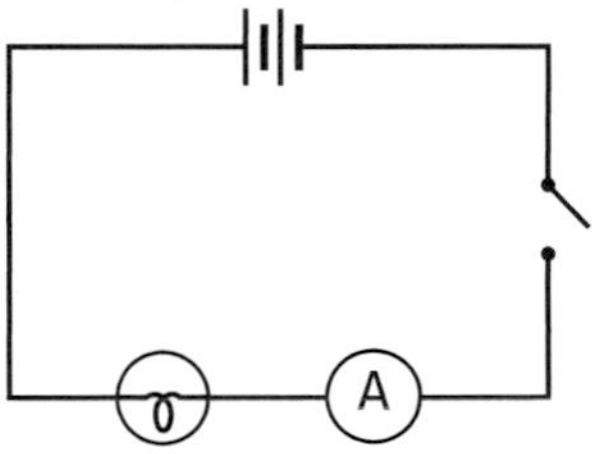

FIGURE 3.4B Schematic diagram of an ammeter in a circuit.

Potential Difference

Potential energy is stored energy that can be used to do something. Electrons get their energy from the potential energy stored in the energy source of a circuit.

Look at Figure 3.5 below. When the electrons leave the battery, they have a certain amount of energy. When they pass through the light bulb, they release energy so that the bulb can light. If we measure the potential energy at points 1 and 2 on the circuit, we will find a difference. That is the **potential difference**. Potential difference is a measure of the energy per coulomb. Potential difference is measured in **volts** (V) using a device called a **voltmeter** (see Figure 3.6). As the electrons pass through the battery again, the energy is continually renewed. Look at Figure 3.5. Will there be a potential difference between points 2 and 3? How about points 3 and 4?

ScienceWise Fact

An electric eel can produce as much as 650 V at 1 A of electricity, enough to kill a horse! Almost 90% of an eel's body is essentially a battery.

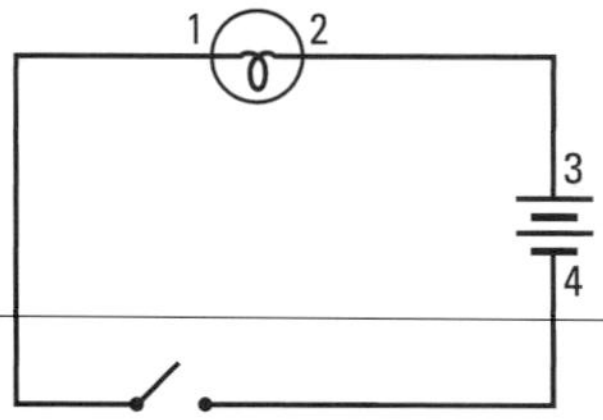

FIGURE 3.5 A schematic diagram of a circuit.

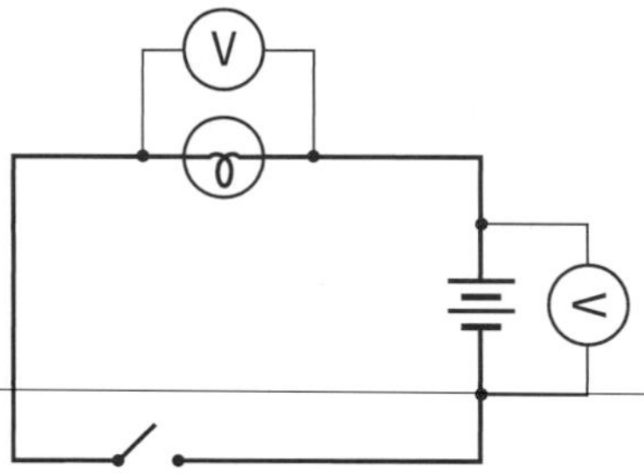

FIGURE 3.6 Voltmeters are not placed directly in the circuit.

Resistance

A material that an electron flows through is called a conductor. Electrons move more easily through some conductors than others. For example, copper is a better conductor than iron. A material that is difficult for electrons to flow through is called a **resistor**. Resistors restrict the flow of electrons.

Resistance is a measure of how easily current can flow through a material. It is measured in **ohms** (Ω) using a device called an **ohmmeter**. A material with a resistance of 2 Ω allows electrons to flow more easily than a material with a resistance of 4 Ω.

Series versus Parallel Circuits

Now you know that electrons need a circuit, or a path, to flow through.

There are 2 kinds of circuits. A **series circuit** (as seen in Figure 3.7) is a circuit set up like a running track. There is only one path for electrons to flow. A **parallel circuit** (Figure 3.8) is a circuit set up like city streets. There are many paths for electrons to flow. In Lab 3A, Series and Parallel Circuits, you will investigate how potential difference, current and resistance compare in different parts of these circuits.

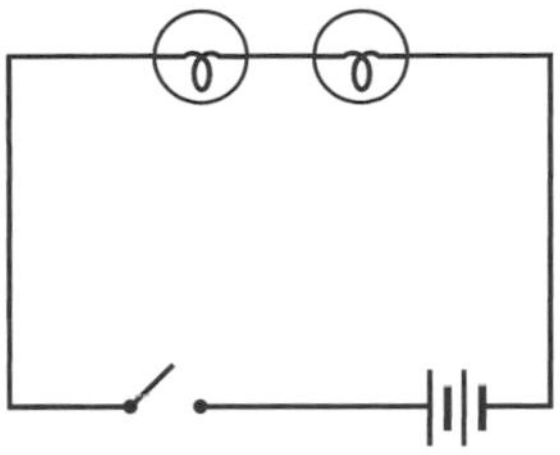

FIGURE 3.7 In a series circuit, if 1 light bulb burns out, the whole circuit turns off. An example of a series circuit is a string of inexpensive festive or holiday lights.

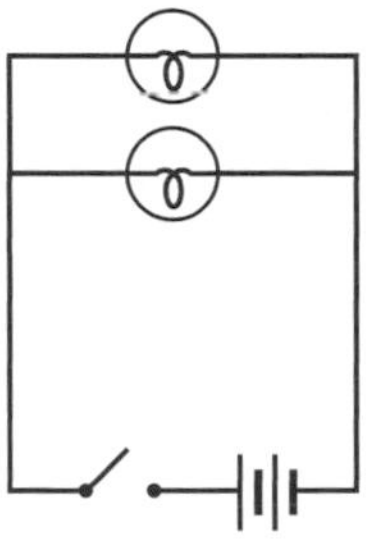

FIGURE 3.8 In a parallel circuit, if 1 light bulb burns out, the circuit still works. Can you give an example of a parallel circuit?

You will need to know the difference between series and parallel circuits for your project, Wiring a New Office.

Be Safe!

- Electricity can be very dangerous. Circuits can safely carry a specific amount of current. If you overload or exceed this safe amount, you can cause a fire.

Figure 3.9 shows a shock hazard symbol. You would find this on the electric devices in your home or workplace. To be safe indoors and outdoors, follow the rules on page 76.

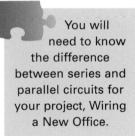

FIGURE 3.9

Indoor and Outdoor Safety

At home

Do not run extension cords under carpets. Extension cords are designed to be used temporarily. If you need one permanently, you should install a new outlet closer to the appliance.

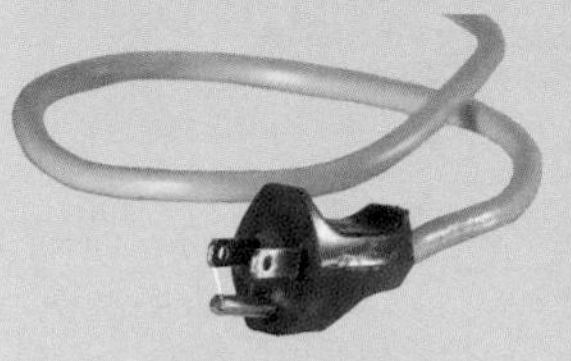

Never cut the ground pin off of a 3-pronged plug.

Never use tacks, staples, or nails to fasten extension cords permanently to walls or baseboards.

Do not plug too many appliances into one outlet. This can overload the circuit. Do not use indoor extension cords outside.

In class

Never connect the positive terminal of an energy source, such as a battery, to the negative terminal without a load in between. This is called a short circuit.

Always have your circuit checked by your teacher before closing the switch.

Outdoors

Never fly a kite or a model plane near overhead power lines.

Never touch an electric wire that has fallen to the ground. Even if the wire does not make a noise or a spark, it is still very dangerous.

Never mix water and electricity. Electricity can travel through water. For example, never mow the lawn with an electric mower when it is raining.

Do not have electric cords near a pool.

In the workplace

Use Canadian Standards Association (CSA) approved equipment.

Follow all guidelines and rules provided.

Practise proper lockout procedures on electric equipment. (Lockout is a safety measure to protect against accidental operation when the operation of the equipment and/or circuits could cause injury to a person.)

FIGURE 3.10 Give other examples of electrical safety that could be practised at home, in class, outdoors, and at work.

Effects of Electricity

Amperes (A)		Effect on the human body
1 A	Necessary to light a 100 W light bulb (enough to kill 20 people)	
0.200 A	Severe burns, no breathing	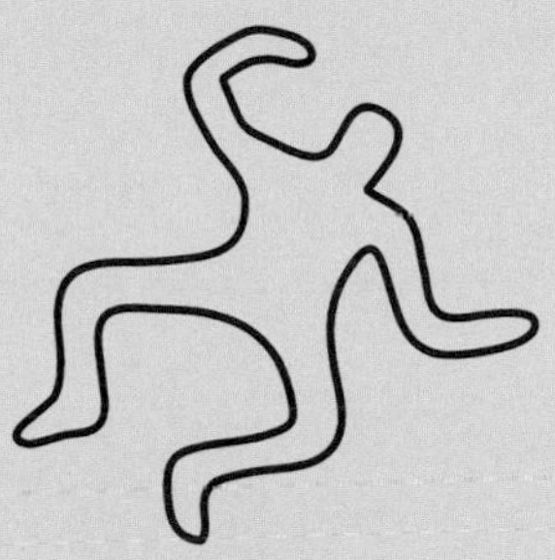
0.050 A	Heart stops pumping (usually causing death)	
0.016 A	Person cannot let go of power source, muscles shake violently, breathing is affected	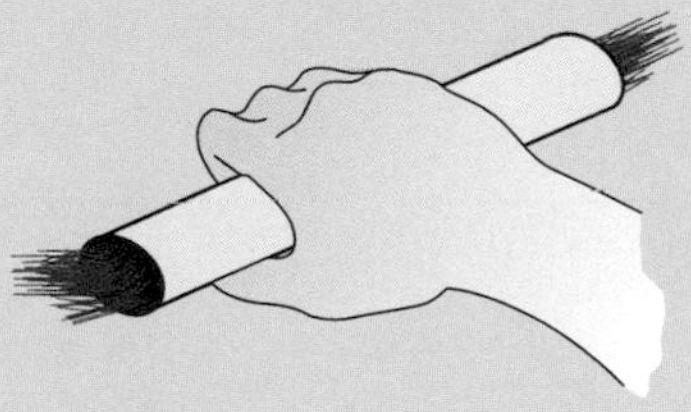
0.005 A	Maximum safe level of current	
0.002 A	Muscles tingle or have a stinging feeling	
0.001 A	You can feel the electricity	

FIGURE 3.11 The effects of electricity on humans.

Be Safe!

To avoid electrocution (death by electric current), follow these steps:

- Protect all outlets, cords, and electric appliances from water.
- Always disconnect from the energy source before working on a circuit.
- Double-check that the circuit is open before you begin your work.

LAB 3A

Series and Parallel Circuits

How do current, potential difference, and resistance affect circuits? Does it matter if the circuit is series or parallel? Now that you have learned about circuits, you will apply that knowledge to constructing them with the help of schematic diagrams.

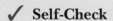

Be Safe!

- Read the procedure carefully before you begin.
- Have your teacher check your circuit before you close the switch.

Purpose

In this lab, you will measure current, potential difference, and resistance in both series and parallel circuits. You will analyze how current, potential difference, and resistance change depending on the type of circuit used.

Materials

- 5 connecting leads
- energy source (12 V)
- 2 light bulbs (4–6 V)
- 1 switch
- multimeter (ammeter, voltmeter, and ohmmeter)

Procedure

Part One: A Series Circuit with 1 Light Bulb

1. Create a data table like Figure 3.12 in your notebook.

Current (A)		Potential difference (V)	Resistance (Ω)
________ A	Across bulb	________ V	________ Ω
	Across battery	________ V	

FIGURE 3.12

2. Construct the circuit (Figure 3.13) without the ammeters or voltmeters.
   - Connect the multimeter to the circuit as an ammeter. Measure the current.
   - Connect the multimeter to the circuit as a voltmeter. Measure the potential difference across the bulb and across the battery.
   - Connect the multimeter to the circuit as an ohmmeter. Measure the resistance across the light bulb.
   - Record your measurements in your data table.

✓ **Self-Check**

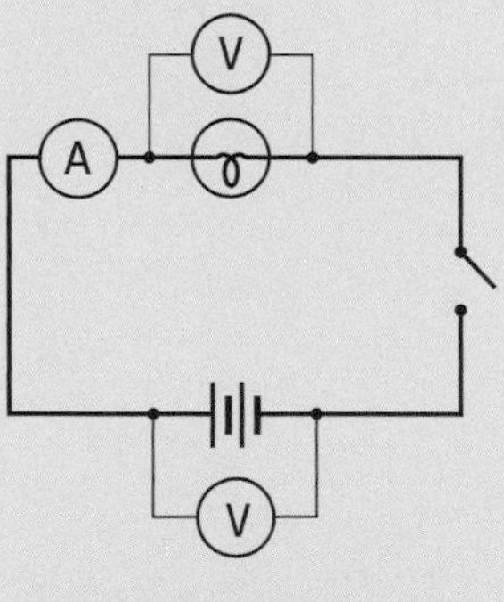

FIGURE 3.13 Compare your set-up with this schematic diagram. If it is different, make any necessary corrections.

Part Two: A Series Circuit with 2 Light Bulbs

1. Create a data table to record your results.
2. Construct the circuit (Figure 3.14) without the ammeters and voltmeters.
   - Use the multimeter as an ammeter. Measure the current through point A and point B.
   - Use the multimeter as a voltmeter. Measure the potential difference across each light bulb and the battery.
   - Use the multimeter as an ohmmeter. Measure the resistance across each light bulb.
   - Record your measurements in your data table.
   - Unwind bulb 2. What happens to bulb 1?

✓ **Self-Check**

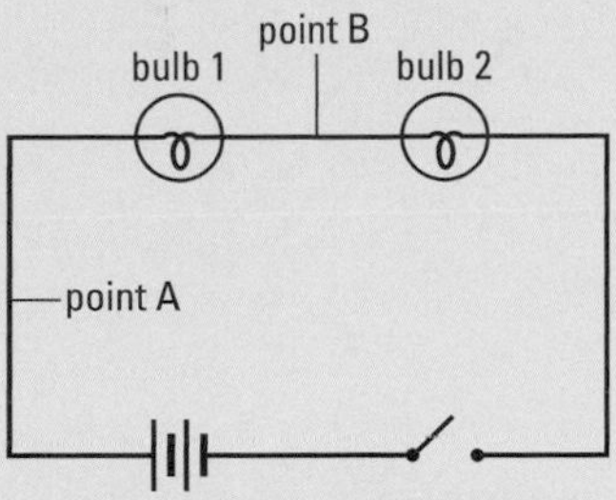

FIGURE 3.14 Compare your set-up with this schematic diagram. If it is different, make any necessary corrections.

Part Three: A Parallel Circuit

1. Create a data table to record your results.
2. Construct the circuit (Figure 3.15) without the ammeters and voltmeters.
   - Use the multimeter as an ammeter. Measure the current through point A and point B.
   - Use the multimeter as a voltmeter. Measure the potential difference across each light bulb and the battery.
   - Use the multimeter as an ohmmeter. Measure the resistance across each light bulb.
   - Record your measurements in your data table.
   - Unwind bulb 2. What happens to bulb 1?

✓ **Self-Check**

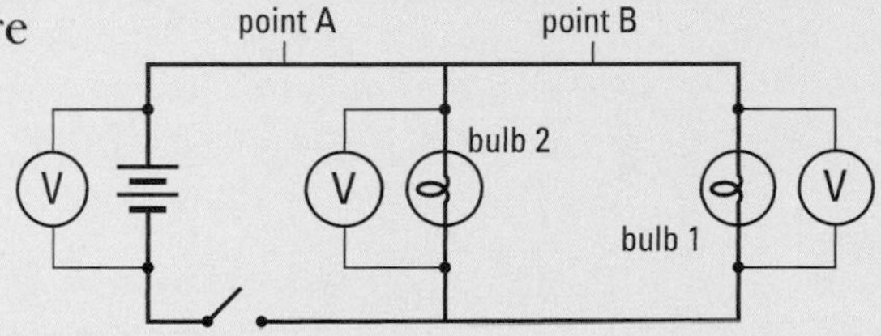

FIGURE 3.15 Compare your set-up with this schematic diagram. If it is different, make any necessary corrections.

Analysis and Conclusion

1. What happens to the current as you add more pathways to your circuit?
2. What happens to the potential difference as you add more light bulbs to a series circuit?
3. What happens to resistance as current changes?
4. What safety precautions did you follow in this lab?

Extension and Connection

5. If you were going to wire a home, would you use series or parallel circuits? Why? What are the disadvantages of your choice?

Series and Parallel Circuits

You now know that in a series circuit, each electron has to pass through every load in the circuit. Everything is arranged in a row, so electrons follow a single path. In a parallel circuit, the electrons flow through all available paths. Electricity has a choice of which path to take around the circuit. Some electricity flows to each load.

Comparing Series and Parallel Circuits

Type of circuit	Current	Potential difference	Resistors
Series	the same throughout	shared between the loads	adding more loads reduces current
Parallel	shared between the paths	the same throughout	adding more loads increases the current

FIGURE 3.16 Table comparing current and potential difference in series and parallel circuits. Resistors affect series and parallel circuits in different ways.

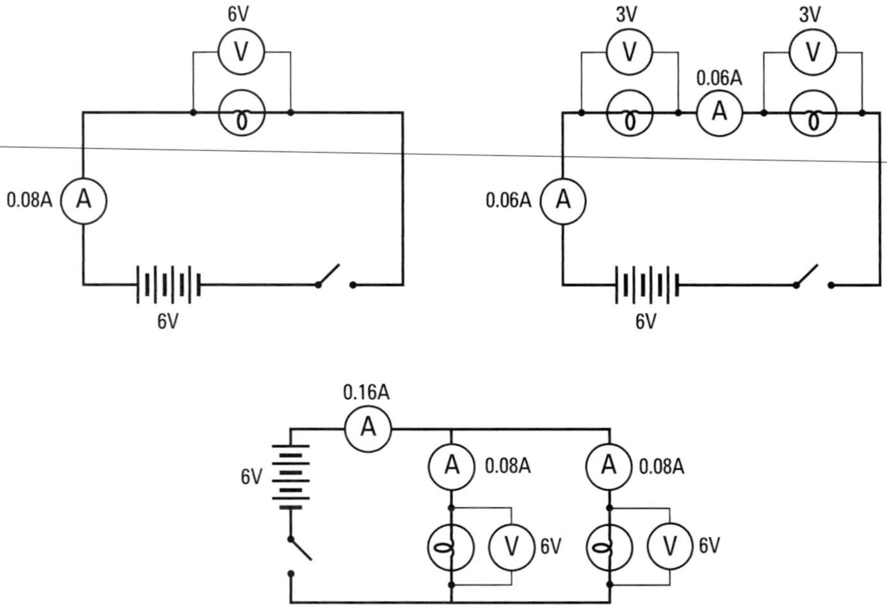

FIGURE 3.17 Solved series and parallel circuits.

Review and Apply

1. Use Figure 3.18 to identify the load and energy source in a flashlight.
2. Why must a plug have at least 2 prongs?
3. Anastasia is helping her dad build a bookcase in their backyard. She gets to use a drill. Suddenly, it starts to rain. What safety advice would you give her and her father? Why?
4. Organize the concepts you have learned in this section in a graphic organizer.

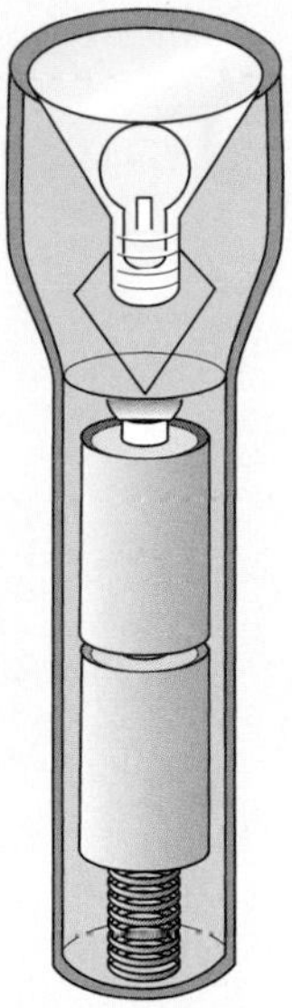

FIGURE 3.18

5. **Drawing and Testing Circuits**

Work with a partner to draw a schematic diagram for each of the following circuits. Construct the circuits you have drawn using the materials from Lab 3A.

- Two light bulbs in series with a switch, battery and ammeter.
- One light bulb with a switch, parallel to another light bulb with its own switch, connected to a battery.

If you were building a circuit at home or in the workplace, you would not use the same materials to construct circuits as you have used in this activity. For example, a 40 W or 60 W bulb would replace the 2 W bulb. For each material used to construct your circuits, try to identify what would be used if the circuit were in a home or business.

3.2 Generating Electricity

We use electricity every day. Electricity comes from many sources, such as generating stations, batteries and cells. But how is the electric current produced? To answer this question, we need to look at the different types of electric currents.

There are 2 types of electric current: direct current (DC) and alternating current (AC). The type of electric current depends on how the current is generated.

Direct Current

Direct current (DC) is the movement of electrons through a conductor from a negatively charged area to a positively charged area. It is a direct flow of electrons. When you measured the voltage of the current travelling through the conductor in Lab 3A, Series and Parallel Circuits, the reading always had the same sign (either positive or negative). This means that the current is travelling in only one direction.

There are a few ways to produce electrons that travel in only one direction in a conductor. One way is through a cell or a battery. Remember, from Section 3.1, that a conductor allows electrons to flow. Examples of materials that allow electric current to flow through them are wires made of aluminum, steel, or copper.

FIGURE 3.19 Cells and batteries are good producers of direct current. Identify which are cells and which are batteries.

How Cells and Batteries Generate Electricity

If you look at any cell, it has 2 terminals: a positive (+) and a negative (−) terminal. Inside the cell, a chemical reaction at the negative terminal produces electrons. Another chemical reaction at the positive terminal uses up electrons. If you connect the 2 terminals, the electrons flow from the negative terminal in the cell to the positive terminal.

A battery is a group of cells connected in series or in parallel. If connected in series, the potential difference will be increased, but if connected in parallel, the batteries will last longer. See Figure 3.19 for examples of cells and batteries.

Alternating Current

Alternating current (AC) is the back and forth movement of electrons through a wire. The most common method of generating alternating current is mechanical-magnetic.

A magnet has a magnetic field. If a conductor passes through this field, it produces an electric current. If the movement of the conductor, relative to the magnet, is in one direction, the current produced also moves in only one direction. Refer to Figure 3.20.

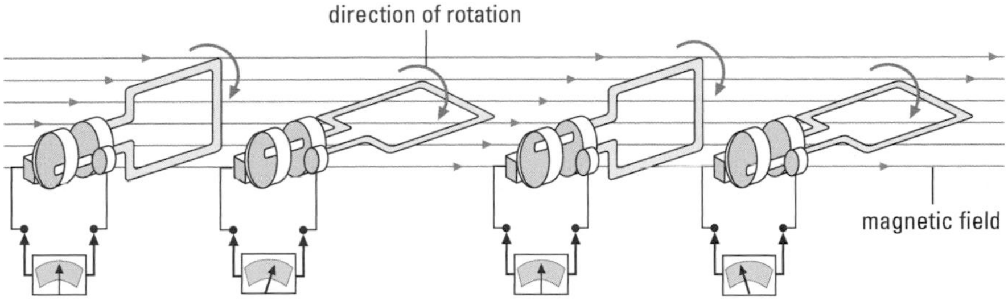

FIGURE 3.20 A generator generally produces an alternating current because the conductor "cuts" the magnetic field in one direction during the first half of the spin and in the opposite direction during the second half of the spin.

Spinning a coiled conductor within a magnetic field is the most common method of generating electricity. The **turbine** turns the generator which produces the electricity.

If moving a conductor in a magnetic field is all we need to produce electricity, why is our society so concerned about future sources of energy? The problem with a turbine is finding the energy to move the magnet or coil. This energy can be provided by gravity (waterfalls), or heat (burning fossil fuels or nuclear reaction).

Ways of Generating Electricity for Society

If you have ever stood under a waterfall, you know that the falling water produces a great deal of force on whatever it hits. If we direct the water to fall so that it turns a turbine, which then turns a generator, electricity is produced.

FIGURE 3.21 These dams produce no pollutants and are not expensive to operate. However, they are expensive to build.

Waterfalls are often manufactured by creating an artificial lake called a reservoir and putting a dam in it. Dams and their reservoirs can upset or destroy ecosystems and flood land. If possible, natural waterfalls such as Niagara Falls are used.

Coal and natural gas generating stations use fossil fuels to heat water to produce steam. The steam drives the turbines which then turn the generator to produce electricity.

Fossil fuels are used all over the world because they are quite easy to obtain and transport. However, fossil fuels are a non-renewable resource. That means when they are all gone, there are no more to use.

FIGURE 3.22 Coal and natural gas power stations produce air pollutants, which—along with cars and trucks—contribute to smog and climate change.

Surf the Web

Go to **www.science.nelson.com**
Follow the links for ScienceWise Grade 11, Chapter 3, Section 3.2. Look at the information under the term nuclear energy. Look at 4 or 5 different links. For each one, ask the following questions:

a) Has the author identified her/himself?
b) Is the author for or against nuclear energy?
c) Does the site provide you with enough facts to allow you to make your own decision about using nuclear energy?
d) Could this site be classified as an advertisement?

Nuclear power plants use radioactive uranium. When uranium atoms are split, they produce heat. The heat is used to produce steam. The steam turns the turbine which spins the generator to produce electricity (Figure 3.24).

Nuclear power produces a great deal of energy with very little fuel. Unfortunately, it also produces radioactive waste, which remains dangerous for thousands of years.

FIGURE 3.23 The Darlington Nuclear Power Plant. Why do you think it is surrounded by water?

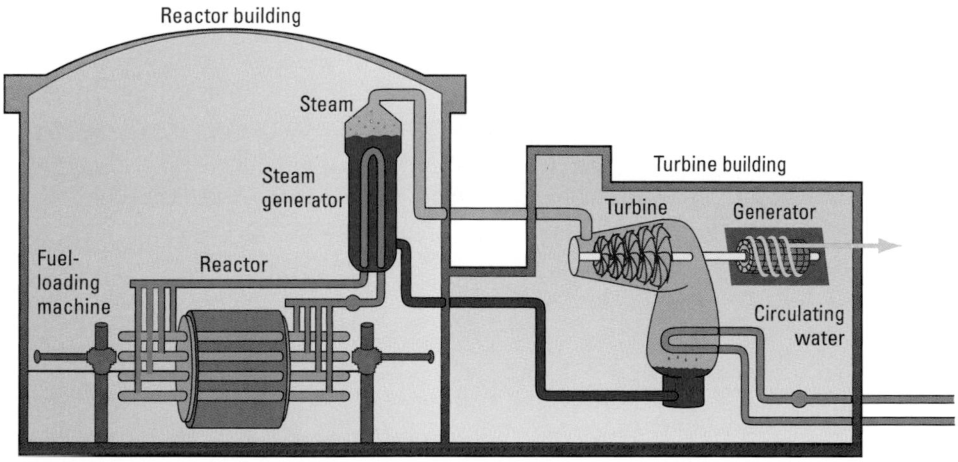

FIGURE 3.24 The basic design of a CANDU nuclear reactor.

LAB 3B

The Voltaic Cell

To observe how DC electricity is produced, you will construct a simple device called a voltaic cell. A voltaic cell works the way a battery works. It converts chemical energy into electrical energy.

Purpose

In this lab, you will observe the factors that affect the production of electricity in a voltaic cell.

Materials

- lab coats
- safety goggles
- 3 connecting leads
- 1 switch
- 2 zinc plates
- 2 copper plates
- 2 graphite plates
- dilute sulphuric acid
- steel wool
- voltmeter
- distilled water
- electrode holder

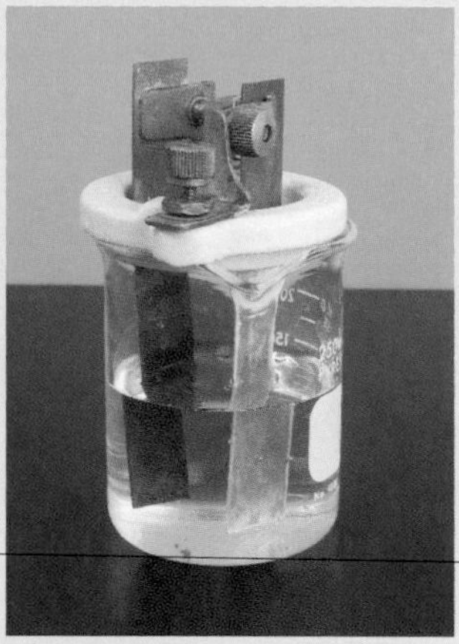

FIGURE 3.25 A voltaic cell.

Be Safe!

- Wear proper safety goggles.
- If you get acid on your hands, rinse them thoroughly with water.

For more information on proper handling, storage and disposal of chemicals, refer to Chapter 1, Section 1.2.

Procedure

1. Copy Figure 3.26 into your notebook.

Electrodes	Potential difference with distilled water (V)	Potential difference with sulphuric acid (V)
Graphite and graphite		
Graphite and zinc		
Zinc and zinc		
Zinc and copper		
Copper and copper		
Copper and graphite		

FIGURE 3.26

2. Clean the two graphite electrodes with steel wool. Construct the voltaic cell as shown in Figure 3.25, using the 2 graphite plates and distilled water.
3. Connect the voltaic cell, the switch and the voltmeter as shown in Figure 3.27.
4. Record the potential difference in your data table.
5. Repeat steps 2, 3, and 4 with each of the other pairs of electrodes, as listed in Figure 3.26.
6. Repeat steps 2, 3, 4, and 5 with sulphuric acid instead of the distilled water.

Analysis and Conclusion

1. What must be true of the 2 electrodes in a voltaic cell?
2. What type of solution should be used in a voltaic cell?

Extension and Connection

3. What other types of solutions might work? Describe how you would test your prediction.
4. In what real-life situation would a voltaic cell be a good energy source? When should another energy source be used instead?

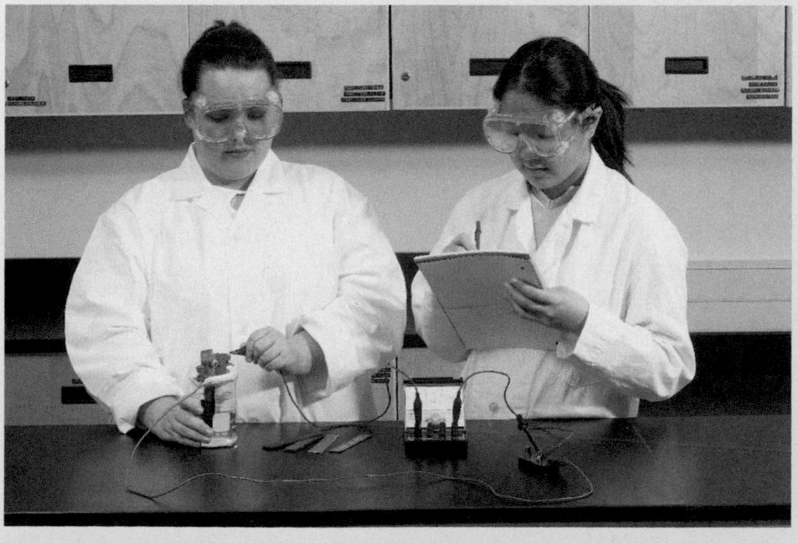

FIGURE 3.27 Getting ready to test the voltaic cell.

LAB 3C

A Simple Generator

Now it is time to build a simple generator to produce electricity. You will use a device called a galvanometer. This device will measure the flow of electricity in your circuit. It is basically the same as the voltmeter that you have used before, except that it shows the size and direction of a current more obviously.

Purpose

In this lab, you will determine the factors affecting the size and type of current produced by a simple generator.

Materials

- solenoid (coiled wire)
- bar magnet
- galvanometer (a current indicator)
- connecting wires

FIGURE 3.28 A simple generator.

Procedure

1. Read the procedure and then design a data table to record your observations.
2. Set up the simple generator as shown in Figure 3.28.
3. Record the reading on the galvanometer without the magnet.
4. Place the magnet inside the solenoid. Record the reading on the galvanometer.
5. Move the magnet slowly into the solenoid. Record the maximum reading.

6. Move the magnet slowly out of the solenoid. Record the maximum reading.

7. Move the magnet quickly in and out of the solenoid. Record the maximum readings.

Analysis and Conclusion

1. Describe, in your own words, how to produce electricity using a magnet and a coiled conductor.

2. How does the speed of the magnet affect the size of the current produced?

3. Is the current produced by moving the magnet in and out of the solenoid direct or alternating current? Explain your answer.

Extension and Connection

4. If electricity is so easy to produce, why do you think we pay for it?

5. Suggest other ways we could spin a turbine that have not been mentioned.

FIGURE 3.29 Setting up the generator.

Surf the Web

Go to **www.science.nelson.com** and follow the links for ScienceWise Grade 11, Chapter 3, Section 3.2. Look at the job description for a power system electrician at Ontario Power Generation.

Review and Apply

1. Why do electric generators tend to produce an alternating current instead of a direct current?
2. Identify 2 situations where direct current is used and 3 situations where alternating current is used.
3. Use your new knowledge to design a generator that is powered by wind. Draw a labelled diagram of your design. Is your invention practical? Why or why not?
4. Work with a partner to list 5 *practical* ways that you could help your home or workplace reduce the amount of electricity it uses. Design a brochure to advertise your ideas. Make sure you consider your audience.
5. What benefits would reducing electricity use have for your home or workplace and for the environment?
6. Add the new concepts from this section to the graphic organizer you started in Section 3.1.

Job Link

If you are looking for a position at Ontario Power Generation (OPG), Tracy Poole may be the person who decides if you will be hired. Ms. Poole is responsible for hiring maintenance and trade staff such as welders and electricians.

FIGURE 3.30 Tracy Poole, Human Resources.

ScienceWise: How do you decide who to hire?

Tracy Poole: Everyone who gets a job at OPG has to take an aptitude test. Another requirement is that they know something about nuclear power, like you would learn in a science course.

ScienceWise: How did you get to your present position?

Tracy Poole: I got my job at OPG right out of high school. I started as a clerk and worked my way up to my present position. Most training is done in-house. I have taken some night school courses, and I found that my experience gained at OPG helped me a lot.

3.3 Electric Components and Wiring

Be Safe!

How can you avoid a short circuit in your home or workplace?

- Replace or repair frayed cords on appliances.
- Replace or repair damaged electric outlets.
- Outlets that spark or have black smudges around them should be replaced immediately.

The amount of current flowing through a circuit may change. Why? How can we regulate the amount of current flowing through a circuit? In this section, we will look at the reasons for fluctuations, or changes in current, and how to protect the circuit during high currents.

Short Circuits

A simple circuit can consist of just a load, an energy source and connecting wires. A load must be in a circuit to avoid a short circuit. A **short circuit** occurs when electrons can get from the negative terminal of an energy source to the positive terminal, without flowing through a load or resistor. Look at Figure 3.31.

Short circuits can be extremely dangerous. The heat generated by a short circuit can cause an electrical fire.

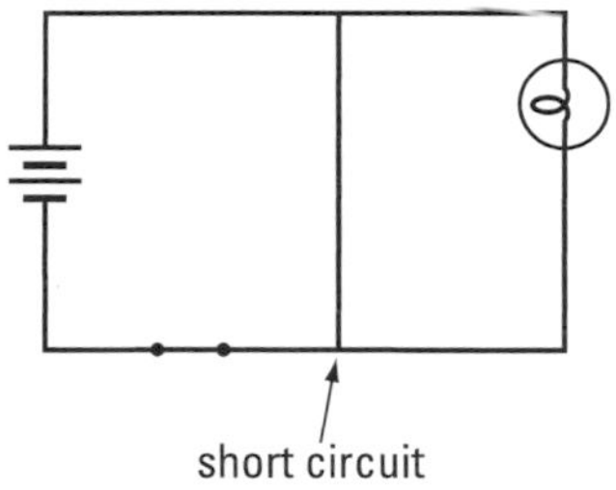

FIGURE 3.31 Electrons will take whichever path is easiest. If there is a path without a load (a short circuit), electrons will take it. This leaves the light unlit and produces a dangerous amount of heat in the conductor. Why do short circuits produce a great deal of heat?

Current, Potential Difference and Resistance

The biggest factor in electrical safety is the current. The current flowing through a circuit depends on both the potential difference and the resistance.

The resistance in a circuit depends on the size of the conductor and the material the conductor is made of. The most common conductor material is copper.

Good conductors have low resistance. Electrons travel through good conductors easily. The current travelling through a circuit with a good conductor will always be bigger than the current flowing through an identical circuit with a poor conductor. Look at Figures 3.32A and 3.32B on page 92. It is like the difference between a paved road and a dirt road of the same size.

Imagine you wanted to reduce the speed of the cars on your street. The town might add speed bumps. These speed bumps would act like resistors in a circuit. You could count the cars passing by your window. If your street is the only way across town, it would be like a series circuit with a resistor.

You will need to know how to avoid short circuits for your project, Wiring a New Office.

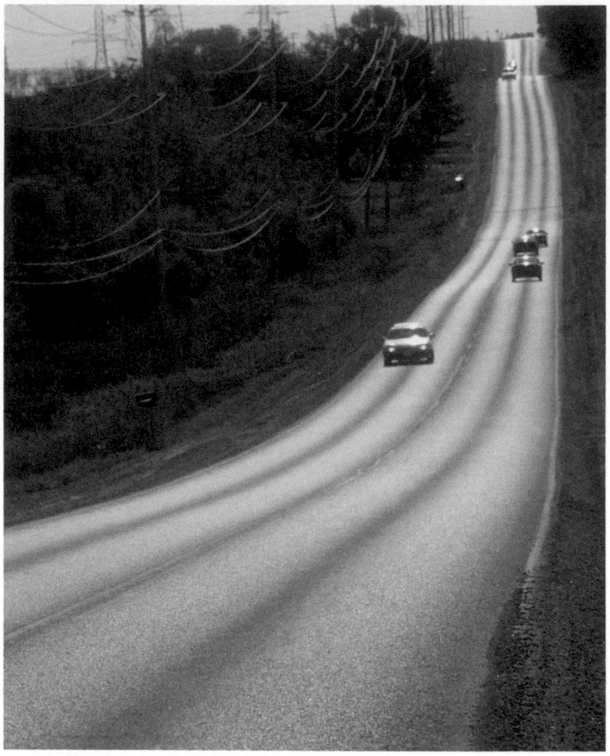

FIGURE 3.32A A paved road is like a good conductor. The high speeds possible mean that many cars can pass a given point in a given time.

FIGURE 3.32B A dirt road is like a bad conductor. Cars cannot travel as quickly on it, so very few cars can pass a given point in a given time.

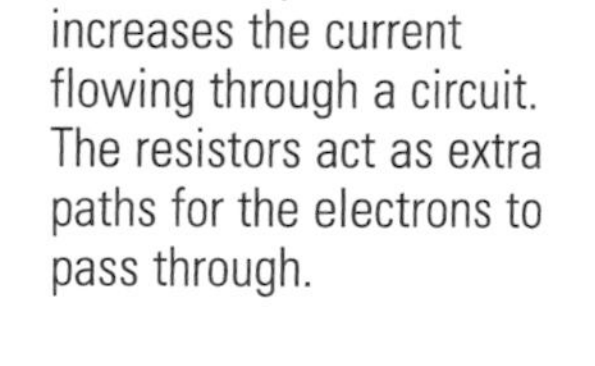

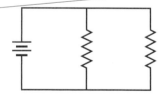

FIGURE 3.33 Adding resistors in parallel increases the current flowing through a circuit. The resistors act as extra paths for the electrons to pass through.

What if there is a second road to go across town that you can also see (in the distance) from your window? It also has speed bumps. If you count the cars on your own street and the other street, you will find that the number of cars that you can see has increased because of the extra street. This is like 2 resistors in parallel (Figure 3.33).

Current in Your Home

When a light bulb burns out in your kitchen, do all of the other lights in your home go out? Of course not! Do you know why this is? It is because your home is wired in parallel.

Did you know that to an electron, an appliance is just like a resistor? It is just one more obstacle in its journey from the negative terminal of the power source to the positive terminal. This produces a problem: with each new path or appliance added to the circuit, more current flows through the circuit. If the current gets too large, it can cause the home wiring to overheat, which may cause a fire. How do we avoid this?

Regulating the Flow of Electricity

Fuses

Fuses are resistors. They are over-current protection devices. Figure 3.34 shows some types of fuses. An **excess current** occurs when more electricity than a wire can handle flows through it. If the current flowing through a wire is too large, the wire will get extremely hot and could cause a fire. Fuses are designed to protect the wire.

Fuses contain a conductor with a low melting point. When the current flowing through the wire gets too large, the conductor melts, breaking the circuit. This will also happen if the current flowing through a wire has too high a potential difference (which will happen in a short circuit). Fuses are labelled according to how many amperes or amps can pass through the wire before this melting occurs.

When you replace a screw-base fuse, it is a good idea to check the top. If the top has a black smudge, it blew because of a short circuit. Repair the circuit before using it again.

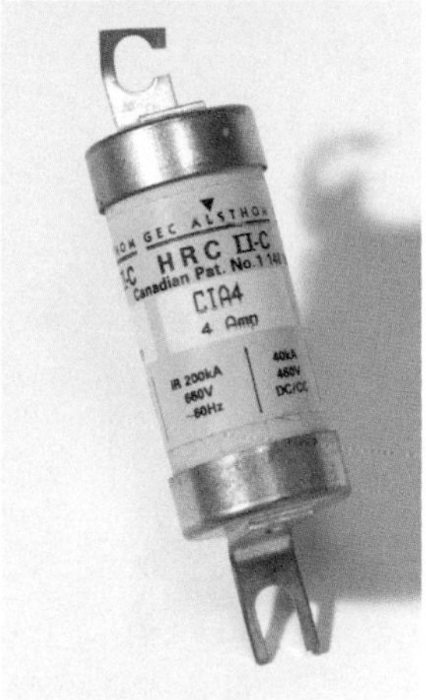

FIGURE 3.34 There are many types of fuses, but they all have the same basic mechanism.

Circuit Breakers

Circuit breakers are switches that are designed to open when too much current flows through them. A bimetallic strip inside the circuit breaker bends away from the circuit when it is heated, opening the circuit.

Circuit breakers are more expensive than fuses but they are reusable. Once tripped (opened by excess current), they can be closed again. They can also be used as simple switches. New homes are being built with circuit breakers that can be switched to the off position whenever work needs to be done on a certain circuit.

Be Safe!

Never use a fuse that has a higher rating than your circuit. If you use a fuse with a higher rating than your circuit, the wiring could overheat and start a fire.

FIGURE 3.35 Circuit breakers in a home (left). A close-up of a circuit breaker (right).

Review and Apply

1. Use your knowledge of parallel circuits and current. Why do you think all homes have fuses or circuit breakers?

2. The 15-amp fuse blows in your stove. You check your supplies and find you only have a 30-amp fuse. Why would it be dangerous to replace the 15-amp fuse with a 30-amp fuse?

3. Kallid goes to the staff kitchen to make himself a cup of tea. He plugs in the kettle to boil water. Everything seems fine at first, but soon his coworkers are complaining that their computers are dead! What happened? What would you tell Kallid to help fix the problem?

4. You have been appointed Health and Safety Representative at the restaurant where you work.
   a) What might you look for with respect to electrical safety?
   b) Design a poster to make your coworkers aware of possible electrical safety hazards.

5. Add the new concepts in this section to the graphic organizer you started in Section 3.1.

6. **Tools of an Electrician**

Many electricians own their own tools and often work independently as freelance contractors. In this activity, you will consider some of the financial decisions a new freelance electrician would have to make.

a) See if you can find all the tools described in Figure 3.37 on page 96, at various hardware and electrical supply stores. Price them and calculate the cost of starting out as a freelance electrician.
b) Electricians often provide their own cable, too. How much does cable cost?
c) Electricians also use tool belts and tool boxes. Research different options for each and their costs.
d) What factors influence the cost of tools?
e) How did you decide whether it was worth it to pay a higher cost for a particular brand of tool or material?

Can you think of other financial decisions an electrician may have to make? Put your information together and present it to your class as a poster, a brochure, a presentation, or a report.

Try This at Home

Home Hazard Survey

Check your home for the following hazards:

1. Look at all the plugs. Are any loose or damaged?
2. Inspect, but do not touch, the electric cords in your house. Are they damaged or frayed?
3. Do you have fuses that blow or circuit breakers that trip frequently?
4. Do you have any circuits that will not work when fuses are replaced or circuit breakers are reset?
5. Are any of the lights dim or flickering?
6. Do you have extension cords under carpets or rugs?
7. Are your extension cords near heaters?
8. Do you have any electrical outlets with too many appliances plugged into them?
9. Look at the electric appliances in your kitchen and bathroom. Are they too close to a sink or bathtub?

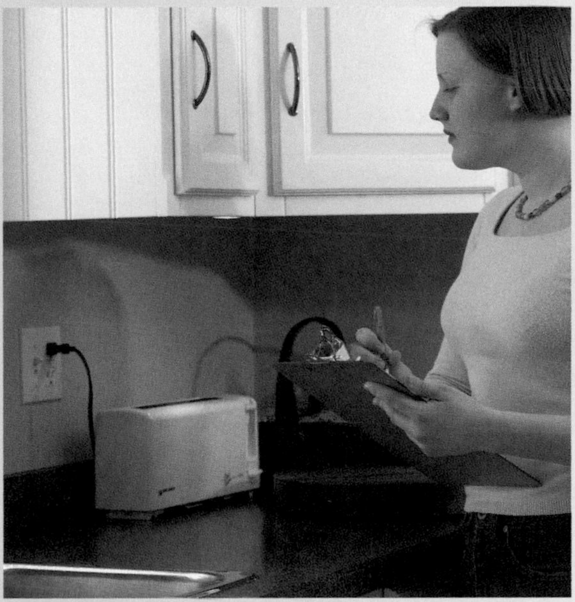

FIGURE 3.36

If you answered yes to any of the above questions, tell your parent or legal guardian so that they can get the problem(s) repaired.

If you answered no to all the questions, give your home an A+ for electrical safety!

Extension

How do you think these 9 problems could be fixed? Discuss your ideas with a partner. Which problems could be safely fixed by you, and which would require an electrician?

LAB
3D Building a Circuit

You will need to know how to build a circuit for your project, Wiring a New Office.

Current, circuits, and switches, now is the time to put it all together! You will design a typical household circuit. Make sure to follow instructions very carefully.

Purpose

In this lab, you will design and construct a circuit for an overhead light with a switch.

Materials

FIGURE 3.37 The materials you will need for your circuit.

Be Safe!

The circuit you will be making is not Canadian Standards Association (CSA) approved. Do not connect it to a 120 V power source at any time.

- Remember to ground the circuit in each of the device boxes.
- Be careful of the edges of the device boxes. They can be sharp.
- Do not test your circuit until the teacher has inspected it.
- Keep your work area clear.
- Read over the entire procedure before you begin. If you have any questions, ask the teacher.
- During the activity, if you are unsure of a procedure, ask your teacher before you try it.

Procedure

1. Cut the NMD 14/2 cable in half. Cut approximately 15 cm of insulation off each end (there are 4 in total) of the 2 NMD 14/2 cables.

2. Strip approximately 2 cm of insulation from the ends of the 2 white and 2 black wires.

3. Insert 1 of the NMD 14/2 cables into the rectangular device box, as shown in Figure 3.38.

FIGURE 3.38 Insert the NMD 14/2 cable into the rectangular device box.

4. Secure the wire by tightening the screw on the inside of the box.

5. ⚠ See Figure 3.39. Use the needle-nose pliers to wrap the bare wire, also called the ground wire, clockwise around one of the middle screws. Tighten the screw. Carefully cut the extra ground wire with the wire cutters. Make sure to show your teacher what you have done before moving to step 6.

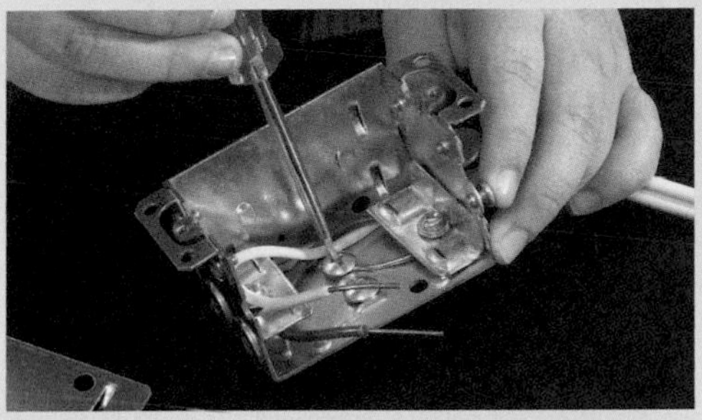

FIGURE 3.39 Securing the wire in this way means that it cannot be pulled out accidentally.

6. If your teacher approves what you have done, continue. Otherwise, correct your work. Insert the other NMD 14/2 cable into the rectangular device box and ground it in the other screw, exactly as you did in step 5. The black and white wires are loose in the rectangular device box.

7. ⚠ Twist the ends of the 2 white wires together. Screw on the connector. Make sure no bare wire is visible.

8. ⚠ The 2 black wires are to be connected to the "bronze" screws on the switch. These screws are on the side of the switch. They are labelled on the back of the switch. Connect the 2 black wires to the switch by using the needle-nose pliers to wrap the end of the wire clockwise around the screw. Tighten the screw. Cut off the excess bare wire (Figure 3.40).

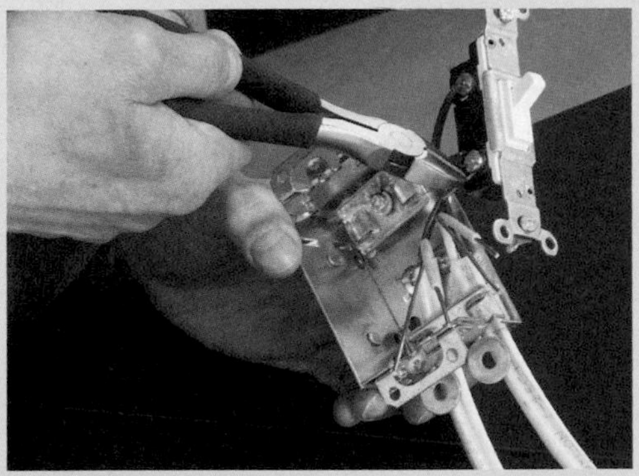

FIGURE 3.40 Step 8.

9. ⚠ Have your teacher inspect your work before you proceed.

CONTINUED

10 Push the wires into the box and screw the switch onto the device box. You have now wired a switch!

11 Compare what you have done to Figure 3.41.

12 Repeat steps 2 to 4 for the octagonal device box, using 1 end of 1 of the NMD 14/2 cables.

13 To connect the black wire on the NMD 14/2 cable to the lamp holder, strip the end of the wire, wrap it around the screw terminal and tighten the screw.

14 Repeat step 13 with the white wire.

15 Push the wires into the device box and attach the lamp holder to it, as in Figure 3.42.

16 Check your circuit to make sure it is correct.

17 Show your circuit to the teacher.

18 ⚠ Your teacher may allow you to test your circuit by connecting it to an energy source. DO NOT CONNECT YOUR CIRCUIT TO 120 V. The circuit you have built is not CSA approved.

FIGURE 3.41 This is what your switch box should look like.

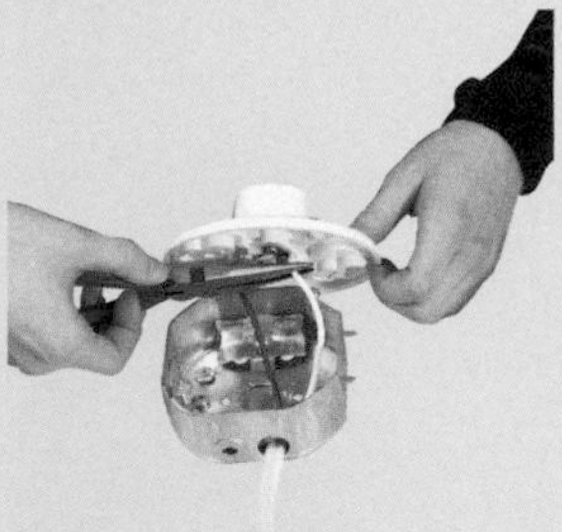

FIGURE 3.42 Connecting the lamp holder to the device box.

Analysis and Conclusion

1 What is the purpose of the ground wire?

2 What is the purpose of the other 2 wires in the NMD 14/2 cable?

3 Draw a schematic diagram of the circuit you have made.

Extension and Connection

4 Describe a situation in your own life when you might have to make a circuit like the one you built today.

5 What safety precautions did you follow during this lab?

6 List three jobs that would require the skill of building a circuit.

3.4 Chapter Summary

Now You Can...

- Describe the components of common electric circuits (3.1; Labs 3A, 3B, 3C, 3D)
- Explain the difference between direct and alternating currents (3.2)
- Describe the functions of components that regulate the flow of electricity in electric circuits (3.3)
- Identify the SI units for potential difference, current, and resistance (3.1)
- Use and describe proper safety procedures for working with electricity at home and at work (3.1; Labs 3A, 3B, 3C, 3D; 3.3)
- Analyze the relationship among potential difference, electric current, and resistance in a complete electric circuit (3.1, Lab 3A, 3.3)
- Describe and identify situations in which electric circuits can be fire hazards or dangers to human life (3.1, 3.3)
- Construct and inspect simple electric circuits (Labs 3A, 3B, 3C, 3D)
- Identify and correctly use equipment to measure potential difference, electric current, and resistance (3.1, 3.3)
- Use safe practices while working with electric circuits (Labs 3A, 3B, 3C, 3D)
- Draw and interpret schematic diagrams of electric circuits (3.1, 3.3)
- Build a circuit using the appropriate tools (Lab 3D)
- Analyze electric circuits, identify any faults, and make corrections (Labs 3A, 3B, 3C, 3D; 3.3)

Concept Connections

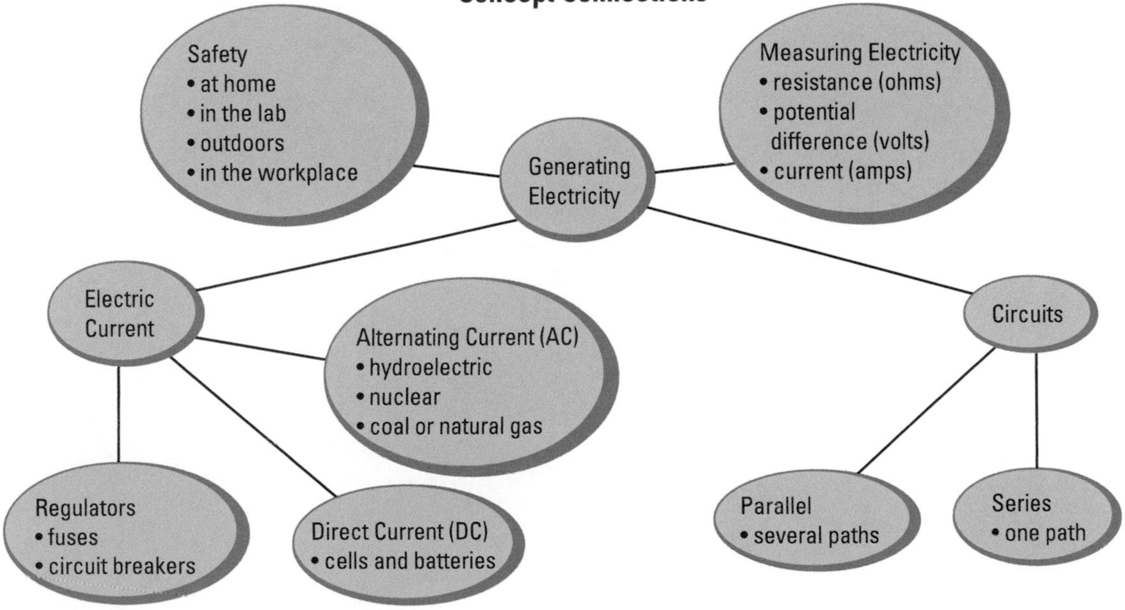

FIGURE 3.43 Compare your completed graphic organizer to the one on this page. How did you do? Can you add any new links to your organizer?

CHAPTER 3 *review*

Knowledge and Understanding

1. For each of the following statements indicate True or False. If False, rewrite the sentence to make it true.
   - **a)** A coulomb is a unit for current.
   - **b)** Ammeters should be connected in series in a circuit.
   - **c)** Voltmeters measure the potential difference in a circuit.
   - **d)** A resistor is a type of insulator.
   - **e)** Fuses are reusable.

2. The Electrical and Utility Safety Association of Ontario (E&USA) recommends that workers not use metal ladders while working on electric circuits. Why do you think they have made this recommendation?

3. Why does adding more appliances to a circuit increase the current?

4. Describe, in your own words, what the schematic diagram in Figure 3.44 shows.

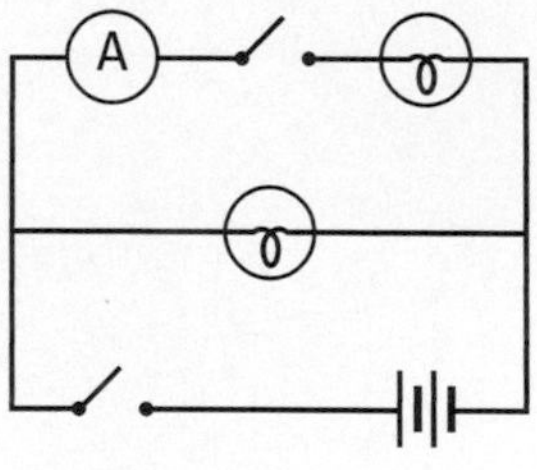

FIGURE 3.44

Inquiry

5. Why are ammeters placed in series in a circuit?

6. Draw a schematic diagram for each of the following:
   - **a)** a closed circuit containing 2 light bulbs in parallel, a switch, and a battery
   - **b)** an open circuit with 2 light bulbs in series, a switch and a battery
   - **c)** an open circuit of **a)**
   - **d)** a closed circuit of **b)**

7. List the things you would look for to determine if a circuit you have constructed is safe. Compare your list with those of 2 classmates. Can you add anything new? Why or why not?

8. You plug an iron into an electric outlet that already has a kettle plugged into it. Both appliances switch off immediately. Use your new knowledge and vocabulary to explain what happened in the circuit.

9. Examine the schematic diagram in Figure 3.45. The light goes off when the switch is closed. Why?

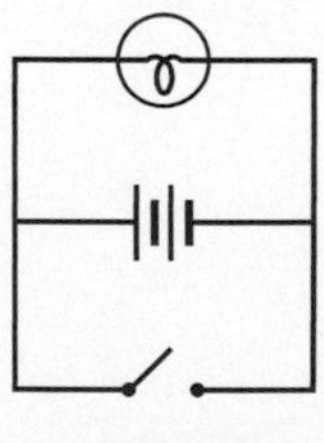

FIGURE 3.45

Making Connections

10. Homes are built with circuit breakers instead of fuses, even though circuit breakers are more expensive. Why do you think this is so?

11. One of the regulations of the Building Code requires that, in a kitchen in a newly built home, the 2 plugs on each outlet must be on separate circuits. What is the purpose of this regulation?

12. Why is it dangerous to fly a kite near a power line?

13. On a cold morning, some cars are hard to start. Explain why this can happen. (Hint: You may want to think about the rates of reaction from Chapter 2).

Communication

14. Ontario's energy demand is getting bigger as the population grows. Several ways of generating electricity were introduced in this chapter. Choose one and explain why it may be a solution to Ontario's problems with air pollution and a growing population. Put your ideas into a letter to be mailed to your MPP (Member of Provincial Parliment).

15. With a partner, write a radio commercial script designed to inform the public of the effects of electricity on humans. Remember, it can only be 30 seconds long!

CHAPTER

4

Practical Electricity

Now you know how electricity works. But how do we use it? In this chapter, you will use your knowledge and skills from Chapter 3 and apply them to buying electrical devices and describing how homes are wired. You will also learn about some of the practical problems and solutions of using electricity. Look at Figure 4.1. How do you think power lines get electricity to our homes? What is a service panel? How do we know what appliances to buy? Are appliances inspected and approved before they are sold?

FIGURE 4.1

What You Will Learn

After completing this chapter, you will be able to:

- Identify and use SI units (4.1)
- Identify household appliances that require 110 V and some that require 220 V to operate (4.1)
- Investigate how electrical devices play a role in the economy of a local community and improve the standard of living (4.2)
- Identify problems and solutions related to the environmental impact of the consumption of electric energy and the disposal of used electrical appliances (4.2)
- Describe common electrical parts that regulate the flow of electricity (4.3)
- Locate, select and analyze information about how electricity gets from the generating station to your home (4.4)

What You Will Do

- Conduct research to prepare a consumer report about a major appliance (Activity 4A)
- Build a circuit using the appropriate tools (Lab 4B)
- Analyze electric circuits, troubleshoot and make changes (Lab 4B)
- Use safe practices while working with electric circuits (Lab 4B)
- Draw a schematic diagram of a standard electric circuit found in a house (Lab 4B)
- Create a household plan for survival in the event of an extended public power disruption (Activity 4C)

Words to Know

acid precipitation
Canadian Standards Association (CSA)
electric power
greenhouse gases
ground fault interrupter (GFI)
joule (J)
kilowatt (kW)
kilowatt hour (kWh)
lightning arrester
neutral wire
nuclear waste
service drops
service panel
surge protectors
tap changing under load (TCUL)
transformer
watt (W)

A puzzle piece indicates knowledge or a skill that you will need for your project, Wiring a New Office, at the end of Unit 2.

4.1 Consumers and Electrical Devices

CD players, televisions, computers, lamps and clock radios are all electrical devices. On the underside of many clock radios or small appliances are symbols from regulatory agencies. But what do they mean to you, the consumer?

FIGURE 4.2 You use a large number of electrical devices every day. Think back to Chapter 3. Which of the above devices use direct current and which use alternating current? Can any use either one?

AC vs. DC Current

Some electrical devices are plugged directly into the AC outlet in your home. Others use batteries or have adapters to convert AC current to DC current. Devices that require DC current tend to be small, like flashlights and some radios. DC energy sources tend to produce a low voltage (values such as 1.5 V–12 V). All large appliances, such as refrigerators, use AC because their energy requirements are higher. The electricity supplied to our homes uses AC current. But how do we know how much energy we use?

Measuring Electricity Use

The SI unit for energy is the **joule (J)**. Have you ever seen an electricity meter attached to a house (Figure 4.3)? It does not measure energy in joules. That is because the joule is too small. So how do we measure electrical energy use? **Electric power** is energy per unit time and is measured in **watts (W)** or **kilowatts (kW)**. Since electric power is energy used in a unit of time, multiplying power by the time interval gives the quantity of energy used.

For example, Hydro wants to know how much electricity is used over a certain time. We pay for our electric energy use in **kilowatt hours (kWh),** that is, 1000 watts of energy each hour.

FIGURE 4.3 Electricity meters measure the amount of electricity being used in the home.

Major Appliances and Energy Efficiency

If an appliance is efficient, it is using most of its power to do what you want it to do and very little to do anything else. For example, an energy efficient light bulb produces light and very little heat. This is exactly what you want it to do, because you want it to produce the light but not the heat. Fluorescent light bulbs are more energy efficient than incandescent light bulbs because they produce less heat.

Nothing is 100-percent energy efficient, but it is a good idea to figure out the energy efficiency of an appliance before you buy it.

Did you know that your refrigerator accounts for 11 percent of the total energy consumed in your home? Major appliances sold in Canada, such as refrigerators, washing machines and dishwashers, are required, by law, to meet minimum energy efficiency standards. They are also required to have an EnerGuide label.

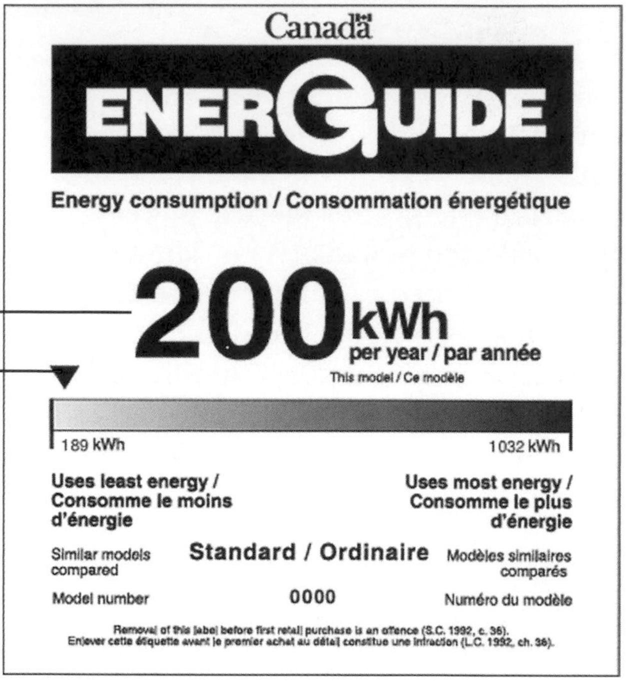

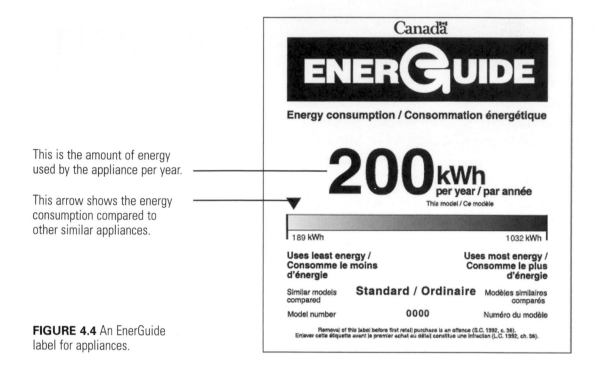

FIGURE 4.4 An EnerGuide label for appliances.

The EnerGuide label helps to inform you before you buy.

The large number tells you the energy in kilowatt hours (kWh) the appliance uses in a year. Less is better—the smaller the number, the less energy it uses and the more efficient the appliance.

Look at Figure 4.4. The arrow on the energy consumption scale tells you how this appliance compares to others like it. You want the arrow to be closer to the left. Why do you think this is?

Most major appliances have a lifespan of 10 to 15 years. So, if you make a bad choice, you are stuck with it for a long while. As well, if the appliance you chose is not energy efficient, you are stuck with the cost. You will practise comparison shopping in Activity 4A.

The Need for Regulation

Besides the EnerGuide label on appliances, it is also important that all electrical devices have an approved logo on them. As you learned in Chapter 3, Section 3.1, a current of 1 A is enough to kill a human being. Most electrical devices draw at least that amount of current. That means that an electrical device can be extremely dangerous if its wiring is damaged. Remember Lab 3D. You made an electrical device, but were not allowed to connect it to a 120 V energy source because an electrical inspector had not approved it.

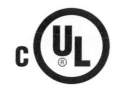

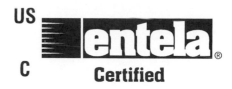

FIGURE 4.5 An electrical device that has been approved for consumer use will have at least 1 of these logos.

Did you know that all electrical devices plugged into electrical outlets approved for use in Canada have a mark of approval on them? The logos shown in Figure 4.5 are from different organizations that have been authorized by the government. Look for these logos on all of the appliances you use at home and at work.

Canadian Standards Association

The **Canadian Standards Association** (CSA) is an association made up of members from many different occupations and backgrounds. It is a not-for-profit organization. That means that it does not make any money. Its goal is to develop a set of standards that address issues like improving public safety and health. Standards are developed by a number of volunteers from many organizations and businesses, consumer groups, and users who would be affected by the standards.

What does it mean if you find the CSA logo on an item you want to buy? What did the manufacturer have to do to be allowed to carry the CSA logo?

FIGURE 4.6 Organizations such as the CSA put consumer products through a formal testing process that includes follow-up inspections. Would their recommendations affect your decision when choosing a stereo to buy? Why or why not?

Buyer Beware

The CSA is not a consumer protection agency and its logo is not the government's stamp of approval. Its logo is a stamp of approval from the CSA only. It means the product meets specific standards, including safety. If an item does not have any of the logos shown in Figure 4.5, you are taking a risk.

Think back to the device you made in Lab 3D. You were careful to construct it properly but it was never tested by an outside agency or electrical inspector. Would it have been wise to plug it into the wall? 120 V is a big risk.

ACTIVITY 4A

Comparison Shopping

When making a major purchase, it is important to do some research and comparison shopping ahead of time. In this activity, you will compare 3 different brands of the same large appliance and determine which is the best buy.

What You Will Need

- pen
- paper
- prices for the appliances chosen
- EnerGuide labels for appliances chosen

What You Will Do

Part 1: The Cost of Energy

1. Choose a large appliance (washer, dryer, dishwasher, stove, or refrigerator) to investigate. Make sure that you can find 3 brands to compare. If you cannot find 3 brands, choose another appliance.
2. Consult the EnerGuide label on each appliance to find out the annual energy consumption and relative energy efficiency.
3. Assume that the cost of electricity is 0.05 cents per kilowatt hour. Calculate how much it would cost to run each appliance for 1 year.
4. Record your data in a table like Figure 4.7A

Part 2: The Cost of the Appliance

1. Prices of appliances can be obtained from catalogues and from advertisements. As well, information about the cost of appliances can be found on websites.
2. Find out the cost of each appliance.
3. Assume that you will use the appliance for 10 years. What is the cost per year of purchasing each appliance? Record this information in your data table.
4. Now add this cost to the operating cost you determined for each appliance in Part 1, step 3. Record this information in your data table under the heading "Total cost of owning per year".

Brand	Cost of operating/year	Cost of purchase/year	Total cost of owning per year	Features

FIGURE 4.7A

Part 3: Features of the Appliance

1. Most appliances have many features that make them unique. Find out some of the features of each appliance.
2. Note some of these features in your data table.

What Did You Find Out?

Using the information that you recorded in your data table, prepare a report explaining what you found out.

- Identify which brand costs the most to operate over a one-year period.
- Include what the per year cost of the appliance would be if you kept the appliance for 10 years.
- Describe the features of each of the three brands.
- Explain which brand you believe would be a wise purchase and give three reasons for your choice.

Making Connections

1. Is the best brand always the one that is cheapest to buy? Explain your reasoning.

FIGURE 4.7B Comparison shopping is useful in determining which appliance to buy.

Review and Apply

1. Why is it important to check for the logos shown in Figure 4.5 when buying an electrical device?

2. Imagine it is your job to develop regulations regarding the design of clock radios. Answer the following:
   a) What kinds of safety features would you require?
   b) Who would you consult to add to your list of safety features?
   c) List any warnings you would require on the clock radio.
   d) Choose 1 of your safety features and describe how you might test it.

3. Your cousin has asked you to help her buy a motorcycle. Two motorcycles are identical in every way except that one has a noisier engine. Which of the 2 motorcycles would probably be more energy efficient? How do you know?

4. With a partner, design and create a brochure to explain how an EnerGuide label works. Gear it to people your own age.

5. In a graphic organizer, organize the concepts you have learned in this section.

6. **Lamp Design**

   This simple lamp would work, but it would never be approved for sale in Canada. Suggest ways to improve the design of this lamp so that it would be approved. Draw a labelled diagram showing your ideas. Compare your diagram to those drawn by other classmates. Go back and make any necessary changes to your diagram.

FIGURE 4.8 Is this lamp safe to use?

Job Link

If you had any questions about electrical safety on the job, Bill Shewan might be the man to call. He is a Technical Communications Consultant with the Electrical and Utilities Safety Association of Ontario (E&USA).

FIGURE 4.9 Bill Shewan, Technical Communications Consultant.

ScienceWise: What is the E&USA?

Bill Shewan: It is the health and safety authority in electrical and utilities. The Ministry of Labour makes the laws and has hired E&USA to make sure they are being followed. Our goal is to reduce the number of electricity-based accidents to zero.

ScienceWise: What do you do at E&USA?

Bill Shewan: I write the manuals that explain what your employer should do to maintain workers' safety around electricity. I also talk to people who have questions about electrical safety. For example, if you work for a contractor who trims trees around hydroelectric wires, you could call me if you had any concerns or questions about electricity.

Surf the Web

Go to **www.science.nelson.com** and follow the links for ScienceWise Grade 11, Chapter 4, Section 4.1. Find out what safety precautions are needed for someone who installs light fixtures.

■

4.2 Environmental Impact

How does the use of electrical devices affect the environment? The effects come from 2 sides. On the consumption side, producing the electricity necessary to run electrical devices can have harmful effects on the environment. On the disposal side, getting rid of electrical devices when we are done using them can also cause problems.

The Consumption Side

Recall from Section 3.2 that moving a conductor relative to a magnet produces electricity. This requires energy to produce the electricity. Each method of using energy for electric production has environmental impacts.

Coal-burning Power Plants

Coal-burning power plants cause a major problem. We usually relate greenhouse gases, such as carbon dioxide, to driving cars. However, coal-burning power plants, which produce a lot of the electricity in some communities, also produce a large amount of the greenhouse gases. Why are they called greenhouse gases?

Earth absorbs ultraviolet radiation from the sun during the day, and then reflects infrared radiation into space. **Greenhouse gases** are gases that absorb infrared radiation, heating up the atmosphere. Refer to Figure 4.10. The effect is similar to that of glass on a greenhouse. If the amount of greenhouse gases in the atmosphere is too high, the temperature of the atmosphere is higher than normal. This disrupts the airflow around Earth and may cause extreme weather conditions, such as tornadoes and hurricanes, far from where the gases were released into the air.

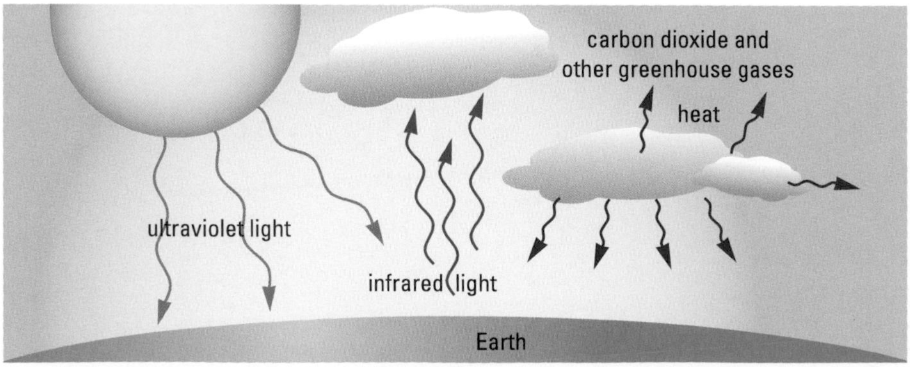

FIGURE 4.10
The greenhouse effect.

The sulphur found in coal is also released into the atmosphere when coal is burned. This produces sulphur dioxide, a highly poisonous gas. When the sulphur dioxide mixes with moisture in the air, it forms acid precipitation. **Acid precipitation** is rain, snow, or hail that is much more acidic than it is supposed to be. It can cause severe damage to forests, crops and buildings.

Nuclear Plants

Nuclear power plants produce very large amounts of energy with very little fuel. They do not produce greenhouse gases. However, they do produce nuclear waste. **Nuclear waste** is made up of the products of the nuclear reactions. They are highly radioactive and remain so for thousands of years. Radioactive substances break down slowly and produce radioactive radiation. Radioactive radiation is made up of particles and energy that can damage living cells. If an organism is exposed to large amounts of radioactive radiation, it can die. As a result, release of these chemicals into the environment can make large areas unlivable for any organism.

FIGURE 4.11 At present, all nuclear waste in Canada is stored at the power plant where it was generated. Nuclear power has been used in Ontario for almost 40 years. What can you predict about the amount of nuclear waste produced by a power plant?

Dams

The dams built for hydroelectric plants are quite large. Hydroelectricity used to be considered an extremely clean and non-harmful way to produce electricity. But the large dams flood the land behind them and can destroy entire ecosystems.

FIGURE 4.12 The Daniel Johnson Dam in Québec.

The dams also lower the water level in front of them, drastically changing the landscape. Aquatic animals that need a certain level of water to live are forced to leave (or die), and land animals (including people) lose their homes. Altering the flow of the river can also destroy the river itself and ruin the drainage of its water system. The result is like a clogged toilet: the river is inactive and the water does not flow.

The more electrical devices we use, the more it is necessary to burn coal at our coal-burning power plants, produce nuclear waste through our nuclear power plants and use dams for hydro-electric plants.

The Disposal Side

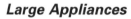

FIGURE 4.13 Most of these electrical devices could have been recycled in some way. Choose an item and suggest how it might have been reused.

The heavy metals (for example, copper, iron and nickel) found in electronic equipment, including computers, stereos and appliances, are harmful to animals and plants. Heavy metals can affect the way organisms live. For this reason, we must use caution when disposing of our electrical devices (see Figure 4.13). In fact, the best solution is to recycle the materials so that they never need to go to the garbage. In Chapter 10, Section 10.2, more disposal options are examined.

Large Appliances

Auto companies have been recycling the metals in old cars for years. The same can be done with large appliances such as refrigerators, stoves, washers, dryers and dishwashers. If the appliance is in good shape, it can be sold to a retailer who is willing to fix it up and resell it. Otherwise, there are companies willing to remove the harmful substances from them and recycle them.

Computers

There are several companies that recycle computers. Most people replace their computers long before they are ready for the garbage. There are many charitable organizations that would appreciate the donation of a used computer. Other organizations are happy to reuse and recycle the parts. The key is to not just throw it into the garbage. The heavy metals that make up the outer case and internal parts are dangerous to our health if they are thrown away.

Batteries

Batteries contain toxic chemicals such as nickel and cadmium. Nickel and cadmium are known carcinogens. Carcinogens are chemicals that can cause cancer. Though most municipalities have rules about how to dispose of large appliances, none have regulations about the disposal of the batteries used in flashlights, Walkmans, or portable radios. Proper disposal of batteries involves separating them from the regular garbage so that they are never put in garbage dumps. Figure 4.14 shows a recycle box for rechargeable batteries. What do you think should be done for non-rechargeable batteries?

FIGURE 4.14 The batteries found in some remote control toys, cordless power tools and cellular and cordless phones can all be recycled in this box.

The Economy and the Environment

Our society depends on electricity and electrical devices. It would be unrealistic to ask everyone to stop using electricity to save the environment. For many people, electricity is necessary to make a living. It is part of the reason for our high standard of living. That standard of living is also paid for by a healthy economy (Figure 4.15).

The economy and the environment are impossible to separate. Many feel that too much attention to the pollution in the environment could hurt the economy. Recycling programs can be expensive and may be paid for through an increase in taxes. That leaves less money to spend on other things. However, others feel that too much pollution hurts the economy. If there is a smog alert in the city, many people who might have gone out shopping, have to stay indoors. If we have too many smog alerts, people may decide to move.

It is a balancing act. Now that you know the 2 sides of the equation—consumption and disposal—you can make a more informed decision.

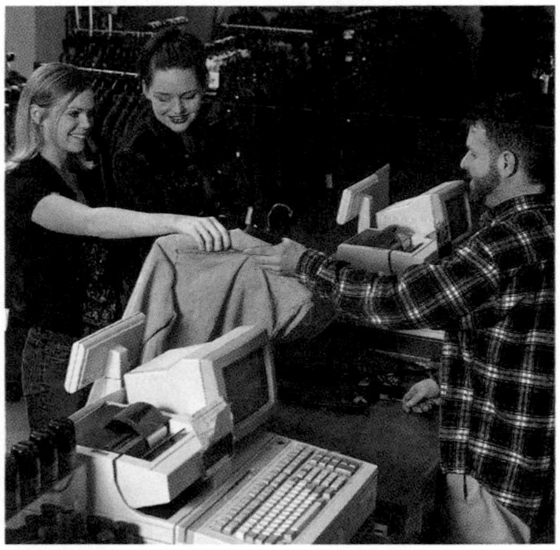

FIGURE 4.15 When people shop, it contributes to the economy. Why do you think this is?

ScienceWise Fact

The population of North America accounts for 8 percent of the world population, yet we produce 50 percent of the world's garbage. Why do you think this is?

Review and Apply

1. Choose 5 electrical devices that you use every day. Figure out how long you leave them turned on each day. What could you do differently to conserve electric energy? Compare your list with a partner and brainstorm ideas.

2. Your municipality has decided to develop regulations for the disposal of household batteries.
   a) Suggest rules that could be put in place. Keep in mind the cost.
   b) Design a poster, promoting the new rules, to be put up in the community.

3. The company you work for is purchasing a new computer system, with new computer terminals for every employee. This means that hundreds of computers are going to be thrown away. Write a letter to your employer outlining the reasons why donating the computers to a local charity would be a better idea.

4. Add the new concepts from this section to the graphic organizer you started in Section 4.1.

5. **Alternative Energy Sources**

So, all we have to do is build hundreds of windmills and solar cells and we can completely replace our nuclear, hydroelectric and coal-burning power plants, right?

Wrong. Wind and solar energy are excellent supplements to our existing power stations. In fact, they could make a significant difference in reducing pollution. Unfortunately, wind and sunlight are just not reliable enough. They could not replace our existing power plants without a huge decrease in our energy use.

Use the information in this section and do any additional research needed to prepare a poem, song, pamphlet, or build a web page, or other creative presentation explaining how people can be more responsible about the electricity they use.

4.3 Home Wiring

The service panel in your home is typically in the garage, basement, or storage area. What is its purpose? In this section, we will look at the wiring in your home in more detail, starting with the service panel and ending with the outlets.

Learning about circuit panels and outlets will help you with your project, Wiring a New Office.

The Service Panel

A typical service panel has 2 110 V–120 V power feeds. Look at Figure 4.16. Each power feed consists of 3 wires, similar to the ones you saw in Lab 3D. The 2 main live wires connect to the main power switch, and the main neutral wire connects to the neutral busbar. The neutral busbar is connected to the earth using any of these ways:

- cold water pipe
- ground rod inserted in the earth
- metal plate sunk in the earth or in the concrete foundation of a building.

Recall the purpose of the circuit breakers from Section 3.3. They protect the circuits in your home from too much current. If you take a look at the breakers in your own home, you will see that some are rated for 30 A and others for 20 A or 15 A. A qualified electrician knows which circuits in the home should be connected to which circuit breakers in the panel.

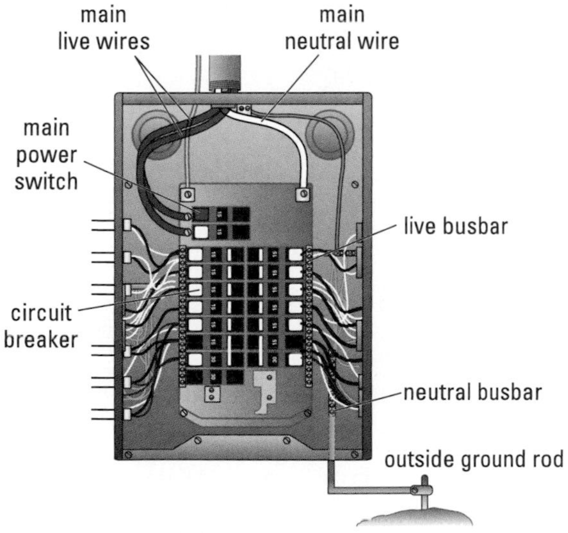

FIGURE 4.16 The **service panel** in your home is the link between the main electrical service in your building and the electrical outlets in your house or apartment.

Be Safe!

Always have a qualified electrician connect circuits to circuit panels.

The 120 V Outlet

A 120 V electric outlet is wired in a similar way to a switch. Look at Figure 4.17. The ground wire is connected to the service panel. The live wire carries 120 V from the service panel to the outlet.

The longer hole on the left leads to the **neutral wire.** It is the path back to the service panel. This wire is only live when there is a connection between the 2 holes. The shorter hole on the right contains a wire that is always live. It carries the current into the device. The bottom hole contains a wire—the ground wire—that leads to the neutral bar in the service panel. This bar is then connected to the earth (refer to Figure 4.16).

Almost all of the electric devices in your home or workplace require 120 V. They are always labelled on the underside or near where the electric cord leaves the device. Devices that require less voltage usually come with an adaptor.

ScienceWise Fact

The purpose of the ground wire is to carry current into the ground (earth) in the case of a short circuit or other potentially dangerous condition. This prevents a person from getting a shock if they touch a faulty or damaged appliance or wire.

The 240 V Outlet

Depending on their energy needs, many stoves and clothes dryers require 220 V–240 V. As a result, many homes are equipped with 2 240 V outlets.

The appliance itself would have a label indicating that it required 240 V, however you could also tell by the different size of the plug.

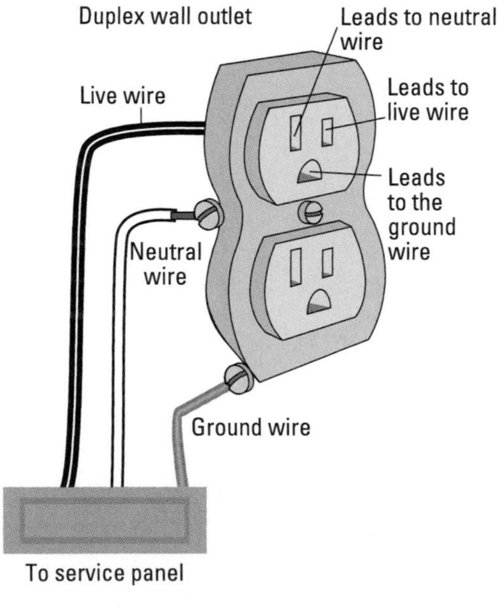

FIGURE 4.17 The wires connected to electric outlets are colour-coded. Why do you think wires are colour-coded?

FIGURE 4.18 The wiring for a 220–240 V electric outlet is quite different from that of a 120 V electric outlet.

Excess Current Protection Devices

Remember the fuses and circuit breakers from Section 3.3? These devices are designed to protect circuits from overheating due to large currents passing through them. Power surges are sudden increases in current. They can be caused by:

- fluctuations in current from the energy source
- short circuits

List 2 other causes of power surges.

Fuses and circuit breakers are found in various devices throughout your home. We have discussed the circuit panel and fuses found in electrical devices. Two other devices containing fuses and circuit breakers are ground fault interrupters and surge protectors.

Ground Fault Circuit Interrupters

Ground fault circuit interrupters (GFCIs) are devices that detect and shut-off unwanted current flow that may produce shock or fire hazard. They are wired like a circuit breaker with a bi-metallic strip that bends when heated, breaking the circuit (Figure 4.19).

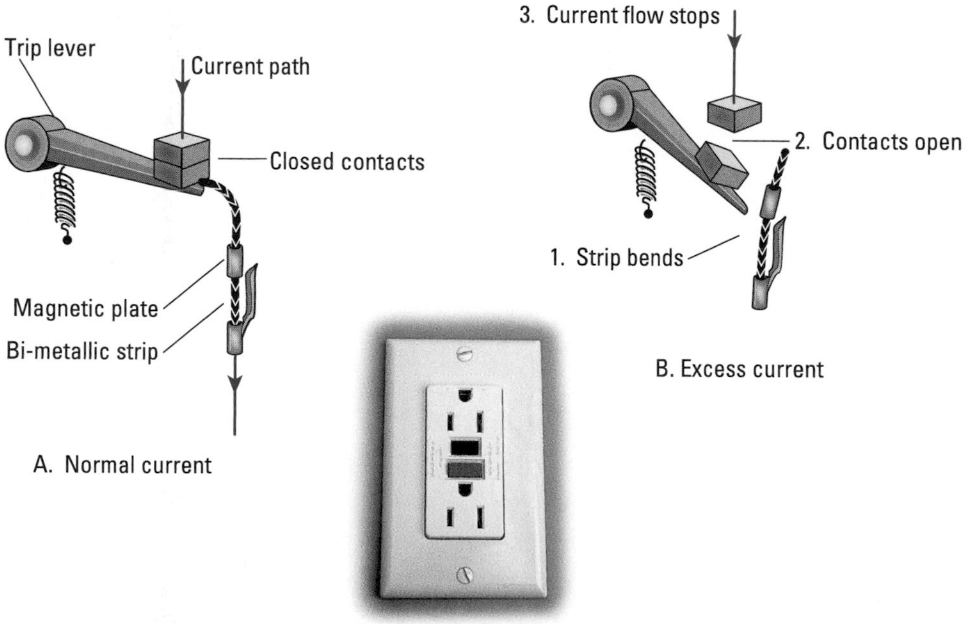

FIGURE 4.19 If the circuit breaker in the GFCI outlet opens the circuit, it can be reset by pressing the red button.

There is always the risk of a short circuit when an electric outlet is near water. If water contacts the outlet, it could provide a path from the live, hot wire to the neutral wire, causing a short circuit. The resulting surge in current would trip the GFCI, opening the circuit.

Surge Protectors

Surge protectors protect the devices connected to them from sudden increases in current. Some contain fuses and some contain circuit breakers. The surge protectors that contain circuit breakers have a reset button so that they can be re-used.

It is always a good idea to connect electronic equipment to a surge-protected power bar because these electrical devices tend to be expensive to replace. A power surge through a computer can destroy a hard drive or a motherboard (the circuit board containing all the parts of the computer).

Surge protectors are not perfect. They cannot protect against extremely high voltages produced in such events as lightning strikes.

Society and Electricity

During the 1960s and early 1970s, many homes were wired using aluminum wiring because it was cheaper than copper wiring. Aluminum is not as good a conductor as copper. To make up for this, a wider gauge of aluminum needs to be used. It is generally 1 size larger than the copper that would have been used.

Aluminum has other disadvantages:

- greater expansion/contraction rate—increases the chance of connections loosening
- less elastic than copper—more likely to be damaged
- corrosion increases resistance and generates a lot of heat

When it was found that aluminum could cause electric fires, the use of aluminum wiring in homes was eventually stopped. Many of the problems were found in the service panels where the aluminum wire connected to another metal, not in the actual wiring of the house. Many homes only need the connection redone. Replacing all of the wiring will not always be necessary. Anyone with aluminum wiring in their home should seek expert advice.

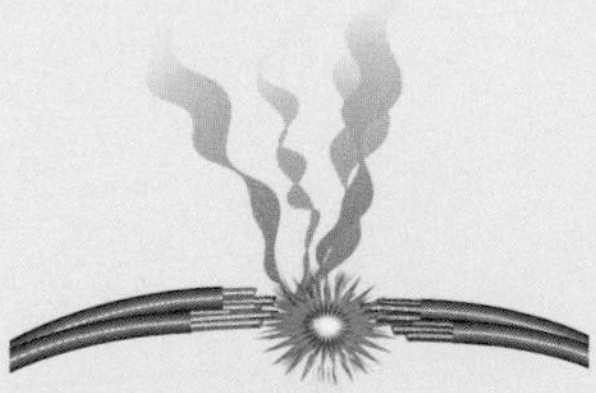

FIGURE 4.20 Aluminum wiring can cause electric fires.

Review and Apply

1. If you choose to connect a circuit directly to a service panel, without an electrician or electrical inspector, it can cancel your home insurance policy. Why do you think this is true?

2. Why should stereos, computers and televisions be unplugged during a lightning storm?

3. Choose 3 electrical devices at home. Find out the following information:
   a) the voltage it requires
   b) the current it draws
   c) the voltage and current required related to what the device is used for (example: production of heat, light, sound, movement)

4. Draw a schematic diagram to represent a motor plugged into an electric outlet, connected to an alternating energy source (use an "m" with a circle around it to indicate the motor). Compare your diagram to that of 2 of your classmates. What suggestions could you make for improving it?

5. Design a circuit for a bathroom (with 2 plugs and a light). Draw the schematic diagram for it using proper circuit symbols. (You may want to refer back to Section 3.1 for a list of circuit symbols you may need.)

6. Add the new concepts from this section to the graphic organizer you started in Section 4.1.

LAB 4B

Home-wiring Model

You will use the skills of building and troubleshooting electric circuits for your project, Wiring a New Office.

Hardware stores often have displays demonstrating how their products can be used. In this activity, you will create a display showing how to wire a circuit for a room the same way that you would in real life. You will also check an electric circuit for faults and correct it.

Purpose

In this lab, you will learn to wire, build and troubleshoot a typical household electric circuit.

Be Safe!

The circuits you will be making are not CSA approved. Do not plug them into a 120 V source. Do not connect your circuit to any energy source until your teacher has approved it.

Materials

Note: Device boxes must be surface boxes for this activity.

- 2-m NMD 14/2 cable
- needle-nose pliers
- octagonal device box
- wire stripper
- 2 rectangular device boxes
- wire cutter
- 12 V energy source
- 1 switch
- flat-head screwdriver
- 1 lamp holder
- Robertson screwdriver
- 1 wall outlet
- 12 V light bulb
- 6 Robertson #8 wood screws
- 1 50-cm by 50-cm piece of plywood or fibre board

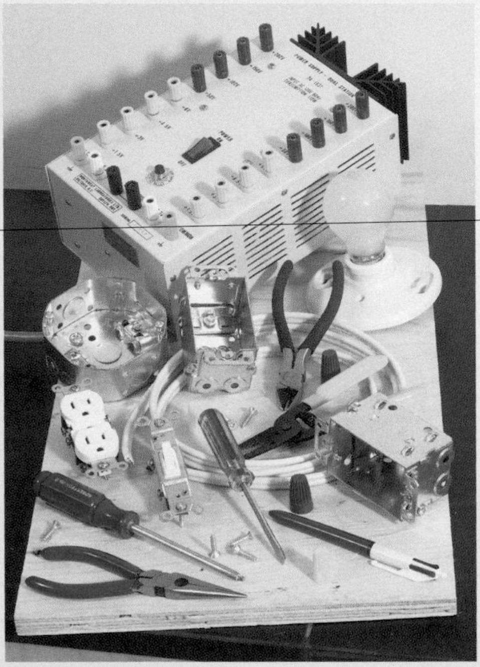

FIGURE 4.21

Procedure

1. Attach the device boxes to the wooden board. Space them so that you have room to label.

2 Carefully cut the NMD 14/2 cable in 3 pieces. Cut 15 cm of insulation off each end of each of the NMD 14/2 cables.

3 Connect 1 NMD 14/2 cable to the octagonal device box and screw the lamp holder to the device box as shown in Figure 4.22.

✓ **Self-Check**

Make sure your box looks similar to this before continuing to the next step.

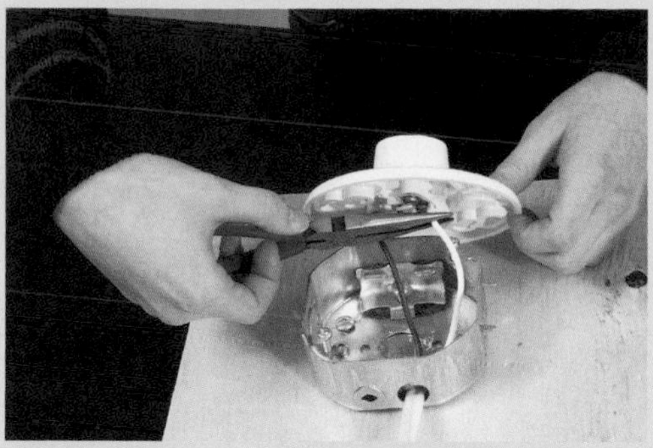

FIGURE 4.22 A lamp holder connected to an octagonal device box.

4 Connect the other end of the NMD 14/2 cable from step 3 to a rectangular device box and wire the switch as shown in Figure 4.23.

✓ **Self-Check**

Make sure your circuit looks similar to this before continuing to the next step.

FIGURE 4.23 A lamp connected to a switch.

5 Connect the outlet to the circuit as shown in Figure 4.24.

✓ **Self-Check**

Make sure your circuit looks similar to this before continuing to the next step.

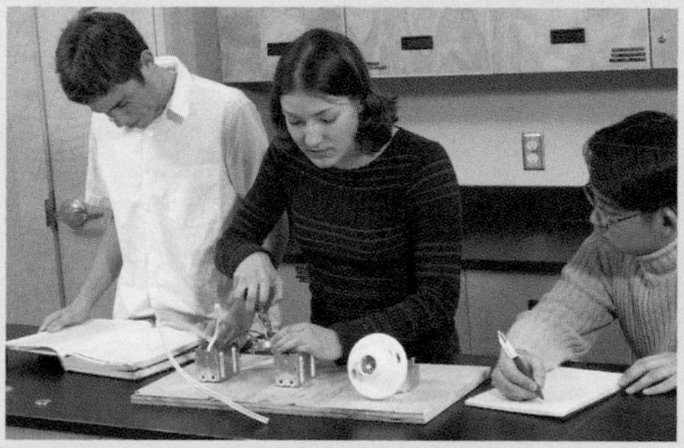

FIGURE 4.24 Connecting the outlet to the circuit.

6 Connect the third NMD cable to the other 2 screws in the outlet (black to black screw, white to silver screw). (This cable would connect back to the service panel if this were in a real room.) Your circuit should look similar to Figure 4.25.

7 Using the appropriate circuit symbols, draw a schematic diagram of your circuit.

8 Go through the checklist provided by your teacher to check that your circuit follows the electrical code.

FIGURE 4.25 A lamp connected to a switch connected to an outlet.

CONTINUED

9. Have another group use the checklist to make sure that your circuit follows the electrical codes. Make any necessary corrections.

10. Label the parts of your circuit.

11. Have the teacher inspect your circuit.

12. Draw a schematic diagram of your circuit and label the main parts.

Analysis and Conclusion

1. Your teacher will sabotage, or interfere with your circuit in one of the following ways:
   - reverse the neutral wire and the live wire
   - leave one wire unconnected
   - use a blown light bulb
   - reverse the ground and neutral wires
   - combination of the above.

2. Now examine the board your teacher returns to you.

3. Troubleshoot the problem(s) and correct them. You may have to connect the circuit to an energy source to do this.

4. What safety practices did you follow in this lab? Why do you think it is so important to follow safety practices when wiring a circuit?

5. If you were to do this lab again, what would you do differently? Why?

Be Safe!

Ask your teacher before you connect the circuit to an energy source.

Extension and Connection

6. Name 3 ways in which this exercise is realistic.

7. **a)** Name 3 ways in which this exercise was unrealistic.
   b) Choose 1 of the unrealistic aspects of this exercise and explain why you think it was done that way.
   c) Make a suggestion as to how the lab could be made more realistic.

4.4 From the Power Station to You

You know from Section 3.2 how electricity is generated, whether it is using nuclear power, coal, or hydroelectric dams. You also know how your home is wired. But how does the electricity get from the power station, also called the electric generating station, to your home, school, or work?

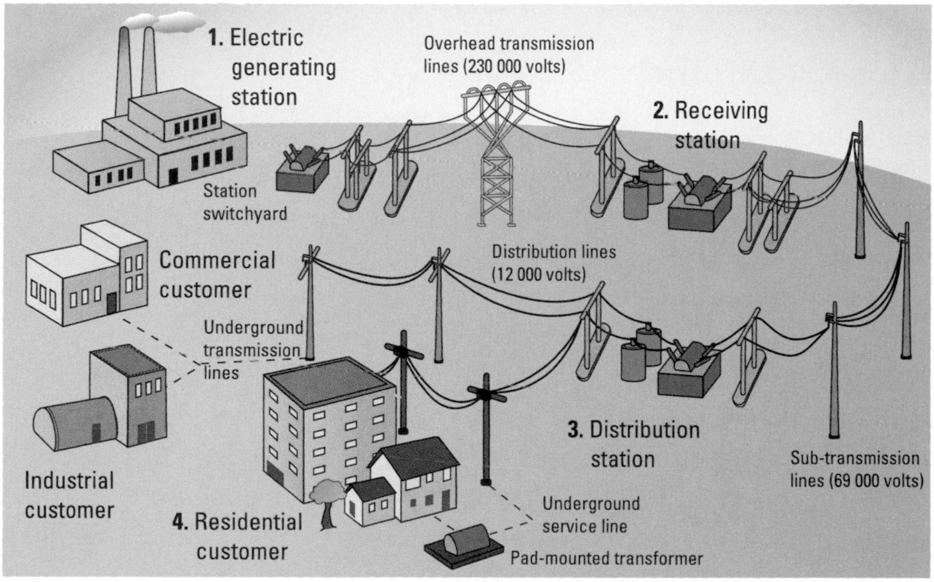

FIGURE 4.26 The path electricity takes from the generator to you. This is the electric grid.

Long-distance Transmission

The electricity generated at the power station has a relatively low voltage. It must travel long distances to get from the station to your home, school, or workplace(Figure 4.26). Power stations use large transformers to increase the voltage to between 69 000 V and 765 000 V. High voltage allows the energy to be transmitted at a low current. This reduces energy loss due to heat along the wires. Transmission lines then connect the power plant to substations (receiving and distribution stations).

Transformers are devices that transfer electric energy from one place to another using induction instead of conduction. In other words, the 2 coils that a transformer is made of are not physically connected.

FIGURE 4.27 The circuit symbol for transformers.

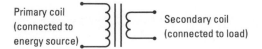

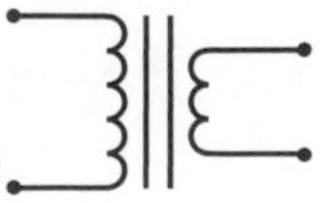

The voltage transferred from the primary to secondary coil depends on the number of turns of the wire in each. See Figure 4.27. If they are equal, the voltage in the secondary coil will be about the same. "Step up" transformers increase the voltage at the secondary coil because the secondary coil has more coils than the primary coil. "Step down" transformers decrease the voltage at the secondary coil.

Closer to Home

Once the electricity reaches a town or city, the high transmission voltage must be "stepped down" to lower levels (about 39 000 V). This occurs at a transmission substation. The voltage is still too high for your home, school and most workplaces.

The next step is to pass the electricity through distribution stations. Here, the voltage is lowered to around 12 000 V. Distribution stations are equipped with many safety features, similar in function to the ones in your home: switches, fuses, circuit breakers and lightning arresters. The switches and circuit breakers use identical mechanisms in distribution stations as they do in your home. They are just designed to take larger currents before they blow or trip. **Lightning arresters** (Figure 4.29, on page 127) are designed to safely guide a lightning strike to the ground without damaging the equipment.

Silicon carbide is a special material. Its resistance to electricity increases at low voltage. That means that in normal conditions,

FIGURE 4.28 These transformers are often disguised as houses. Why do you think this is?

no electricity is conducted. However, its resistance is greatly reduced at high voltage. When lightning strikes, the surge of electricity reduces the resistance in the silicon carbide block, allowing the current to flow to the ground. As soon as the surge has passed, the resistance rises again and no current flows.

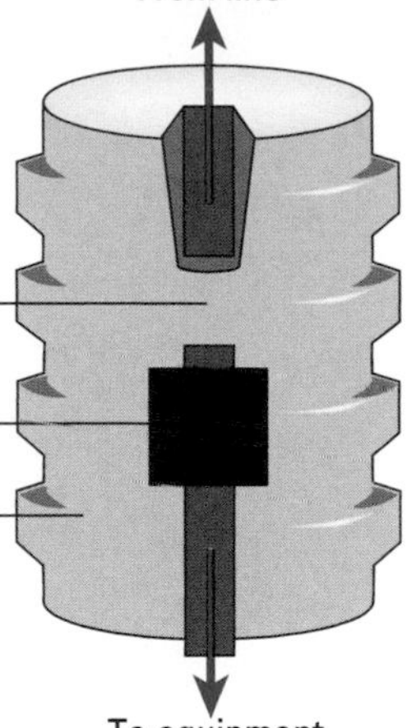

FIGURE 4.29 A lightning arrester.

Fluctuations in Voltage

We expect the voltage in our homes, schools and workplaces to remain constant. In other words, lights should not become dimmer or brighter for no reason and our electronic equipment should not be exposed to power surges. The voltage on power lines does vary, or fluctuate depending on the amount of load—number of devices or appliances using the electric energy—being drawn by customers. For example, the voltage will decrease when everyone turns on their air conditioners in the summer, or in the evening when many people turn on their televisions.

How does the power company deal with this?

Power companies use a method known as **tap changing under load (TCUL).** These taps automatically adjust the output voltage of the transformer to match a predetermined voltage at some point down the line.

In Your Neighbourhood

You may have noticed the green boxes (Figure 4.30) in your neighbourhood or the grey buckets at the top of your hydro poles. These are transformers that "step down" the voltage to 120/240 V service for your home, school, or workplace.

The conductors from these transformers are called **service drops.** They are made up of the 3 wires you saw in Section 4.3 (2 live and 1 neutral).

FIGURE 4.30 The "green boxes" are the last transformers before an underground service enters a home. Why are children told not to play on them?

At Your Home

Before the conductors enter your home, they pass through a meter to measure the amount of electricity used. From there, they pass through the service switch (the on/off switch for the entire building) and into the service panel.

Review and Apply

1. Why is electric heat such an expensive method of heating a home?

2. Distribution and transmission substations are expensive to build and maintain. Why does the electric company not reduce the voltage of the electricity once, at the transformers in the "service drops" in local neighbourhoods?

3. In a group, imagine you are hired to help to plan the electric grid. For each of the following, what would be your most important consideration: safety, convenience, or cost? Explain your reasoning.
   a) Location of transmission stations
   b) Number of distribution stations
   c) Whether to use overhead or underground wires
   d) Location of distribution stations

4. Add the new concepts in this section to the graphic organizer you started in Section 4.1.

5. **In Your Neighbourhood**

   Look around your neighbourhood.
   - Is the service drop for your home above or below ground?
   - Where is your nearest substation?
   - How far are you from the power plant?
   - Can you locate the power lines leading from the power plant?
   - See if you can trace the electricity from your power plant to your home.

   On a map, draw the path the electricity in your home follows from the plant to your service panel. You may have to do some research.

Electromagnetic Fields (EMF) around Power Lines

In 1979, concerns were raised that the electromagnetic fields (EMF) around power lines were causing cancer in the people who lived near them. This caused many people to worry about living near power lines.

Since then, many studies have been done to determine if EMF is dangerous to human health. The result:

- No conclusive evidence that cancer levels are higher in individuals who live near electric power lines.

Some people say "case closed." Others are still worried that the evidence does not rule out the possibility of a problem. Is the above statement enough of an assurance for you? Only you can decide.

FIGURE 4.31

Surf the Web

Go to **www.science.nelson.com** and follow the links for ScienceWise Grade 11, Chapter 4, Section 4.4 to find out more information about EMF. Use the information you find to support 1 of these statements: "I am not concerned about EMF because..." or "I am concerned about EMF because..."

CASE STUDY

The Ice Storm of 1998

What Happened?

From January 5 to 10, 1998, an extraordinary ice storm occurred. It was extraordinary for a few reasons:

- It rained for a total of 80 hours over several days (more than double the amount of freezing rain that normally occurs in eastern Canada in a year!).
- It directly affected more people than any previous weather event in Canadian history.
- It stretched from Kitchener and the Muskoka region in Ontario to western Québec and the Eastern Townships to the Fundy coast of New Brunswick and Nova Scotia.

What Was the Damage?

Freezing rain clings to whatever it lands on, forming a sheer layer of ice on roads, trees, hydro wires and buildings. Since it rained for so long, the ice just continued to build on trees and other structures until they could no longer hold the weight. There were many effects of this storm, but we will focus only on the power outages.

The collapse of both the power lines and telephone cable meant that the people experiencing the storm were left without electricity for weeks.

a) Make a list of all of the things you use each day that require electricity. Circle the ones you absolutely could not do without.

Since the storm occurred in the middle of the winter, many residents were left without heat for their homes. Millions of people were forced to move in with relatives or into a shelter. One million households in Québec and Ontario were without power.

FIGURE 4.32 The ice grew so heavy that hydro towers collapsed. Do you think that the electric company could have planned for this? Why or why not?

b) If your family were forced to evacuate your home, where would you go? Do you have relatives in a nearby city?

Under the weight of the ice, 120 000 km of power lines and telephone cables, 130 major transmission towers and about 30 000 wooden utility poles collapsed. With such extensive damage to the electric grid—the system of power lines between power stations—simply repairing it was not enough. Major sections had to be rebuilt. The electric grid in eastern Ontario took 50 years to build. Now a storm had severely damaged it in a matter of days.

The storm itself lasted only 5 days, but many residents had no power in their homes for 2 or 3 weeks. Some people had to wait until February to get their power back.

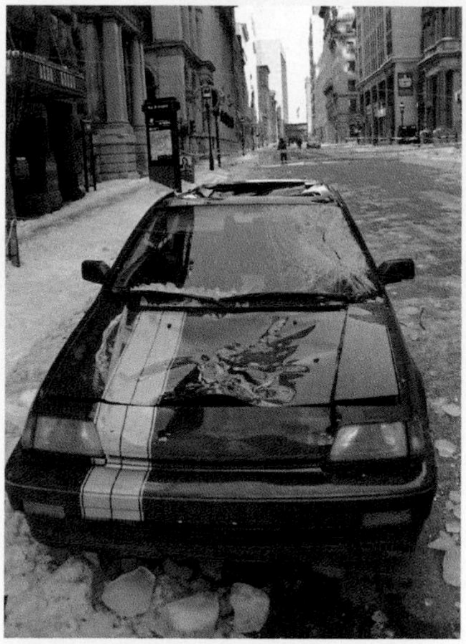

FIGURE 4.33 Many businesses were forced to close because of the power outage. Here is a usually busy street in downtown Montreal, completely empty because of the danger of falling ice from buildings. Describe 2 economic consequences of the ice storm.

c) How would you adjust to being without electricity for 2 weeks? What would you have to do differently?

Eastern Ontario and western Québec are very likely to get storms. Many of those affected by the storm questioned the wisdom of having so much of the electric grid above ground. Many people wondered if the ice storm would have been as big a disaster if the hydro lines had not been affected.

Analysis and Communication

1. Why do you think the electric utility companies had so many of the power lines above ground? With a partner, brainstorm ways they could have helped prevent the lengthy power outages.

Making Connections

2. Choose a local business you would be interested in owning, or if you have a part-time job consider the type of business you work for. Brainstorm and make a list of everything related to this business that requires electricity. What would happen if you had no electricity for 2 weeks? What would you do? Your business would probably have to close temporarily. How would you earn a living?

ACTIVITY 4C

Are You Ready?

Chances are you have experienced a power outage before. In the event of a storm or accident, your electric power could be cut off for a few minutes to a few hours or days. It is important to be prepared for these kinds of emergencies.

In this activity, you will develop a plan for dealing with emergencies as a result of a power failure or other electrical problem.

What You Will Need

- pen and paper

What You Will Do

1. Prepare a chart with the headings shown below.
2. Refer to the headings below. Brainstorm as a class what immediate action you would take at home in each case. Write your suggestions under the appropriate heading.
3. Make a second chart with the headings *Essential* and *Non-essential.*
4. List each of the electrical devices in your home under one of the 2 headings.
5. Next to each of the essential devices, indicate the most important to the least important by using numbers, stars or some other system of your choice. Example: Have the most important device be number 1.
6. Now, imagine your day. Go through what you do in a typical day and write the things you need for it. Exclude the non-essential electrical devices you identified in step 3. Replace the essential electrical devices with an alternative. *Remember that during a power outage, your lifestyle will change.*
7. Make a list of items that you feel should be included in an emergency kit for your survival in the event of a one-week power failure in the middle of the winter, if you will be remaining in your home.
8. Suppose you are evacuated and have to leave your home. Make a list of items you feel you should have in an emergency kit that you can carry on your back.

Electric fire	Overloaded circuit/ Blown fuse	One-day failure (pole down)	One-week failure (ice storm)

9 Think about your family. Can you think of any necessities for them that have not been included in your emergency kits in steps 7 and 8? Add them now.

10 You have your emergency kits prepared. But, there are still a few questions to be answered. Answer the questions below as best you can. If needed, ask your family for help.

FIGURE 4.34 An emergency kit, prepared by Emergency Preparedness Canada.

a) In the event of an emergency, cell phones and local phone lines would probably be unavailable. Where would you all meet if separated?

b) Which relative, outside of town, would be your common contact if you are separated? (Long distance phone lines would probably still be available.)

c) Where are the following shut-off valves in your home?

i. gas
ii. water
iii. electricity

What Did You Find Out?

1 After going through this activity, do you feel you are better prepared for an emergency than before you started it? Explain your answer.

2 Some families have considered what to do in case of a fire. Most families have not thought about what to do in any other type of emergency. List 2 reasons why you think this is true.

3 Will you make sure your family is prepared for an emergency now? Why or why not?

Making Connections

4 Imagine you are charged with designing an emergency preparedness booklet to help people in your community prepare for a 3-week power outage. Plan and design a 5-page booklet to be distributed to households in your community.

5 Talk to a school custodian. Find out how emergencies due to power outages are handled. After completing this activity, can you suggest any ways your school could improve its plan?

Be Safe!

Be Safe! Never shut off the gas in your home unless it is absolutely necessary. A licensed professional must turn it on again.

Job Link

Emergency Preparedness Team

You have probably seen or heard stories on the news about disasters. There are always many people picking through rubble or taking care of the injured. You probably do not know that most of those people are volunteers like 19-year-old Kerry Chalmers who volunteers with the St. John Ambulance Brigade.

ScienceWise: How long have you been involved in the organization?

Kerry Chalmers: I've been a member of the St. John Ambulance Brigade since I was 14.

ScienceWise: How did you end up in the Emergency Preparedness team for your community?

Kerry Chalmers: It isn't really voluntary if you are in the Brigade and have standard first aid training. We run through simulations to be ready if something happens.

ScienceWise: How can a person join?

Kerry Chalmers: Just sign up. The Brigade will train you.

FIGURE 4.35 Kerry Chalmers, Volunteer, St. John Ambulance Brigade.

SAFE GUARD is a national program that brings together government, private and voluntary organizations that are part of the emergency planning, response and recovery community.

Here is a list of some of the organizations that coordinate the network of volunteers in your community, who are prepared in case of an emergency:

Canadian Red Cross
Emergency Preparedness Canada
Emergency Measures Ontario
St. John Ambulance Brigade

Surf the Web

What happens if a disaster strikes in your city or town? Are there enough employees to handle it? What is the government's role? Visit www.science.nelson.com and follow the links for ScienceWise Grade 11, Chapter 4, Section 4.4 to find out.

4.5 Chapter Summary

Now you can...

- Identify and use SI units (4.1)
- Identify some household appliances that require 110 V and some that require 220 V A to operate (4.1)
- Conduct research to make a consumer report about a major appliance (Activity 4A)
- Investigate how electrical devices play a role in the economy of the local community and improve the standard of living (4.2)
- Identify problems and solutions related to the environmental impact of the consumption of electric energy and the disposal of used electrical appliances (4.2)
- Build a circuit using the appropriate tools (Lab 4B)
- Analyze electric circuits, identify faults and make corrections (Lab 4B)
- Use safe practices while working with electric circuits (Lab 4B)
- Draw a schematic diagram of a normal electric circuit found in a house (Lab 4B)
- Describe common electrical components that regulate the flow of electricity (4.3)
- Create a household plan for survival in the event of an extended public power disruption (Activity 4C)
- Locate, select and analyze information about how electricity gets from the generating station to your home (4.4)

Concept Connections

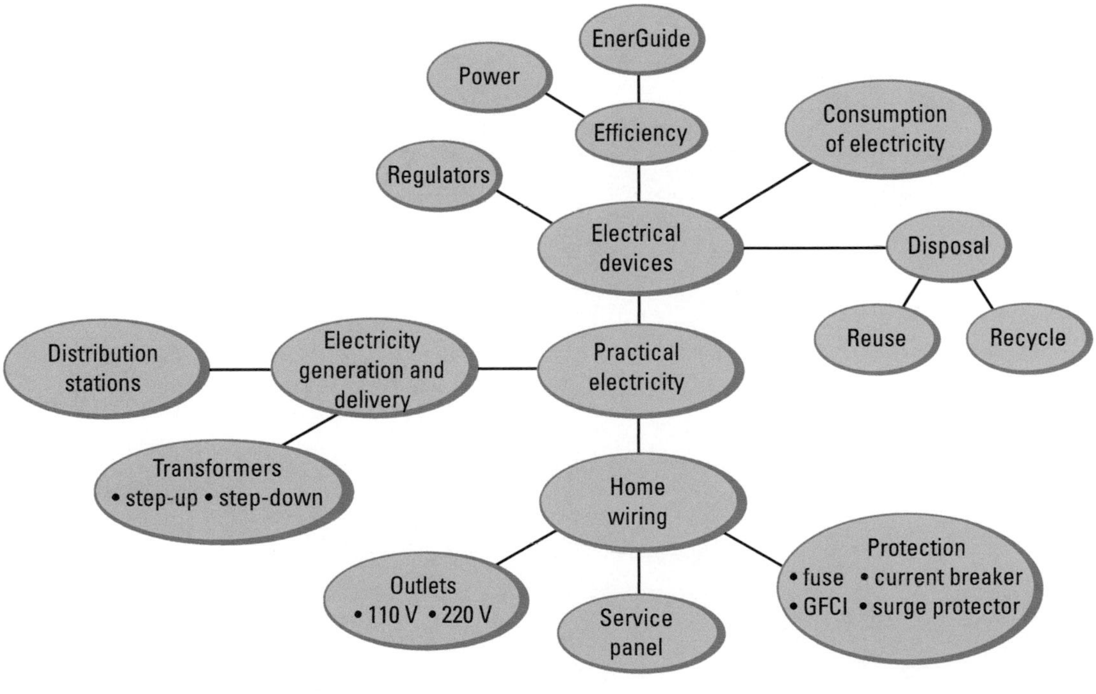

FIGURE 4.36 Compare your completed graphic organizer to the one on this page. How did you do? Can you add any new links to your organizer?

CHAPTER 4 *review*

Knowledge and Understanding

1. Explain, in your own words, how each of the following devices works.
   a) Fuse
   b) Circuit breaker
   c) Lightning arrester

2. Most electrical devices release some energy as heat. The elements on an electric stove are almost 100 percent efficient. Why?

3. Draw the following chart in your notebook and fill it in.

	Nuclear power	Hydroelectric energy	Coal and natural gas
Advantages			
Disadvantages			

Compare your answers with a classmate's. Add 1 new advantage or disadvantage to your chart.

4. The electric grid includes all of the components and wires from the power station to the home, school, or workplace. Name as many components of the electric grid as you can.

Inquiry

5. Design an investigation to determine which of 2 microwave ovens (of identical size) is more efficient. Assume you are able to measure the amount of energy the microwave oven uses.

6. In your notebook, create and fill in the following chart for a room in your house such as the kitchen, living room, or den. List all of the electrical devices in the room under the heading "Item."

Item	Is it currently on?	Is it currently being used?	Is it older than 5 years?

Now take a look at your chart. Is energy being wasted or used wisely in this room? How could you make the room more energy efficient?

7 Your workplace is experiencing a brown-out (decrease in voltage). Which part in the substation is probably not working properly? Explain your reasoning.

a) Lightning arresters
b) Fuses
c) Taps (used in TCUL)
d) Circuit breakers

Making Connections

8 Rashid wants to buy a new refrigerator for his parents' anniversary. The salesperson shows him a few but refuses to let him examine the EnerGuide labels closely. What advice would you give to Rashid?

9 Think of a small appliance in your home that contains a motor (blender, hand mixer, can opener). Suppose the motor stops working. List any parts of the appliance that could be re-used.

10 Why is it dangerous to get an electric outlet wet?

11 A bird can sit on a power line, but if you were to touch a power line while standing on the ground, it could kill you. Why? Explain your answer.

12 Willa wants to open up the green transformer box across the street from her home. "After all," she says, "it is only 110 V in there." What would you tell Willa about electrical safety?

Communication

13 Write a story, suitable for a 5-year-old to read, about how electricity gets from the power station to your home. You may want to work with a partner.

14 Draw a schematic diagram using the proper circuit symbols for a laundry room with 1 outlet and an overhead light and a fan (use the resistor symbol with a square around it for the fan).

15 In a group, prepare a video or radio show explaining why you think nuclear power is a better or worse energy source than hydroelectricity (make sure you include at least 3 reasons). You may want to make a practice tape of your presentation, then as a group agree on how you could improve it, and then re-tape it.

PUTTING IT ALL TOGETHER

Wiring a New Office

More and more small businesses are being run out of home offices. Before you can redo your basement and open up shop, it is important to check with your town, city, or municipality. They may have zoning bylaws that must be met before a business can be run out of a home.

The Project

You have decided to open a home office in your basement. You will determine the requirements of your municipality. You will also draw a schematic diagram for the electric wiring and determine the cost to do the renovation of the wooden studs and electric wiring (excluding the hook-up to the service panel).

What You May Need

The materials you use will vary from group to group, depending on your design. You may need the following materials:

- paper
- pencil
- ruler
- a copy of the building code (The building code is published by the Ontario government and must be purchased from them. Your local library should have a copy of it.)
- catalogues and flyers from local hardware stores
- NMD 14/2 cable
- wire stripper
- needle-nose pliers
- device boxes
- wire cutter
- lamp holder
- screwdrivers
- wall outlets
- light switches
- plywood or fibre board

What You Will Do

1. Research the bylaws in your municipality. Find out if you can build a home office in the basement, like the one in Figure 1B.

2. List your municipality's requirements and restrictions.

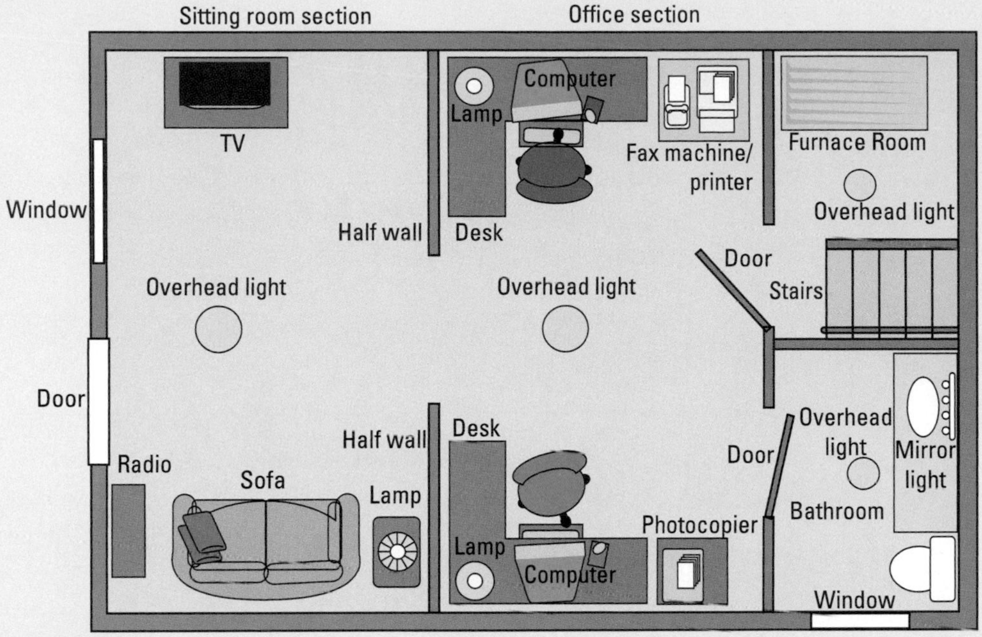

FIGURE 1B Your home office will be designed to have working space for 2 people and a sitting room with a television and a stereo. There will also be a bathroom. Each area, or room, has its own overhead light.

3 A carpenter friend takes care of the wooden studs that form the frames for the rooms. You have decided to wire the electrical yourself, but are leaving the hook-up of the circuit panel to an electrician.

Draw a schematic diagram for the circuits in each room of the basement in Figure 1B. Remember that each NMD cable includes 2 wires. Assume the circuit panel is in the furnace room.

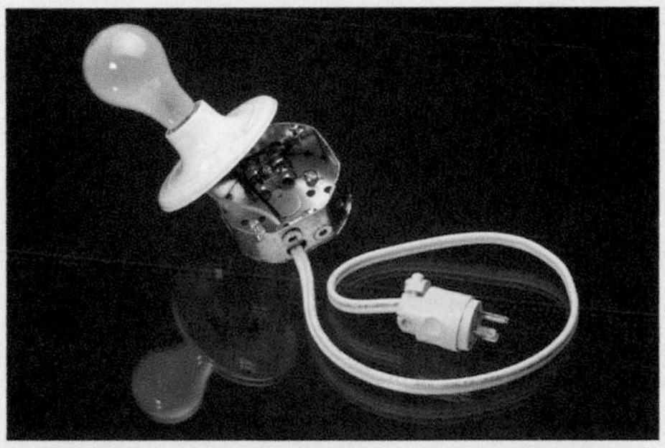

FIGURE 2B A simple lamp. The 2 wires connecting the bulb to the energy source are inside the single NMD 14/2 cable.

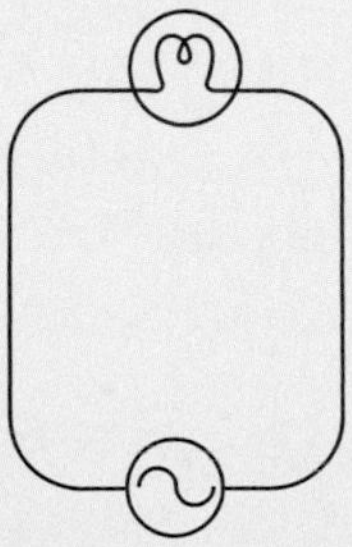

FIGURE 3B The schematic diagram that matches the lamp.

CONTINUED

4. Determine the materials necessary to complete the electrical part of the renovation (excluding any computer cables, as you have decided to hire someone else to do that).

5. Use flyers and catalogues and visit local hardware stores to determine the cost of purchasing the materials. In your notebook, fill in the following chart.

Item	Quantity	Cost per item	Total cost	Store

6. Make sure you add up the "Total cost" column to determine the cost of purchasing all of the materials.

7. Choose either the sitting room or the office space. Construct a model of the room with the circuits that you designed for it. You may wish to look at Lab 4B for help.

8. Answer the following questions.
   a) Why is it important to understand your municipality's bylaws before doing major renovations?
   b) Why is there a single building code for all of Ontario instead of one for each municipality?
   c) Why is it a good idea to have an electrician run your circuits to the service panel?
   d) List 2 advantages and 2 disadvantages to doing your own electric wiring or hiring someone to do it for you. Support your thinking.

Assessment

9. Look at other groups' models. What did you think they did well? What did you like best about your group's model? If you were to do this activity again, what changes would you make? Why?

UNIT 3

Micro-organisms

CHAPTER 5

Characteristics of Micro-organisms

Micro-organisms are all around you. A **micro-organism** is any living thing that is too small to see with the naked eye. Micro-organisms are in the air, in water, on plants and animals, and even on people you meet. Although some micro-organisms can make us sick, most are harmless. Many are, in fact, very useful. Look at the photographs below. Some of these people need to be careful about harmful micro-organisms in their workplace. Others use helpful micro-organisms to do their job. What do you know about the role of micro-organisms in each of these occupations? Are these micro-organisms helpful or harmful? Do you know of any other occupations where workers must have some understanding of micro-organisms in order to do their jobs?

FIGURE 5.1

What You Will Learn

After completing this chapter, you will be able to:

- Describe the characteristics of 4 groups of micro-organisms, using a classification system and correct scientific terms (5.1)
- Describe the basic characteristics of 4 groups of micro-organisms (5.2, 5.3, 5.4, 5.5)
- Compare the life cycles of 4 groups of micro-organisms and explain how they reproduce (5.2, 5.3, 5.4, 5.5)
- Describe some of the ways that micro-organisms can help us and can hurt us (5.2, 5.3, 5.4, 5.5)

What You Will Do

- Classify micro-organisms according to their basic characteristics and communicate your results in a flow chart (Activity 5A)
- Grow samples of micro-organisms on Petri dishes from items in your classroom and communicate your results in data tables and diagrams (Lab 5B)
- Carry out an investigation using prepared slides and wet mounts of micro-organisms and communicate your results on data tables and diagrams (Lab 5C)
- Identify micro-organisms that grow on food samples and compile, organize and interpret your data using data tables and diagrams (Activity 5D)
- Follow safety procedures when working with micro-organisms in the lab (Labs 5B, 5C, 5D)
- Use a microscope appropriately (Lab 5C)
- Work co-operatively with classmates to compile information on the costs to society of 1 micro-organism, and report your findings in a booklet (Activity 5E)

Words to Know

anatomy
asexual reproduction
bacteria
blue-green algae
binary fission
budding
chlorophyll
cytoplasm
filamentous
fragmentation
fungi
life cycle
micro-organism
monera
mould
nucleus
parasite
photosynthesis
physiology
chloroplast
protist
protist algae
protozoa
sexual reproduction
species
spore
virus
wet mount
yeast

A puzzle piece indicates knowledge or a skill that you will need for your project, Micro-organisms at Work, at the end of Unit 3.

5.1 In a Class of Their Own

Whether you are at home, at work or at school, you are always in contact with micro-organisms. Some micro-organisms can hurt you and some micro-organisms are useful. Therefore, it is important to be able to identify the different kinds, or species, of micro-organisms and know something about where and how they live and reproduce. A **species** is a group of similar organisms that are capable of breeding with one another and producing offspring. For example, dogs and cats are 2 different species of organisms.

To help identify different micro-organisms, scientists have classified them according to certain characteristics. Micro-organisms that share the same characteristics are placed in the same group. Classifying organisms, or placing them into groups, helps us to know what characteristics we can expect the micro-organisms in a group to have.

You will need to know how to classify micro-organisms to complete your project, Micro-organisms at Work.

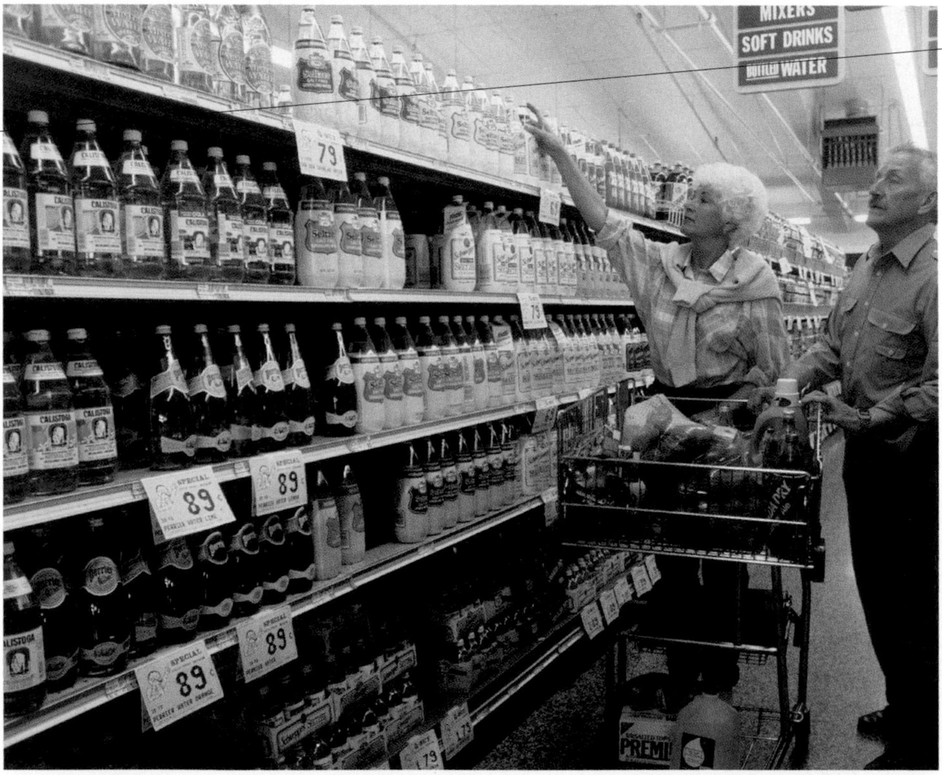

FIGURE 5.2 How is classifying micro-organisms similar to classifying items in a grocery store?

Classifying Micro-organisms

To classify something, it is useful to start with general shared characteristics and then move to more specific characteristics. The general characteristics help you to place items in large groups. The specific characteristics help you divide the large group into smaller groups. For example, when you are sorting laundry, you might first divide bedding from clothing, then further subdivide the bedding into sheets, pillowcases and towels, and the clothing into shirts, pants, socks and underwear.

All micro-organisms can be placed into one of 4 categories: monera, protists, fungi and viruses. Each of these categories includes many species of micro-organisms, which makes them similar to the categories of "bedding" and "clothing" in the example of sorting laundry.

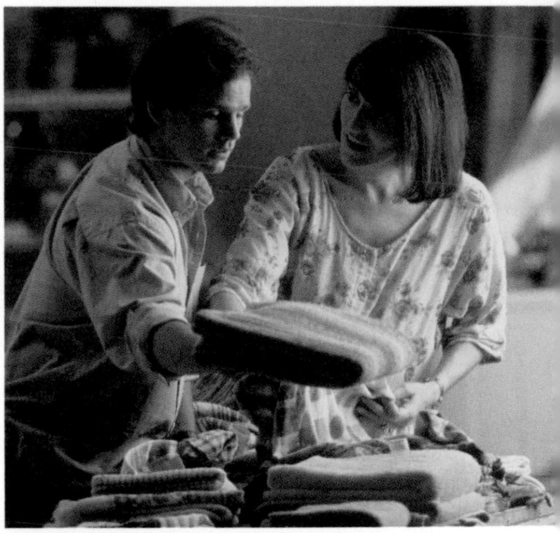

FIGURE 5.3 In order to sort laundry, you place items in different categories according to their similarities and differences.

Monera

Monera are micro-organisms composed of 1 cell that does not contain a cell nucleus. The cell **nucleus** is a special structure in some cell types that contains the genetic material. In monera, the genetic material floats in the **cytoplasm,** a jelly-like substance found in all types of cells. Monera usually reproduce only by **asexual reproduction,** which is reproduction without the exchange of genetic material.

Figure 5.4 shows 2 very different examples of monera. Some monera can cause diseases; for example, certain species of monera cause strep throat or food poisoning. Many monera are helpful organisms that break down and recycle the components of living things after they have died. Other monera species are a food source for aquatic animals.

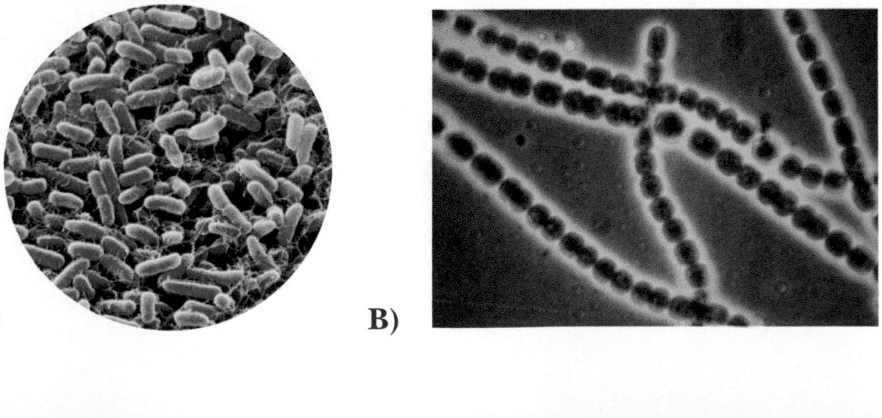

A) **B)**

FIGURE 5.4 A) Bacteria cells; B) Blue-green algae cells. These organisms are both members of the monera group, because they have only 1 cell, which has no nucleus.

Protists

Protists are micro-organisms that are usually composed of only 1 cell, but they have a cell nucleus. Most protists undergo only asexual reproduction. You might have seen the examples of protists in Figure 5.5 in other years. What do you know about how these micro-organisms live and reproduce?

A)
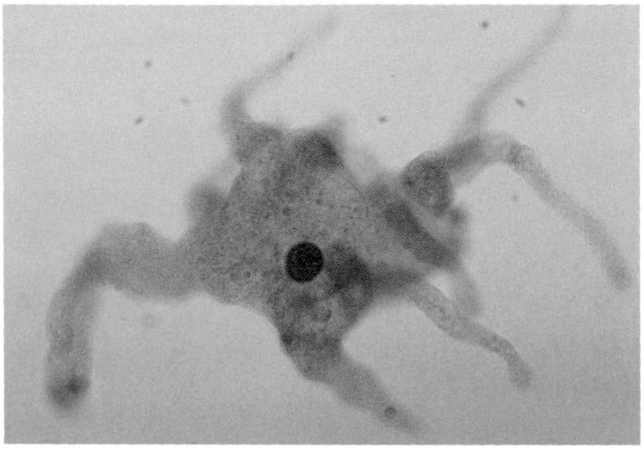

B)
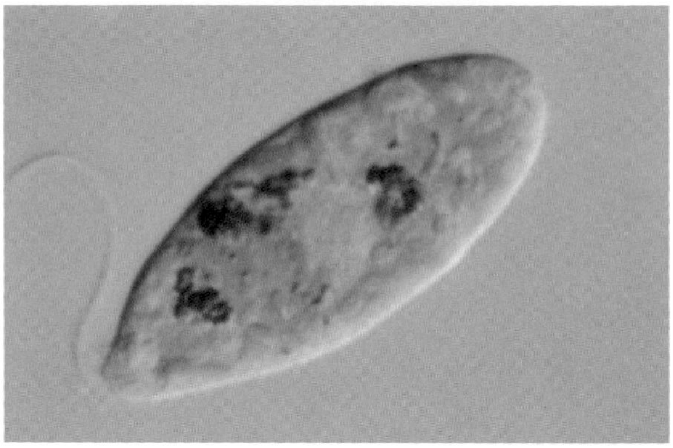

FIGURE 5.5 A) *Amoeba* and B) *Euglena* are both protists. What characteristics do they have in common?

Fungi

Micro-organisms that are **fungi** are composed of at least 1 cell that contains a cell nucleus. In this way, fungi are similar to protists. However, most fungi undergo both asexual and sexual reproduction. **Sexual reproduction** is reproduction that involves the exchange of genetic material. Figure 5.6 shows you 2 examples of fungi that are micro-organisms, a mould and a yeast.

A)
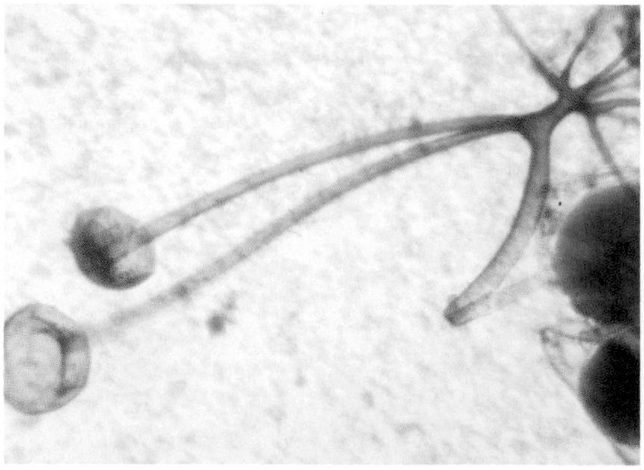

B)
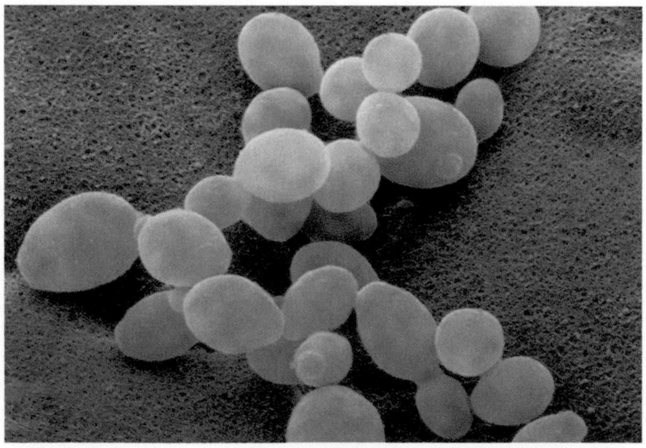

FIGURE 5.6 A) Mould cells and B) yeast cells. Mould and yeast that is visible to the eye is actually composed of many cells.

Viruses

Most living things are composed of cells, either a single cell or many cells working together. Viruses, however, are not made of cells at all. Instead, **viruses** are micro-organisms made up of only genetic material wrapped in protein molecules. Different species of viruses have different genetic material and different proteins.

You will need to know about the classes of micro-organisms to complete your project, Micro-organisms at Work.

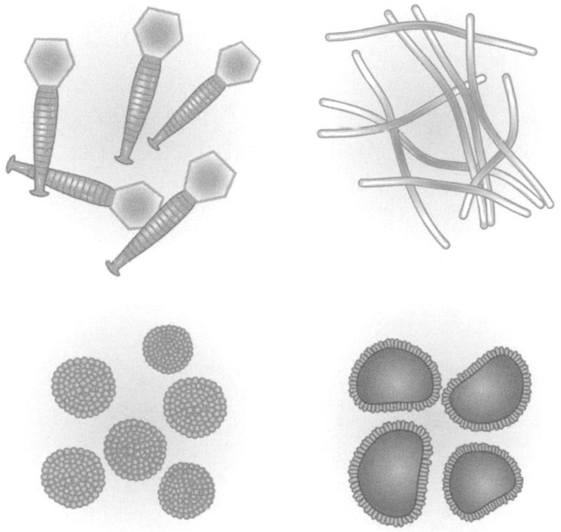

FIGURE 5.7 Examples of virus shapes. Scientists can recognize different viruses by their different shapes.

ScienceWise Fact

Scientists have identified over 5800 different species of micro-organisms. This number probably represents only 3 percent to 27 percent of the actual number, which means there might really be as many as 193 000 species!

ACTIVITY 5A

Classification Keys

One tool that scientists use to identify organisms is a classification key. To identify an organism with a classification key, you must do 2 things. First, you must observe and identify the characteristics of the organisms. Second, you must follow the steps in a flow chart, which contains questions you must answer. These will lead you to the identity of the organism.

In this activity, you will work with 3 or 4 classmates. You will review how a classification key works and then create your own classification key that would allow someone to figure out in which group a micro-organism belonged: monera, protist, fungi, or virus.

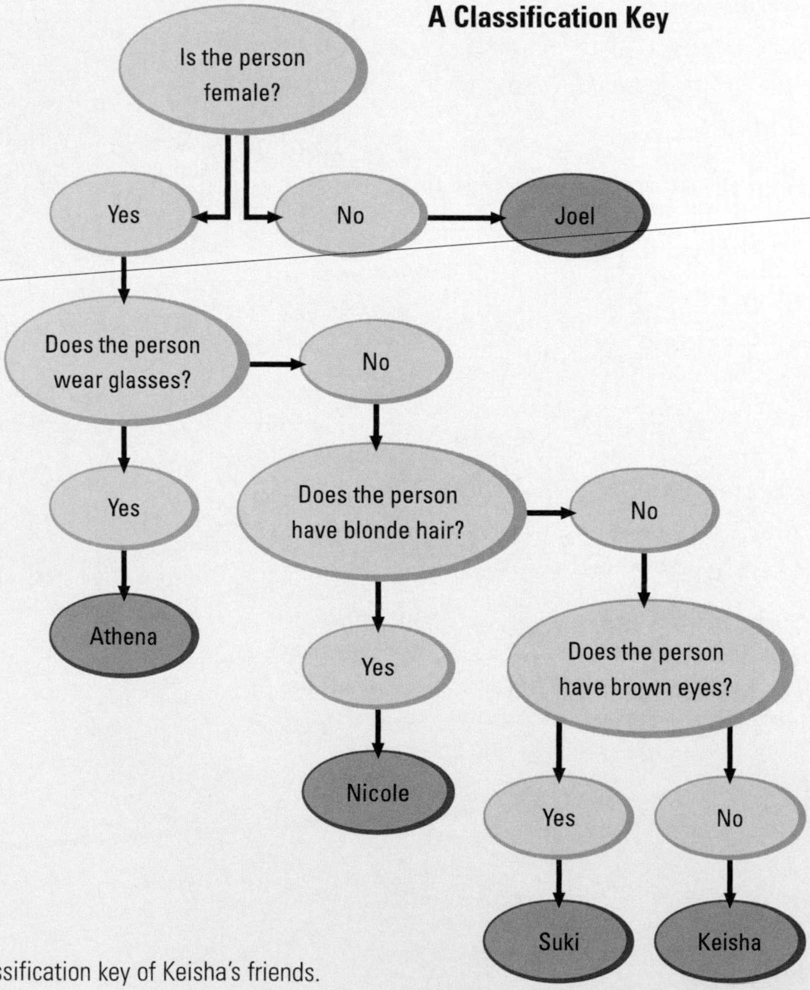

FIGURE 5.8 Classification key of Keisha's friends.

What You Will Need

- pen or pencil
- Bristol board

What You Will Do

1. Figure 5.8 shows a classification key that a student created of her friends, based on some of their characteristics. Follow the arrows down the key. Notice how the key provides 2 choices based on a question and then breaks in 2 directions based on the answers to these questions.

2. At each fork in the classification key in Figure 5.8, identify:
   a) the question being asked and
   b) the characteristic used to separate the individuals.

3. Prepare a list of all the characteristics that are found in members of monera, protist, fungi and viruses.

4. Working with 1 group of micro-organisms at a time, brainstorm a series of questions that would allow someone to decide if a micro-organism was a member of that group. Your questions must be answerable with "yes" or "no." For example, a question to decide if a micro-organism is a monera could be, "Does this micro-organism have cells with a nucleus?"

5. When you have completed your questions for all the groups, organize them into a flow chart. Draw your finished flow chart on your Bristol board.

6. Switch charts with another group. See if you can follow that group's flow chart. Identify any steps with which you had trouble.

7. Meet with the members of all of the other groups. Discuss what you liked and what you did not like about their chart. What features of their keys did you think were done well? Were any parts of their keys confusing?

What Did You Find Out?

1. Explain how a key makes it easier to decide how to classify a micro-organism.

Making Connections

2. Filing documents in an office is 1 example of using a classification key at the workplace. List 3 other examples of how classification can be used in the workplace.

Review and Apply

1. Make a list of at least 5 different examples of tasks that you do in your daily life in which you use classification. For each example, write a sentence explaining why you use classification to accomplish that task.

2. In a sentence, identify the group composed of micro-organisms that are made of cells but do not contain a cell nucleus.

3. In a chart, summarize the similarities and differences between monera and protists.

4. In a sentence, identify the group composed of micro-organisms that are not composed of cells.

5. Both protists and fungi are composed of cells and have nuclei. Explain the difference between these 2 groups of micro-organisms.

6. Bottled water is always sterile, which means that it does not contain any micro-organisms. Imagine that you open a sealed bottle of sterile water, take a quick drink and then immediately replace the lid. Is the water still sterile? If your answer is yes, justify your choice. If your answer is no, justify your choice and then describe where the micro-organisms came from.

7. Organize the concepts you have learned in this section in a graphic organizer.

8. **A "Class" Project**

Working in a group of 2 or 3, choose 1 of the following workplace settings: a restaurant, a hospital, or an office. Brainstorm ways that classification would be used in this workplace. When you have identified as many ways as possible, summarize your ideas in a chart. Then, choose a spokesperson to present the ideas on your chart to the class.

Working on your own, explain in a short paragraph how you used classification to make your chart.

Surf the Web

To find related careers that require classification skills, visit **www.science.nelson.com** and follow the links for ScienceWise Grade 11, Chapter 5, Section 5.1.

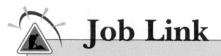

Job Link

Retail Sales Clerk

Retail sales clerks are the ultimate classifiers. They sort, classify and maintain information related to retail activities, such as displaying goods, keeping inventories, tracking prices and taxes, and keeping sales records.

FIGURE 5.9 Sales clerks have to do a lot of classifying.

Responsibilities of a Retail Sales Clerk

- greet customers and assist them in finding the merchandise they are interested in purchasing
- advise customers on the use and care of merchandise and provide advice about products and services
- register, check and process incoming merchandise
- prepare reports and documents for ordering merchandise and reporting sales
- prepare merchandise for display
- keep track of the numbers of items that are both in stock and have been sold (maintain inventory records)
- prepare sales agreements and accept cash, cheque, credit card, or debit payments
- operate computerized inventory and ordering systems

Where do they work?

- in retail businesses or in wholesale businesses that sell to the public, such as factory-direct sales centres

Skills for the Job

- good classification skills are a must
- a friendly, people-oriented personality
- typing and computer operation skills may be required
- ability to communicate clearly, both verbally and in writing
- ability to work both as a team member and independently

Education

- a secondary school diploma is usually required
- specific courses or training may be required by some businesses
- demonstrated sales ability and knowledge of products may be required in businesses that sell specialized or expensive products, such as computers or sports equipment

5.2 Monera

You will need to know about monera to complete your project, Micro-organisms at Work.

Recall from Section 5.1 that micro-organisms in the group monera are made of cells but have no nucleus. Monera can be subdivided into two groups: bacteria and blue-green algae.

Physiology and Anatomy of Bacteria

Most of the monera that you encounter in daily life are bacteria. Bacteria have been found in everything from air to water, and from the sub-zero arctic ice to the vents of active volcanoes. Where would you expect to find bacteria in the places shown in Figure 5.10?

FIGURE 5.10 Bacteria are found in many different places and play many different roles in our lives.

Physiology refers to the way the body of an organism works. Your physiology, for example, includes the way your digestive system works to feed your cells. **Anatomy** is the structure of organisms. For example, your anatomy includes 2 arms, 2 legs, a torso and a head.

Bacteria are monera that cannot make their own food. Bacteria usually feed by releasing chemicals to break down a food source into particles that are small enough to enter the cell. Different species of bacteria have different shapes, either rod-shaped, circular, or spiral (Figure 5.11A). All bacteria have a cell wall and do not have a nucleus (Figure 5.11B).

ScienceWise Fact

Each square centimetre of your skin averages about 100 000 bacteria.

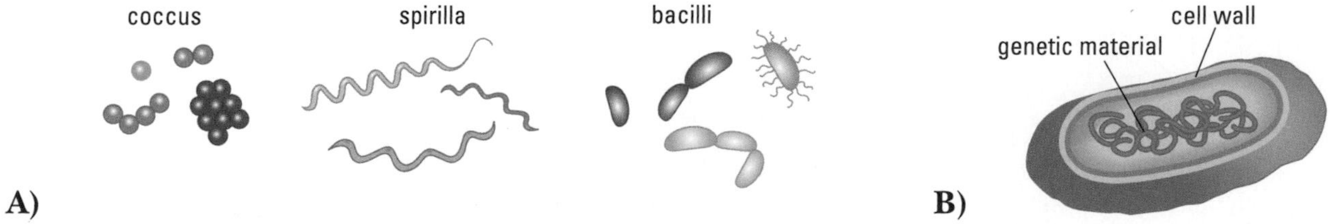

FIGURE 5.11 A) The 3 basic shapes of bacteria cells; B) Anatomy of a common species of bacteria called *E. coli*.

Physiology and Anatomy of Blue-green Algae

Blue-green algae are monera that can make their own food. This fact separates blue-green algae from bacteria. Blue-green algae make their food by **photosynthesis,** a process that captures the sun's energy and uses it to convert carbon dioxide gas to food. This process requires a chemical called **chlorophyll,** which gives the blue-green algae their colour (Figure 5.12). Since they are monera, all blue-green algae have no cell nucleus. Unlike bacteria, blue-green algae can only survive in water.

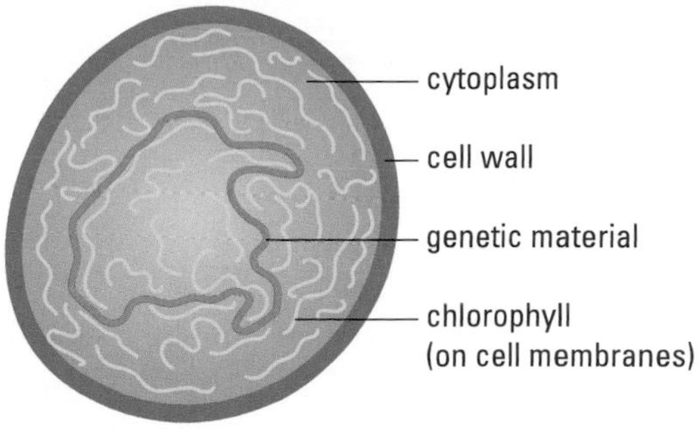

FIGURE 5.12 Chlorophyll is the chemical that allows blue-green algae to make their own food.

Reproduction and Life Cycle of Monera

The **life cycle** of an organism refers to the stages that occur from the time the organism is first formed to when it first reproduces. All monera undergo asexual reproduction by the process of binary fission. **Binary fission** is the division of a cell into 2 equal halves (Figure 5.13) This process can take as little as 20 seconds to complete.

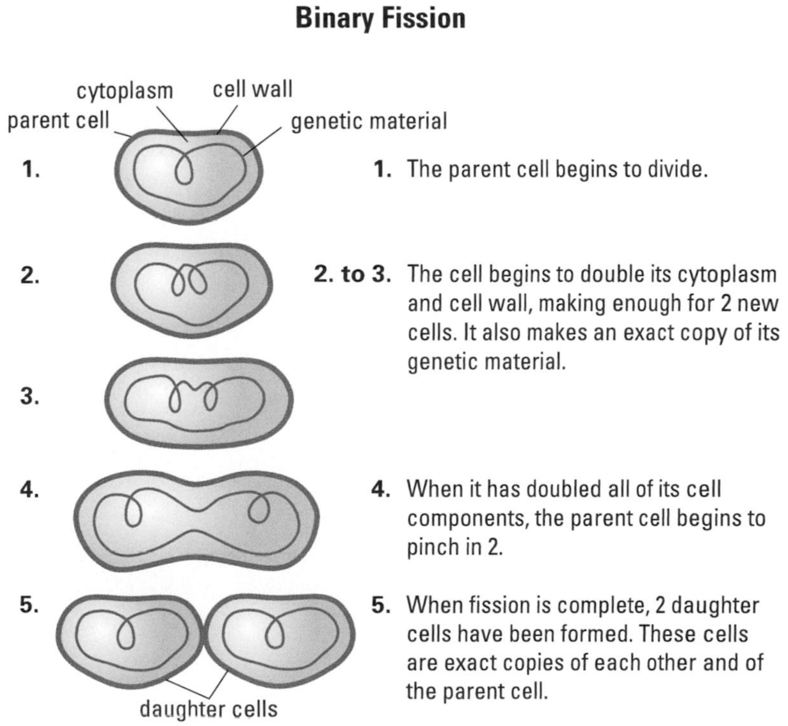

Binary Fission
cytoplasm
cell wall
parent cell
genetic material
1.
1. The parent cell begins to divide.
2.
2. to 3. The cell begins to double its cytoplasm and cell wall, making enough for 2 new cells. It also makes an exact copy of its genetic material.
3.
4.
4. When it has doubled all of its cell components, the parent cell begins to pinch in 2.
5.
5. When fission is complete, 2 daughter cells have been formed. These cells are exact copies of each other and of the parent cell.
daughter cells

FIGURE 5.13 After binary fission, the 2 new cells are about the same size.

LAB
5B

Bacteria in the Workplace

Be Safe!

- Do not swab your mouth or cough onto a Petri dish to collect bacteria.
- Dispose of your Petri dish and swabs according to your teacher's instructions.
- Wash your hands thoroughly after this lab.
- Do not touch your mouth, eyes, nose, or ears when working with micro-organisms.
- Do not open your Petri dish after you have collected your samples.

Humans sometimes create areas that contain just the right conditions for bacteria to survive. Bacteria need a certain temperature range and a source of food and water to live. Because some bacteria can cause disease, finding out about the kinds of places in which bacteria survive is a good way to keep healthy at home and on the job.

Purpose

In this lab, you will look at the kinds of bacteria that are in your classroom and where they are. You will grow and identify bacteria from common items that could be found in many workplaces.

Materials

- 1 Petri dish with agar
- permanent marker
- tape
- 4 sterile cotton swabs
- distilled water

Procedure

1. Create a data table in your notebook, using the headings in Figure 5.14.

Section	Item swabbed	Observations	Sketch

FIGURE 5.14

2. Obtain a Petri dish with agar, and 4 sterile swabs. With a permanent marker, mark 4 equal sections on the bottom of the Petri dish and label each section from 1 to 4, as shown in Figure 5.15.

FIGURE 5.15 Divide your plate into quarters.

3. Choose an item in the classroom that would likely be found in many workplaces. For example, you might choose a computer keyboard.
4. Carefully wet the sterile swab in distilled water and run it over the surface of the item you chose in step 3.

5 Lift the upper lid of the Petri dish as shown in Figure 5.16. Gently run the swab in a zigzag pattern across 1 section of the nutrient agar. Be careful not to tear the agar surface. Close the lid of the Petri dish. Dispose of the swab according to your teacher's instructions.

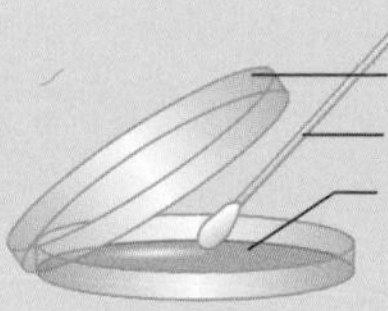

FIGURE 5.16 Open your Petri dish just a little bit and run the swab gently across the surface of the agar.

6 In the appropriate section of your data table, record the item that you tested.

7 Repeat steps 3 to 6 for 3 other items in your classroom.

8 Replace the upper lid of the Petri dish. Tape the top and bottom lids in the form of an "X" with masking tape to seal the Petri dish.

9 Write your name and the date on the Petri dish. Store the Petri dish in a dark cupboard at room temperature for 3 or 4 days.

10 Without opening it, observe the bacteria on your Petri dish. In your data table, write a description and draw a sketch of the bacteria on each section of the Petri dish.

11 Dispose of your Petri dish according to your teacher's instructions.

Analysis and Conclusion

1 List the items you swabbed in order of the amount of bacteria that grew, from the most to the least. Include all the different types of bacteria. You do not need to estimate actual numbers of bacteria.

2 Think about the characteristics of the items you swabbed, and the order of your list from most to least bacteria. Suggest reasons for the amount of bacteria that grew from each item, in point form.

FIGURE 5.17 How can you reduce the number of bacteria in your classroom?

Extension and Connection

3 With 2 or 3 classmates, brainstorm ways to reduce the amount of bacteria on workplace objects in your classroom. Make a list of your ideas.

4 Draw a map of your kitchen at home. With a red "X," mark the places you would be most likely to find bacteria. Explain why you marked these areas.

Review and Apply

1. Two different groups of micro-organisms are classified as monera. Give the names of these 2 groups.
2. Using modelling clay, create models that show how the shape of the cells can be used to help identify different species of bacteria.
3. Compare how bacteria and blue-green algae get food.
4. Create a Flip-chart animation that shows how monera reproduce by binary fission.
5. Draw a labelled diagram of a bacteria cell and a blue-green algae cell. In a sentence, identify the characteristic that allows you to distinguish between these 2 types of cells.
6. Imagine that you left a package of raw meat on the kitchen counter at 8:00 A.M. There is 1 cell of bacteria on the meat. At 8:15 A.M., this cell reproduces. There are now 2 bacterial cells. At 8:30 A.M., the bacteria again reproduce, so there are now 4 cells. If the bacteria continue to reproduce every 15 minutes, calculate the number of bacterial cells that would be on the meat at 12:00 A.M., at 2:00 P.M., and at 3:30 P.M. Do you think the meat would still be safe to eat at 3:30 P.M.? Why or why not?
7. Some people thaw frozen meat at room temperature, as shown in Figure 5.19. Do you think this is a good practice? Give reasons for your answer.
8. Add the new concepts from this section to the graphic organizer you started in Section 5.1.

Time	Number of bacteria cells
8:00 A.M.	1
8:15 A.M.	2
8:30 A.M.	4
12:00 A.M.	
2:00 P.M.	
3:30 P.M.	

FIGURE 5.18 Use a table like this or spreadsheet software to help you calculate your answer to question 7.

FIGURE 5.19

5.3 Protists

You may encounter protists every day, but you probably do not know they are there. Protists are always found in water; that is, they are aquatic organisms. Protists are the main food of many aquatic organisms, from other micro-organisms all the way up to large whales. Through photosynthesis, protist algae produce two-thirds of the world's oxygen. Some protists cause deadly diseases, such as malaria and African sleeping sickness.

You will need to know about protists for your project, Micro-organisms at Work

Protists can be subdivided into 2 smaller groups: algae, which include all species of algae except for blue-green algae; and protozoa. Figure 5.20 shows an example of micro-organisms from these 2 sub-groups.

A) 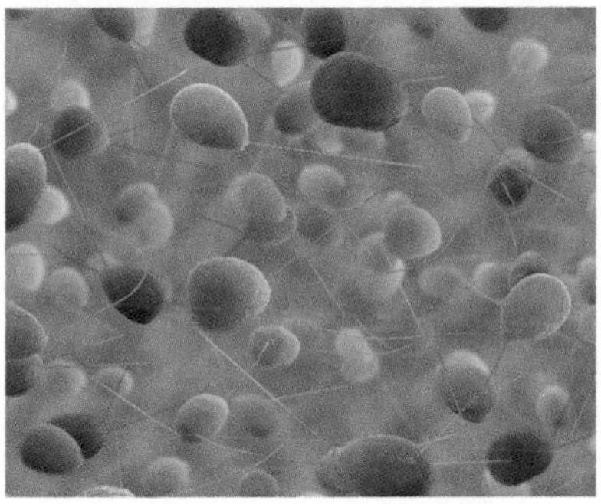

B) 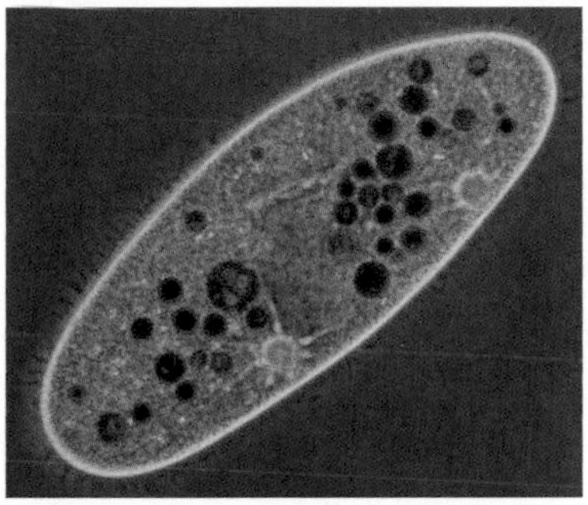

FIGURE 5.20 A) A species of green algae. B) A species of protozoa. These protists may look different from one another, but they have characteristics in common. What are these characteristics?

Anatomy and Physiology of Algae

Protist algae are protists that are plant-like. Inside every protist algae cell you will see a nucleus that contains the genetic material and at least one **chloroplast**, which is a cell structure that carries out photosynthesis (Figure 5.21). This is different from the blue-green algae, which contain no nucleus and no chloroplasts. Protist algae also *have a cell wall* and produce their own food through photosynthesis. This is why this sub-group of the protists is said to be plant-like.

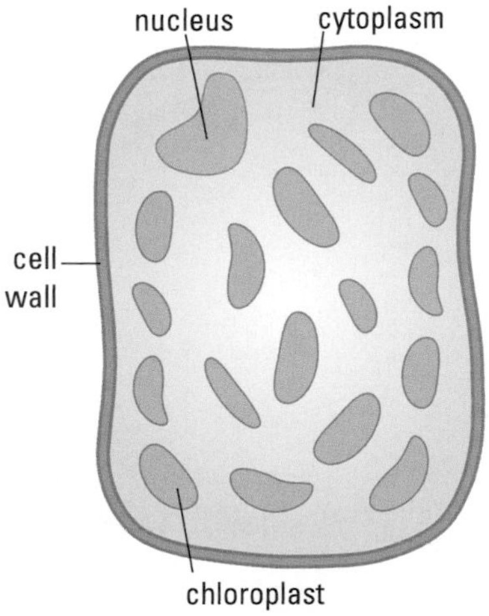

FIGURE 5.21 The anatomy of a protist algae cell.

Anatomy and Physiology of Protozoa

Protozoa are protists that are animal-like. There are many different sizes and shapes of protozoa. Protozoa usually have only 1 cell, and always have a nucleus but *no cell wall.* Most protozoa cannot produce their own food, and so are said to be animal-like. Species of protozoa get their food in the following ways:

- by capturing and eating other organisms;
- by decomposing dead organisms;
- by absorbing chemicals from the water, or;
- by being a parasite.

A **parasite** is an organism that lives on or inside another living organism and gets its food from that organism.

Some Examples of Protozoa

Micro-organism	Description
Amoeba 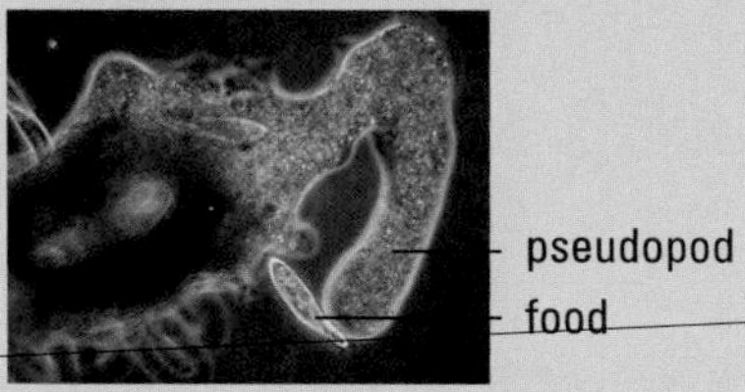	*Amoeba* uses pseudopods or "false feet" to move. An *Amoeba* feeds by surrounding an organism with its pseudopod, then taking the organism inside the cell membrane. The organism is then broken down and used by the *Amoeba* for energy and nutrients.
Paramecium 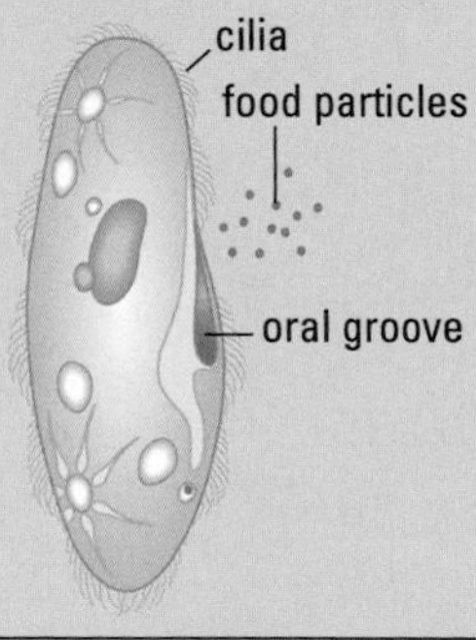	A *Paramecium* feeds by moving its cilia, which are tiny hair-like projections on the cell membrane. Cilia also help *Paramecium* to feed by sweeping food particles into its oral groove (mouth).
Plasmodium 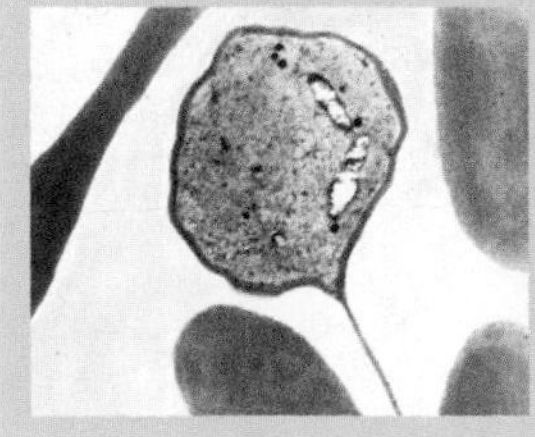	*Plasmodium* are parasitic protozoa that can cause malaria in humans. Malaria causes fever, and chills, and can damage internal organs. More than 1 million people die per year from malaria.

FIGURE 5.22 These micro-organisms all look very different, but they are all protists. What characteristics do they all have in common?

Reproduction and Life Cycle of Protists

Most protist micro-organisms usually undergo asexual reproduction by binary fission. Recall from Section 5.2 that monera reproduce by binary fission as well, but these micro-organisms do not have a nucleus. Many protists can also reproduce sexually. The life cycle of protists can range from several hours to just a few days. Figures 5.23 A and B show the 2 very different life cycles of the protists *Amoeba* and *Plasmodium*.

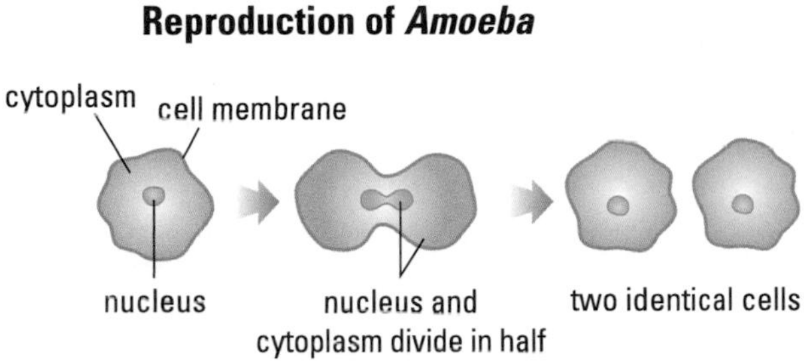

FIGURE 5.23A The life cycle of *Amoeba* includes only asexual reproduction by binary fission.

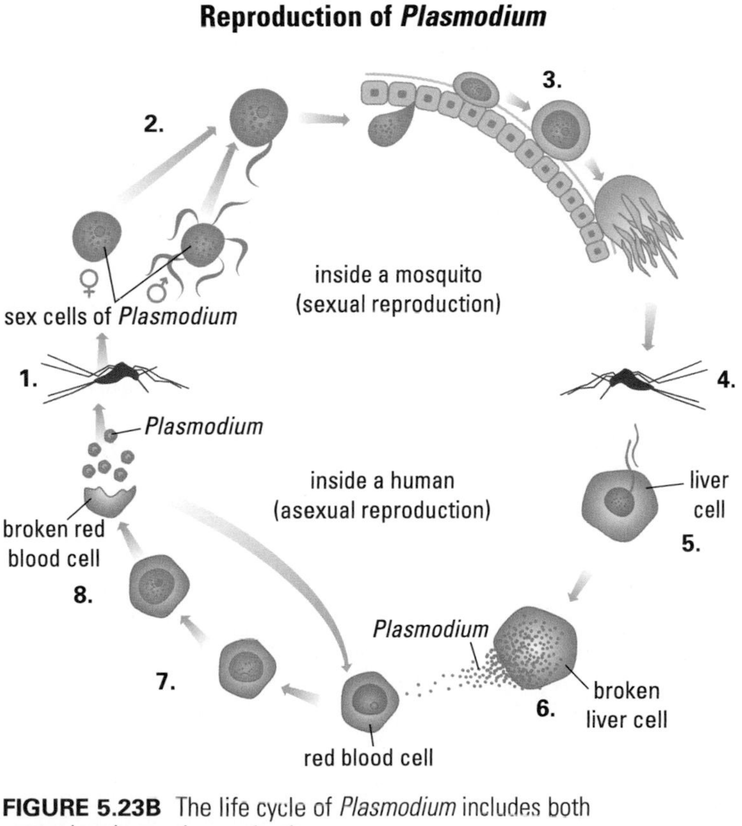

1. A mosquito bites an infected human and takes up *Plasmodium* sex cells.
2. The sex cells join (sexual reproduction) and make a new individual of the sexual form of *Plasmodium*.
3. The sexual form of *Plasmodium* develops into a structure that produces many copies of the asexual form, which are released into the saliva of the mosquito.
4. The mosquito bites another human, releasing the asexual form of *Plasmodium* into the human.
5. The asexual form of *Plasmodium* infects the liver cells of the human.
6. The asexual form of *Plasmodium* multiplies by asexual reproduction, eventually breaking the cell.
7. The asexual form of *Plasmodium* infects red blood cells, and continues to multiply by asexual reproduction.
8. A few cells of *Plasmodium* become sex cells, which are taken up by another mosquito to begin the process again.

FIGURE 5.23B The life cycle of *Plasmodium* includes both asexual and sexual reproduction.

LAB 5C

Looking at Protists

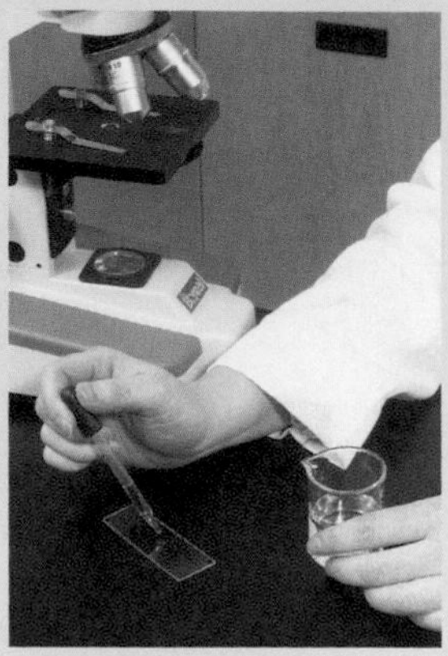

FIGURE 5.24
Preparing a wet mount.

Protists can be found in many different workplaces. For example, protists are likely to be on golf courses and other landscaped areas, in farm ponds and even in the puddles on a playground. What do these micro-organisms look like?

Purpose

In this lab, you will observe the characteristics of live and prepared specimens of protists. You will prepare your own wet mounts and draw and label accurate sketches of the protists you observe.

Materials

- live samples of *Amoeba* and *Paramecium*
- microscopes
- protist-slowing agent
- toothpick
- prepared slides of *Amoeba* and *Paramecium*
- slides and cover slips
- eye-dropper

Be Safe!

- Do not touch your mouth, eyes, nose, or ears when working with micro-organisms.
- Wash your hands thoroughly after this lab.
- Dispose of the protist cultures according to your teacher's instructions.

Procedure

1. Divide a clean sheet of blank paper to form 2 equal sections. Label each half as follows: *Amoeba* at 400× magnification; *Paramecium* at 100× magnification.

2. On a second sheet of paper, create a data table using the headings in Figure 5.25.

Species	Characteristics found in all protists	Characteristics not found in all protists

FIGURE 5.25

3. Place a prepared slide of *Amoeba* on the stage of your microscope. Focus the image starting with the 10× objective lens, then switch to the 40× objective lens.

4. Record your observations in your data table, and sketch the micro-organism.

5. Add 1 drop of live *Amoeba* culture to a clean microscope slide. Carefully lower a cover slip onto the drop, being careful to avoid making air bubbles. This method of preparing a sample for viewing is called a **wet mount**.
6. View the wet mount with the 10× objective lens. Record your observations in your data table.
7. Sketch the movement of the micro-organism from the wet mount.
8. Repeat steps 3 to 6 for *Paramecium*.
9. Get a clean slide. Add 1 drop of protist-slowing agent to the centre of the slide. Add 1 drop of the *Paramecium* sample to the protist-slowing agent. Gently mix the drops with a toothpick.
10. Place the slide on the stage of the microscope and focus the wet mount under the 10× objective lens.
11. Sketch the movement of *Paramecium*. Record any additional observations in your data table.

Analysis and Conclusion

1. Compare the movement of *Amoeba* to that of *Paramecium*. Do you think movement is a useful characteristic in telling these 2 species apart? Justify your response.
2. Explain why you added the protist-slowing agent to the *Paramecium*.
3. State the characteristics that all protists share. On your diagrams, highlight the shared characteristics of protists that you were able to observe.

Extension and Connection

4. Explain why scientists who study micro-organisms look at both prepared slides and wet mounts.
5. Look at the drawings of a few of your classmates. What are the similarities? Were there any differences? Explain why 2 people looking at the same organism might make different observations.

Review and Apply

1. Describe the characteristics of protists that allow them to be distinguished from monera.

2. Create a poster showing a labelled diagram of a protist algae cell and a *Paramecium* cell. On your poster, identify the characteristics that allow you to classify both of these organisms as protists, and those that allow you to classify one as an algae and the other as a protozoan.

3. In your notebook, create a table that compares the similarities and differences of the feeding and locomotion of *Amoeba* and *Paramecium*.

4. Compare how algae and protozoa obtain food.

5. Describe where you might encounter protists in each of the following workplaces: a pool-cleaning business, a plumbing business and a pet shop. Based on your descriptions, what do all these workplaces have in common that allows protists to survive?

6. You work for the Ministry of the Environment, taking water samples. In one of your samples you find a protist that is green in colour. What organism would you suspect it to be? How could you find out if you were right?

7. Add the new concepts from this section to the graphic organizer you started in Section 5.1.

Surf the Web

The protozoan species *Euglena* has characteristics that are both plant-like and animal-like. Go to **www.science.nelson.com**. Follow the links for ScienceWise Grade 11, Chapter 5, Section 5.3. Look at the information under *Euglena*, and answer the following questions:

a) How do *Euglena* feed?

b) Based on your research, do you think *Euglena* are more like animals or more like plants?

■

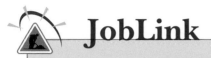

JobLink

Aquaculture Worker

Aquaculture involves raising fish and other aquatic organisms. People working in aquaculture need some knowledge of protists, because many of these organisms can be harmful to the animals that are being raised.

Responsibilities of an Aquaculture Worker

- maintain stocks in facilities such as aquariums or stocked ponds
- test, maintain and write reports on water quality
- maintain computer- or paper-based inventories of organisms
- prepare organisms for shipping to customers
- identify the presence of harmful micro-organisms and take appropriate steps to control them
- may be responsible for handling cash purchases and answering customer questions in retail businesses

FIGURE 5.26 One area in which aquaculture workers are involved is in the breeding of ornamental fish.

Where do they work?

- fish hatcheries, government facilities and fish processing facilities
- aquarium suppliers and retail sellers

Skills for the Job

- attention to detail and ability to meet very high standards of cleanliness
- ability to problem-solve, since conditions of organisms under aquaculture can change rapidly and cause extensive loss of stock
- good organizational skills, to ensure that scheduled tasks are completed on time
- ability to work as part of a team, since most aquaculture facilities employ a group of people with different skills, who must work together
- must be able to learn on the job

Education

- a secondary school diploma may be required
- a college diploma or experience in aquaculture is usually needed

5.4 Fungi

What do you think of when you hear the word "fungus"? Chances are, you do not think of cheese, yogourt, beer, or bread. However, all these things are made with the help of fungi. Other fungi can make us ill, such as the fungus that causes athlete's foot.

Many fungi decompose dead plants and dead animals, and wastes. These actions are important in keeping the environment healthy. Some fungi decompose things that people use, such as food, clothes, wood and paper. This can cause unhealthy conditions, or force people to make expensive repairs.

Anatomy and Physiology of Fungi

All fungi are made up of cells with a nucleus and a cell wall. Fungi cannot produce their own food. In other words, fungi do not photosynthesize. Instead, they obtain their food from other organisms, or by decomposing matter in the environment. Some fungi are also parasites. Some examples of fungi are shown in Figure 5.27. You might have heard the words "mould" and "yeast" before. Did you know these micro-organisms are classified as fungi?

You will need to know about fungi to complete your project, Micro-organisms at Work.

Although fungi can come in many shapes and sizes, there are 2 common shapes: round to oval single cells and long thread-like, or **filamentous,** cells. Scientists have divided fungi into 2 subgroups, based in part on their shape. **Moulds** are fungi that are usually filamentous and **yeasts** are fungi that are usually round or oval single cells. Most fungi change their shape from one form to the other as they go through their life cycle.

Some Examples of Fungi

Micro-organism	Description
Penicillium 	*Penicillium* mould has a dense brush-like appearance, with round structures at the end of branches. One species of *Penicillium* produces the drug penicillin. Others are used to make cheese, and others can cause diseases.
Bread mould 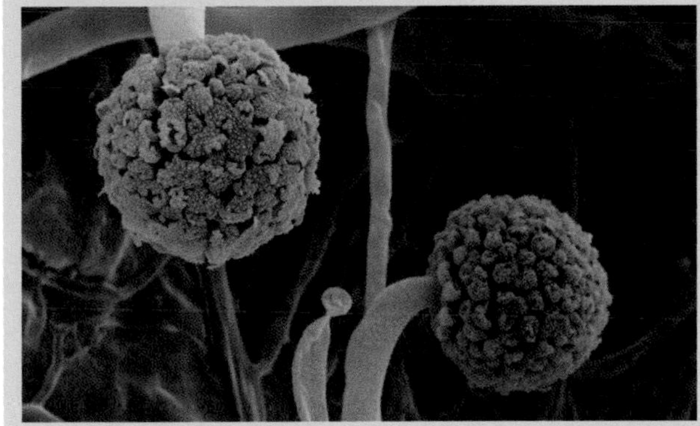	Bread mould is made of long thread-like cells. Some of these might have a round cap on top, which is a reproductive structure. Other moulds often grow on crops during wet conditions and can destroy the plants if it is not controlled.
Yeast 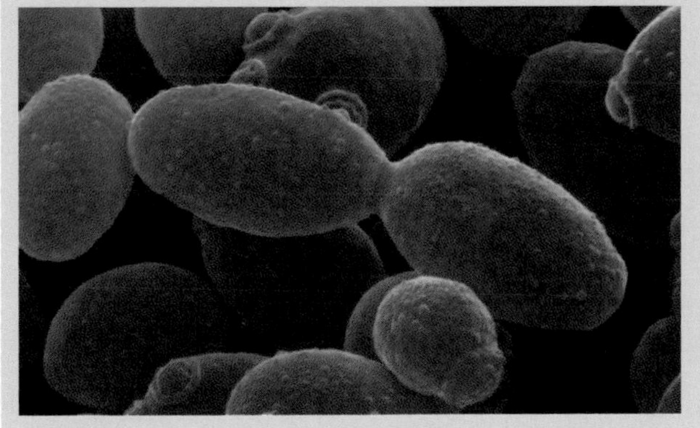	Yeast cells are round to oval. Yeast are always composed of 1 cell, except when they are undergoing reproduction. Some species of yeast are used to make foods, such as bread and beer, but others cause diseases.

FIGURE 5.27 These micro-organisms all look very different, but they are all fungi. What characteristics do they all have in common?

Reproduction and Life Cycle of Fungi

The life cycle of all fungi usually includes both sexual and asexual reproduction. Asexual reproduction in fungi does not occur by binary fission, but by the processes of fragmentation, spore production and budding.

Yeasts

Yeasts usually reproduce asexually through a process called budding. **Budding** is the division of a cell to form 2 new cells, in which the new cell is always much smaller than the parent cell (Figure 5.28). When budding starts, a bulge called a bud forms on the yeast cell. When the bud grows large enough, it will break off to form a new yeast cell. This process occurs so quickly that new buds will often form on older buds even before they have broken away.

Yeast can also reproduce sexually: two yeast cells unite and form 1 single cell. This new cell can then immediately begin to bud and form new individuals, or it might first divide into equal halves, and then begin to bud.

Reproduction of Yeast

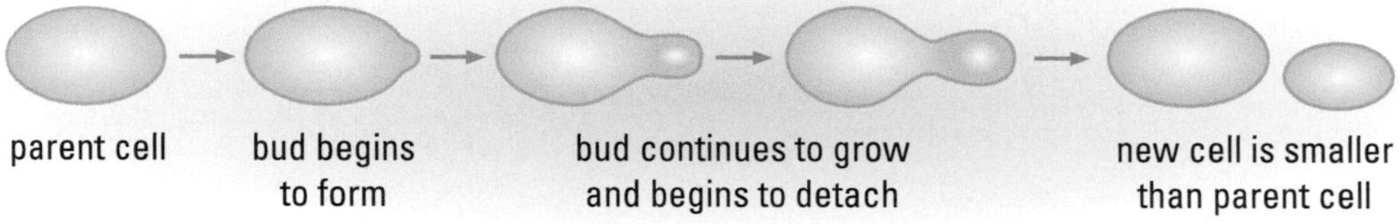
parent cell
bud begins to form
bud continues to grow and begins to detach
new cell is smaller than parent cell

FIGURE 5.28 In asexual reproduction by budding, the new cell is always smaller than the parent cell.

Moulds

Moulds can reproduce in 3 ways (Figure 5.29). They can reproduce by **fragmentation**, which is the formation of small pieces, by spore formation, or by sexual reproduction. **Spores** are special structures, similar to seeds, which allow the mould to spread to a new area. Fragmentation and spore formation are both forms of asexual reproduction.

Reproduction of Mould

Type of reproduction	Description
Asexual 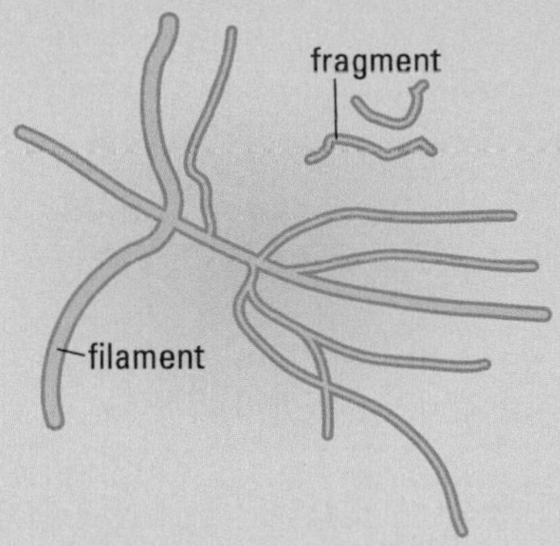	Filamentous mould cells undergo fragmentation by dividing into unequal portions. One mould cell can fragment into many pieces at the same time, which will form many new individuals.
Asexual 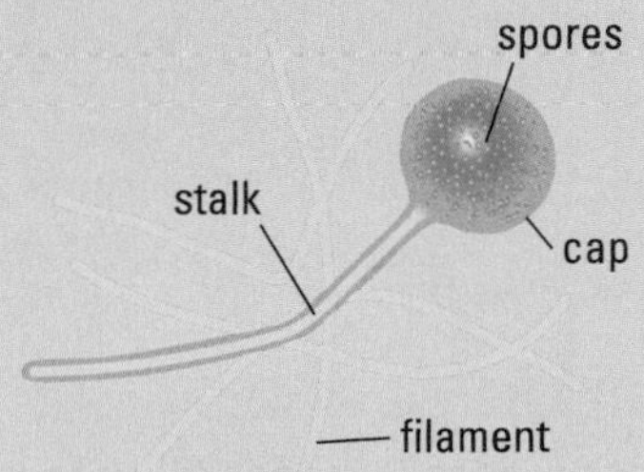	During spore formation, the mould cell changes shape entirely. For example, this mould has formed a stalk structure topped with a round cap. The cap forms millions of spores, which can be carried by wind or water to a new place.
Sexual 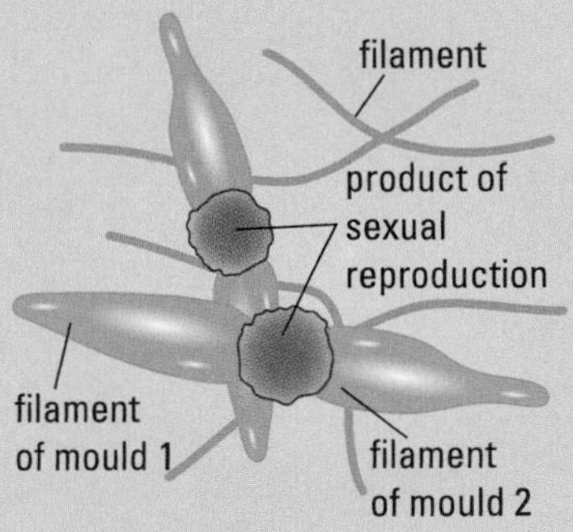	During sexual reproduction, part of the filaments of 2 different moulds exchange genetic information to produce an entirely new mould. This new mould begins as the structure labelled "product of sexual reproduction" on the diagram here.

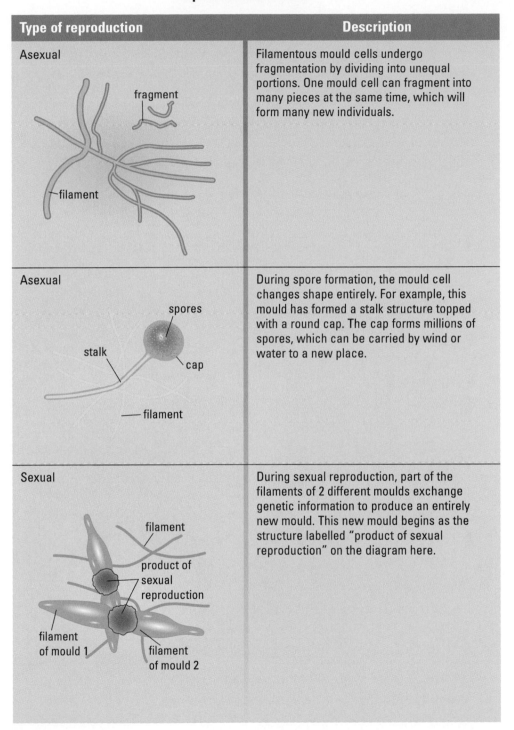

FIGURE 5.29 Mould cells change shape during their life cycle. When is the mould filamentous?

LAB

5D Looking at Fungi

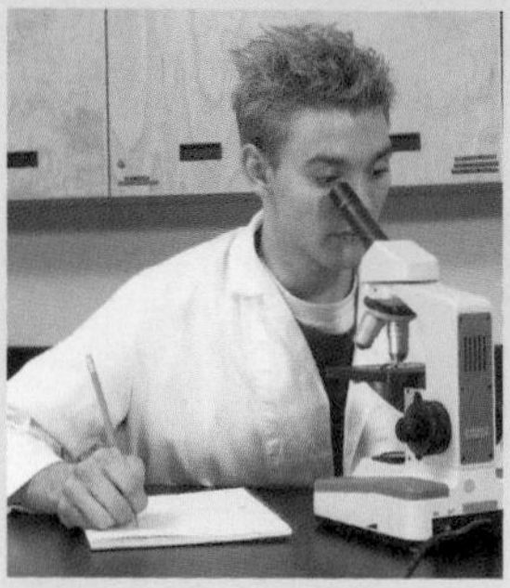

FIGURE 5.30 Some mould structures can only be seen under magnification.

An important role of many fungi is to recycle the chemicals in organisms after they have died. Unfortunately, sometimes fungi can go to work on our food. As they break down this food, some fungi produce chemicals that can make humans sick.

Purpose

In this lab, you will allow fungi to grow on some common food items, and then observe the characteristics of these organisms.

Materials

- hand lens or dissecting microscope
- kitchen knife
- bread
- 2 Petri dishes
- masking tape

Be Safe!

- Do not open the sealed Petri dishes at any time.
- Dispose of your Petri dishes according to your teacher's instructions.
- Wash your hands thoroughly after this lab.
- Do not touch your mouth, eyes, nose, or ears when working with micro-organisms.
- Be careful using the knife.

Procedure

1. Wipe a piece of bread over a tabletop or floor to collect mould spores.
2. Break off a piece of bread that is about the size of a Petri dish (Figure 5.31). Place the bread into 1 of the Petri dishes. Add a small amount of water. Your bread piece should be slightly moist, but not wet.
3. Close the lid of the Petri dish, and securely seal the edges with masking tape.
4. Cut a small slice of fruit and leave it exposed to the air for several minutes. Place the fruit slice into the other Petri dish, and sprinkle it with water.
5. Close the lid of the Petri dish, and securely seal the edges with masking tape.
6. Store the Petri dishes in a dark, cool place for several days.

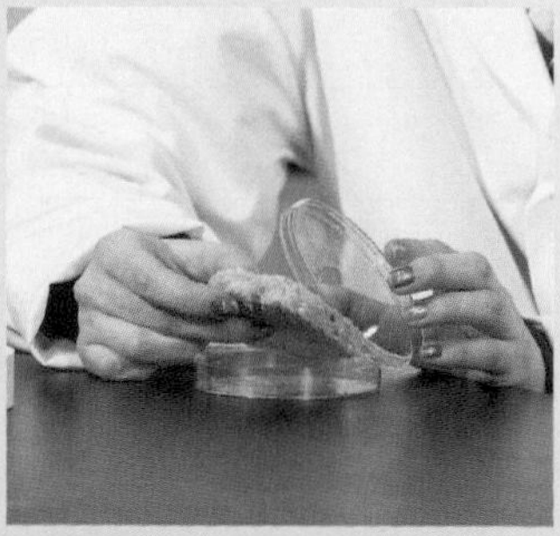

FIGURE 5.31 Your food samples must be small enough to fit in the Petri dish.

7. Create a data table in your notebook, using the headings in Figure 5.32.

Date	Food Item	Description	Diagram

FIGURE 5.32

8. Do not open the Petri dishes at any time. Examine the stored food items with a hand lens or dissecting microscope every day for 2 to 10 days. Record your observations on your data sheet.

9. When the mould on your food items turns black, stop making observations. Dispose of the Petri dishes as instructed by your teacher.

FIGURE 5.33 Observe the mould cells only by looking through the sealed Petri dish.

Analysis and Conclusion

1. Do you think there was more than 1 type of mould growing on each of the food items? Give reasons for your answer.

2. Why did you need to add water to the Petri dishes?

3. Did the mould cells undergo reproduction during the experiment? Explain your answer.

Extension and Connection

4. Explain why it is important to throw out food that has gone mouldy.

5. Describe a situation in your own life where you found that food had gone mouldy. Your description should include where, how long, and under what conditions the food was stored.

Review and Apply

1. List the characteristics of fungi that allow us to distinguish them from protists and from monera.

2. Draw one diagram of filamentous fungi and a second diagram of round single-celled fungi. Label the structures in your diagrams.

3. Create a chart or poster that shows the similarities and differences between yeasts and moulds.

4. Many young people (and adults) think that fungi are always harmful. Create a collage, using clippings of pictures, drawings, or words to illustrate how fungi can be both harmful and beneficial to humans.

5. Imagine you are working in a bakery. Explain why it would be important to wear gloves when placing bread into bags, referring to fungi in your answer.

6. Add the new concepts from this section to the graphic organizer you started in Section 5.1.

7. **Fungi Life Cycles**

   Work in a small group. Copy each method of reproduction of the yeast from Figure 5.28 and the moulds from Figure 5.29 onto large, unlined index cards. Each card should show only 1 method. Make your drawings as clear as possible, using colour. On the back of each card, write the name of the type of fungi (mould or yeast) and the method of reproduction. When all the cards are finished, shuffle them together and test each other's knowledge of the reproductive methods of yeasts and moulds.

Try This at Home

Safety and Moulds

Some indoor moulds produce chemicals that can make people sick. For example, black mould is a slimy, greenish-black substance that often grows in buildings. If you are exposed to black mould, you might experience tightness in your chest, coughing, fatigue, nosebleeds, rashes, or fever.

Black mould grows on areas such as damp or wet wood, ceiling tiles, wallpaper, or cardboard. Because it can be hard to tell if the mould in a building is harmful, people who work or live in buildings with mould must always treat it as if it were harmful, in order to stay safe.

Are there any areas in your home that are growing mould? Conduct a survey of your home, concentrating on those areas that are most likely to support the growth of moulds. Most moulds will appear grey to black. Remember that although most moulds are harmless, you should treat all moulds as if they were harmful, in order to stay safe.

Be Safe!

- If you are allergic to moulds, do not carry out this survey.
- Any mould has the potential to make you ill. Wear household gloves while you are conducting your survey.
- Do not touch your mouth, eyes, nose, or ears while you are conducting your survey.
- Wash your hands thoroughly when you are finished.

Use the following list to guide your search for mould:

1. Inspect any areas where water is used regularly. Check the tiles and caulking in the bathroom. Look for black stains or slimy build-up. Inspect the kitchen sink and counter.
2. Inspect any areas where food is stored. Include not only the food in your refrigerator, but the parts of the refrigerator itself. Are there any stains on the seal around the door?
3. Mould often grows in areas we do not know are damp. Check in the cabinets under sinks, and around plumbing joints. If you have a basement or live below street level, check the corners of the walls.

If you found any mould in your inspection, discuss with your parent or guardian what strategies you could use to destroy the mould. Depending on where it is, first clean off the mould with household bleach. Then, try to reduce the amount of moisture in that area. For example, your parent or guardian may need to check for leaking faucets or loose plumbing joints. If the mould keeps coming back, it is likely that more drastic measures will be needed to cure the problem, such as re-caulking a tub or replacing a worn-out faucet.

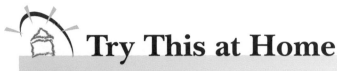

5.5 Viruses

You will need to know about viruses for your project, Micro-organisms at Work.

If you have ever had a cold or the flu, you already know something about viruses. Many viruses cause disease. Viruses are not made up of cells. Viruses are very small; in fact, they are the smallest known organisms. The largest virus is only about the same size as the smallest bacteria.

Anatomy and Physiology of Viruses

There are many different kinds of viruses, but all viruses are made of genetic material wrapped in protein. Protein is a chemical that is the main building block of all organisms. Scientists identify different viruses by both the genetic material they contain and by their shape. Figure 5.34 shows the shapes of some different examples of viruses.

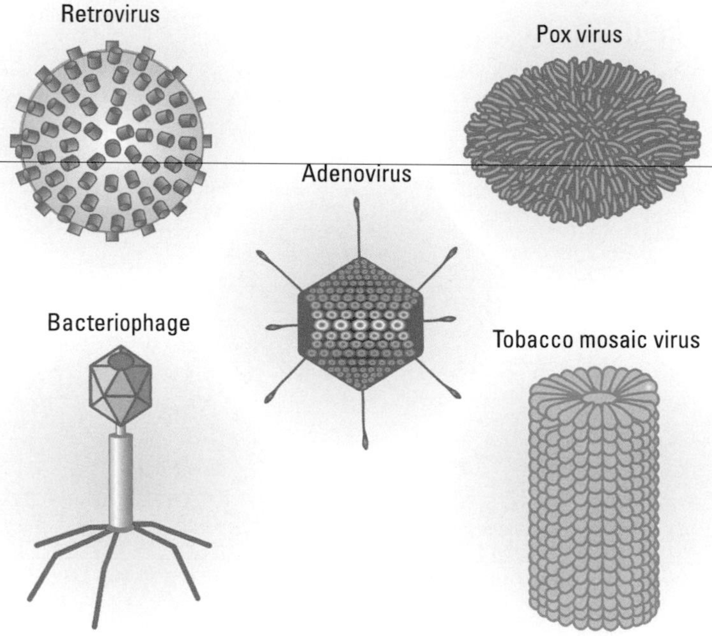

FIGURE 5.34 Examples of virus shapes. Compare the shapes of each of the viruses shown here.

Because they are only genetic material and protein, viruses cannot survive unless they are inside another living organism. In other words, all viruses are parasites. There are viruses that are parasites on people, on animals, on fish, on plants and even on bacteria.

Why does a virus need to live inside another living organism? Because it is only made up of protein and genetic material, a virus has no way of getting its own food, or of moving, or even of reproducing. Viruses depend on the organisms in which they live to provide everything they need to survive and to reproduce.

Reproduction and Life Cycle of Viruses

Like all organisms, viruses must reproduce. Viruses are the only living things that are not able to reproduce by themselves. To reproduce, viruses take over the cell they are living in and force that cell to make copies of the virus (Figure 5.35). This, unfortunately, often means that the cell cannot do the things it needs to do in order to keep itself alive. Instead, the cell will be forced to make many copies of the virus, until the cell finally dies. This is why viruses almost always make us sick.

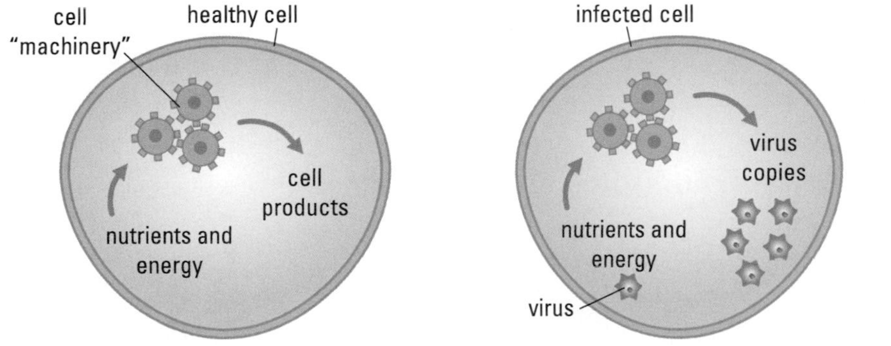

A. The cell's "machinery" works to make products for the cell.

B. The virus forces the cell's "machinery" to make copies of the virus.

FIGURE 5.35 Once the virus has taken over, the cell has no choice but to work for the virus instead of for itself.

Surf the Web

Viruses often make us sick. What diseases do viruses cause? Visit **www.science.nelson.com** and follow the links for ScienceWise Grade 11, Chapter 5, Section 5.5, to find some examples of viruses that cause diseases in humans.

CASE STUDY

Tattoos and Hepatitis B

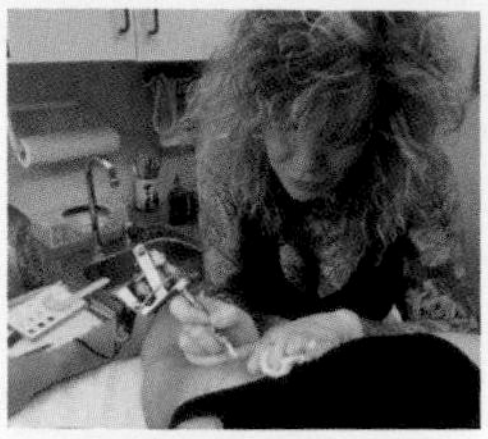

FIGURE 5.36 Should you be concerned about micro-organisms in a tattoo parlour?

Why do tattoo artists need to be concerned with bacteria and viruses?

Although most tattooing is safe, there are some health risks if the tattoo artist does not know how to avoid spreading micro-organisms. One micro-organism that can be spread by tattooing is the virus that causes the disease hepatitis B.

What is a tattoo?

Tattoos are created by injecting ink into the skin, using a needle (Figure 5.37). The needle penetrates the top layer of the skin and the tattoo ink mixes with the cells underneath. The cells on the surface of your skin are constantly replaced, but those beneath the skin surface are not. This means that the tattoo will last a person's entire life, although it will fade and even blur.

The Importance of Hygiene in Tattooing

Anytime you puncture your skin, you increase the chances of micro-organisms entering your body. When micro-organisms enter your body, you might get sick. Therefore, it is extremely important that everything that touches you when you are getting a tattoo be extremely clean, especially the tattoo needles. Tattoo needles should either be sterile disposable needles, or else be sterilized every time they are used.

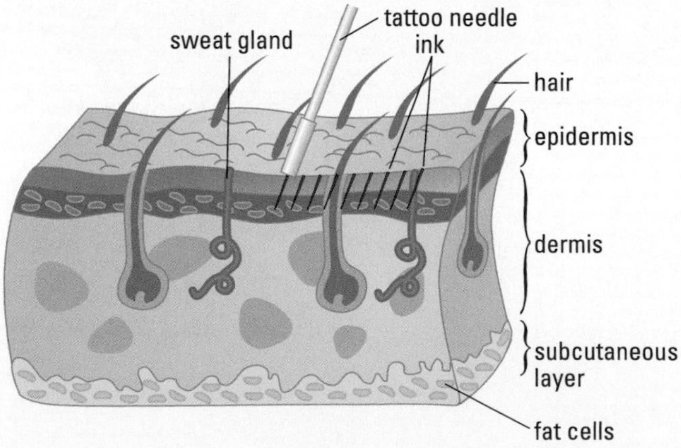

FIGURE 5.37 The ink is placed below the top layer of skin cells, which are constantly replaced.

If the tattoo artist uses non-sterile needles, there is a good chance that clients could get a serious disease, such as hepatitis B. This disease is caused by a virus and is spread when someone comes in contact with the blood of a person with the disease. There is always a small amount of bleeding under the skin surface during tattooing. Hepatitis B can be fatal. About half of the people who get hepatitis B do not feel sick. Others feel like they have the flu when they first become ill. A small number of people with hepatitis B develop dark-coloured urine and a slight yellowish tint to their skin and eyes over time. If it is left untreated, hepatitis B can lead to liver failure or liver cancer.

a) How can you protect yourself from getting hepatitis B from a tattoo needle?

b) Suggest some things you might look for, or ask about, in a tattoo parlour that would indicate that the tattoo artist knew how to avoid spreading hepatitis B.

Responsibilities of the Tattoo Artist

In Canada, tattoo artists do not have to be licensed. However, Health Canada provides guidelines describing how tattoo artists can prevent and control the spread of micro-organisms in their workplace. If a tattoo artist follows these guidelines, there is less chance of spreading harmful micro-organisms. The safe working guidelines for tattoo artists include:

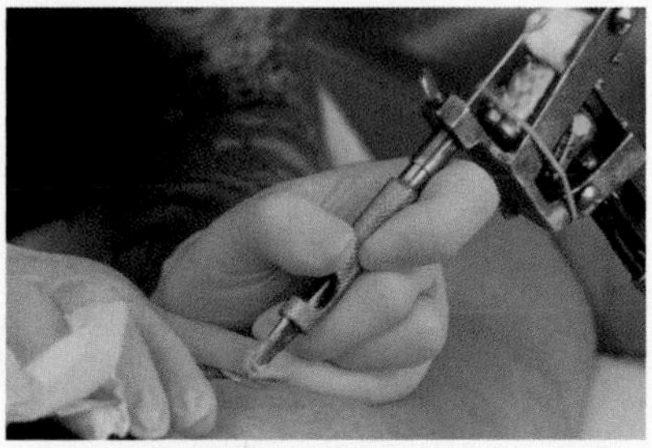

FIGURE 5.38 What would you need to know in order to create a safe workplace if you were a tattoo artist?

- Always use sterile disposable needles.
- Wear gloves and do not touch your eyes, mouth, ears or nose.
- Open the ink bottle with a clean tissue and prevent the open mouth of the bottle from touching anything.
- Bandage clients with packaged sterile bandages.
- Wash your hands after every procedure.
- Never tattoo someone if you have uncovered cuts, sores, or hangnails.
- Dispose of used needles properly.

c) Explain why these safety procedures are important.

CONTINUED

Responsibilities of the Client

If you are getting tattooed, you must choose a tattoo parlour that practises proper hygiene. Here are some things you can do to help ensure your safety:

- Look to see if the tattoo parlour is clean.
- Ask questions. For example, you could ask, "How do you sterilize your equipment?"; "Are the needles and other materials single-use only?"; "Do you wear gloves?"
- Be sure that safety measures are followed, and make sure all needle packages are opened in front of you.

If you want to get a tattoo, always have it done by a reputable tattoo artist. Discuss tattooing with your parents or guardians first. You might also talk to your family doctor about risks associated with tattoos.

d) What additional health risks would there be if you got a tattoo from someone who was not a reputable tattoo artist?

Analysis and Communication

1. Explain why tattooing puts people at risk of getting hepatitis B.
2. Do you think that tattoo artists should have a licence or diploma? Explain.
3. Is hepatitis B the only disease that can be contracted by poor hygiene standards in a tattoo parlour? Justify your answer.

Making Connections

4. Do you think there should be a minimum age requirement for individuals who want a tattoo? Explain.
5. You have decided to get your body pierced. In point form, outline the things you should look for where you plan to have the piercing done, to ensure that you will be protected from harmful micro-organisms.

ACTIVITY 5E

Viral Investigation

In this activity, you will use electronic and print resources to research the influenza virus. You will use the information you find to create an information booklet on the influenza virus.

What You Will Need

- access to a library or the Internet

What You Will Do

1. Working in pairs, research answers to the following questions:
   a) How does the influenza virus spread from person to person?
   b) How can people avoid getting influenza?
   c) What can people do to feel better if they do get influenza?
2. Using the facts from your research, create an information booklet that will help the public understand how the influenza virus can affect their health and what they can do to protect themselves from this virus.

FIGURE 5.39 Your finished booklet could look like this example.

What Did You Find Out?

1. Look at the booklets of at least 2 of your classmates. What do you like about their booklets? What do you think could have been done better?
2. Consider your own booklet. Based on what your classmates did, is there anything you think you might change if you had the chance? Write 1 or 2 sentences describing any changes you might make.

Making Connections

1. Imagine that you are sick at home from the influenza virus. Your supervisor at your part-time job calls and says that she needs someone to come in to work an extra shift, or she will lose an important customer. What is the most responsible decision in this situation? Explain your answer.
2. Do you think that a high-school student is likely to encounter the influenza virus? Explain your answer. Would someone in the workplace be likely to encounter the influenza virus?

FIGURE 5.40 How could this person have avoided getting sick from the influenza virus?

Review and Apply

1. Describe the characteristics of viruses that allow us to distinguish them from fungi, protists and monera.
2. In 2 or 3 sentences, explain why viruses are parasites.
3. Draw and label a diagram of a virus.
4. Create a chart that shows how viruses reproduce.
5. Do viruses need food? Explain your answer.
6. Name 2 diseases that are caused by viruses.
7. Add the new concepts from this section to the graphic organizer you started in Section 5.1.
8. **The West Nile Virus**

The West Nile virus is named after the West Nile region of Uganda, where the virus first appeared in 1937. Most people who have this virus either do not feel sick, or feel like they have a mild case of the flu. This virus can sometimes cause meningitis, an inflammation of the lining of the brain and spinal cord, or encephalitis, an inflammation of the brain. The West Nile virus was first reported in North America in 1999.

In groups, research the spread of the West Nile virus in North America since 1999. Find out where it was first found and where it was found in the following years. When you have finished your research, create a map of the spread of the West Nile virus in North America. In one corner of the map, list the ways that this virus is spread.

FIGURE 5.41 Birds can also be affected by the West Nile virus.

5.6 Chapter Summary

Now You Can...

- Classify monera, protists, fungi and viruses (5.1)
- Describe the anatomy and physiology of monera (5.2)
- Describe the anatomy and physiology of protists (5.3)
- Describe the anatomy and physiology of fungi (5.4)
- Describe the anatomy and physiology of viruses (5.5)
- Compare the life cycles of examples of monera, protists, fungi and viruses (5.2, 5.3, 5.4, 5.5)

Concept Connections

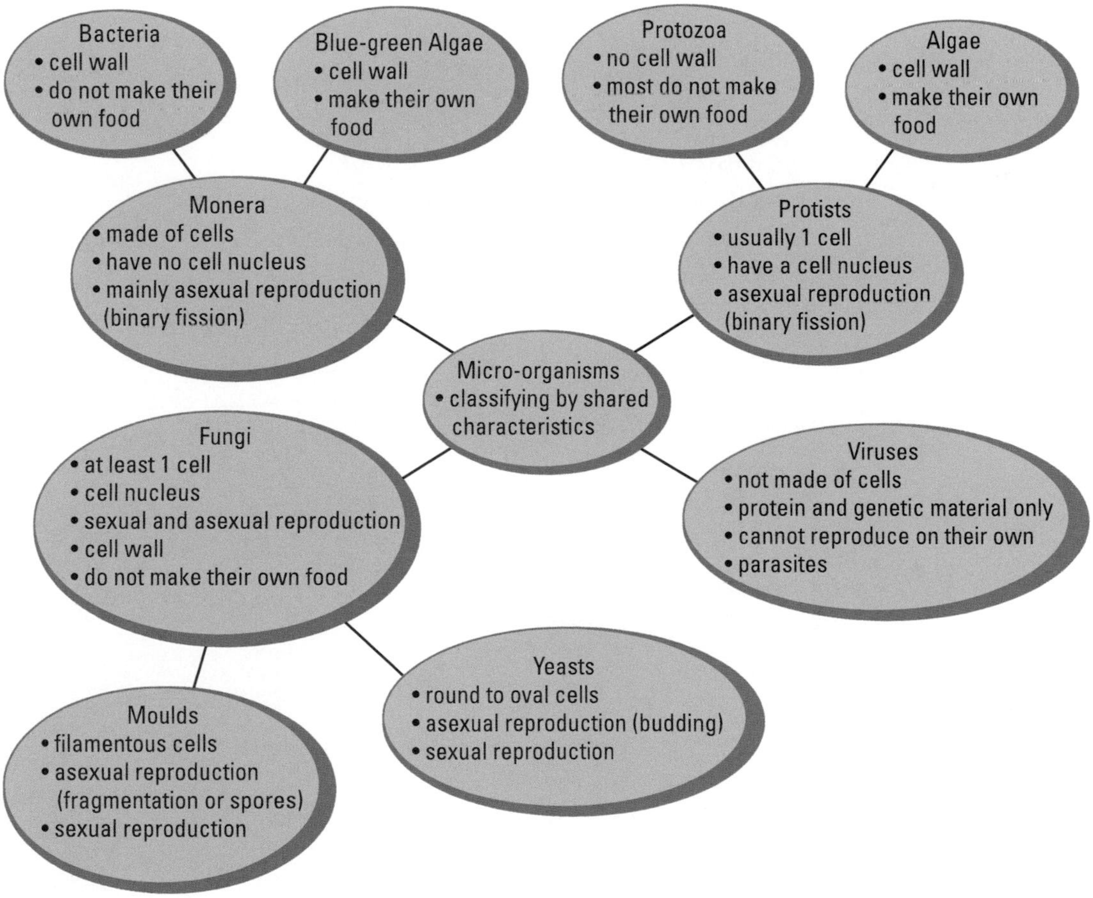

FIGURE 5.42 Compare your completed graphic organizer to the one on this page. How did you do? Can you add any new links to your organizer?

CHAPTER 5 *review*

Knowledge and Understanding

1. Match the group of micro-organisms on the left with the description on the right.

1. Monera	**A.** composed of 1 cell, have a cell nucleus and most undergo only asexual reproduction
2. Protists	**B.** composed of 1 cell, have a cell nucleus and undergo both asexual and sexual reproduction
3. Fungi	**C.** parasite
4. Viruses	**D.** composed of 1 cell without a cell nucleus

2. Figures 5.43A to 5.43D are examples of 1 of the following micro-organisms: bacteria, yeast, protozoa, or virus. Match the type of micro-organism with the correct figure number.

3. Identify which of the following groups of micro-organisms have a cell wall: algae, protozoa, bacteria, blue-green algae, viruses, and yeast.

4. Identify which of the following can make their own food through photosynthesis and those that can not: algae, protozoa, bacteria, yeast, moulds, and viruses.

5. Moulds can undergo asexual reproduction in 2 different ways. Create a labelled diagram of each of these 2 ways.

6. Make a table or chart that shows the similarities and differences in the life cycles of bacteria, protists, viruses, and fungi.

Inquiry

7. Draw a diagram illustrating the correct way to prepare a wet mount of a live sample of micro-organisms for viewing under a microscope.

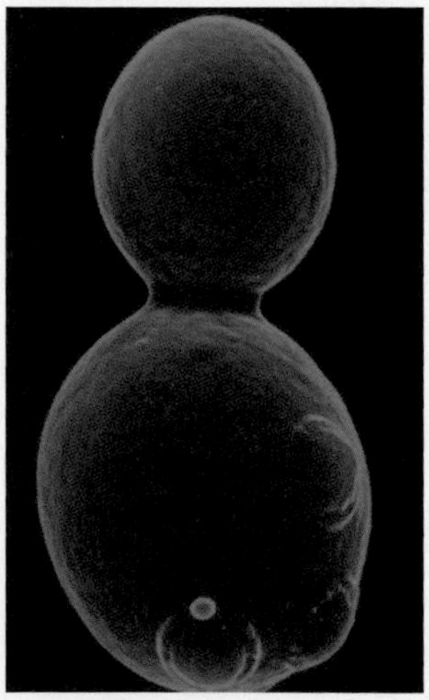

FIGURE 5.43A

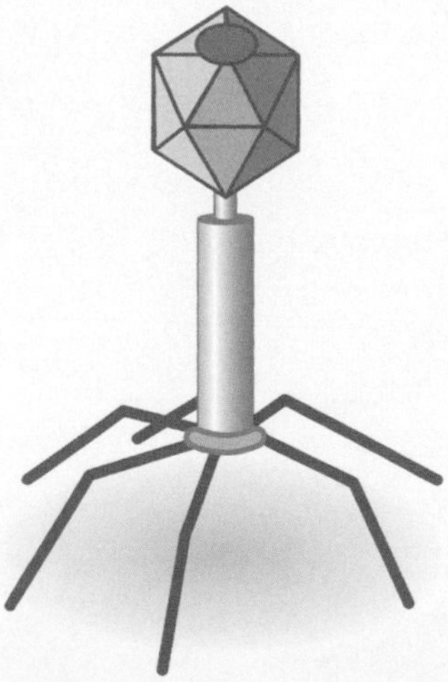

FIGURE 5.43B

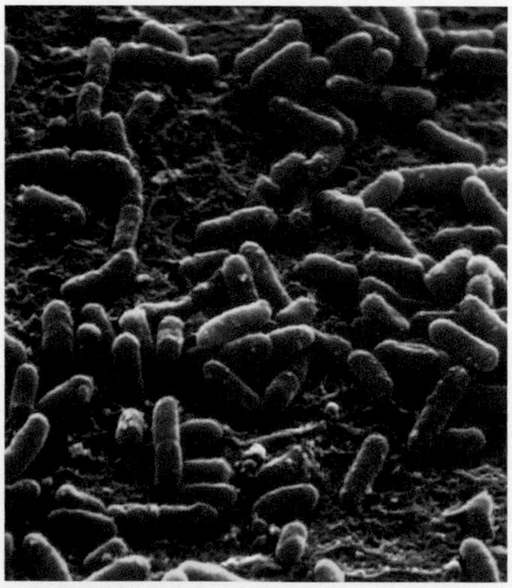

FIGURE 5.43C

8 You have been assigned to monitor your classmates' safety during a lab in which you are working with living micro-organisms. Make a list of the safety precautions that students should follow in this situation.

9 You need to grow a sample of bacteria cells and a sample of protists. Identify which sample you must grow in water and which on a Petri dish.

Making Connections

10 In a short paragraph, explain why all of the instruments and machinery in a food-processing plant must be free of micro-organisms.

11 Go through the employment section of the newspaper and find jobs that require knowledge of micro-organisms. Choose 1 of these jobs and write a brief report on how knowledge of micro-organisms is used in this job. Share your report with the rest of the class.

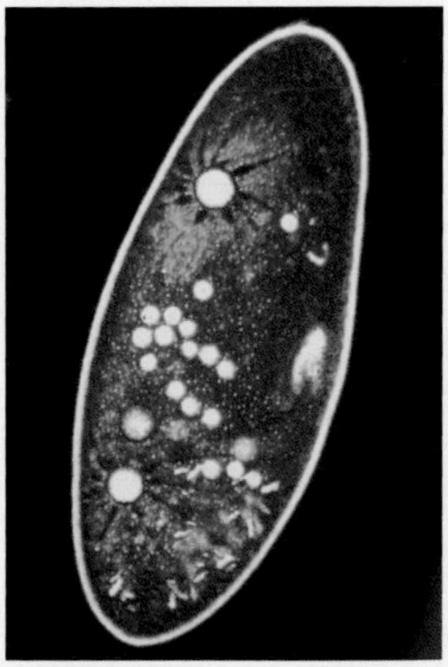

FIGURE 5.43D

12 You are working for a cheese company that uses mould to produce some of its cheese. Explain why workers in the company must regularly check what type of mould is growing on the cheese.

Communication

13 In a group of 3 or 4 students, create a trivia card game made up of 10 questions and answers about reproduction in micro-organisms. When you are finished, exchange games with another group, and play their game. Evaluate their game. Was there anything that did not work very well? Was there anything you really liked?

14 Explain whether you think fungi are harmful, beneficial, or both harmful and beneficial to humans. You must give reasons for your answer.

15 Make a collage from newspaper and magazine clippings, showing how micro-organisms and cleanliness are connected in the workplace.

CHAPTER 6

Micro-organisms and Human Life

No matter what kind of work we do, all of our lives are affected by micro-organisms. Consider the situations shown in Figure 6.1. In each of these situations, the people are benefiting from the presence of micro-organisms. At the same time, there are also micro-organisms that could harm these people. What kinds of micro-organisms do you think are beneficial in each of these situations? What kinds are harmful?

FIGURE 6.1

What You Will Learn

After completing this chapter, you will be able to:

- Describe how bacteria, protists, viruses and fungi are useful to humans (6.1, 6.2, 6.3, 6.4)
- Describe how bacteria, protists, viruses and fungi cause diseases in humans (6.2, 6.4)
- Describe the nature and function of vaccines (6.4)
- Describe some of the challenges to controlling harmful micro-organisms (6.1, 6.2, 6.3, 6.4)
- Identify careers that deal with micro-organisms (6.1, 6.2, 6.3, 6.4)

What You Will Do

- Conduct and report on research about an issue related to micro-organisms (Activities 6A, 6D)
- Conduct an experiment to investigate the behaviour of micro-organisms in breaking down vegetable scraps (Lab 6B)
- Prepare yogourt using micro-organisms (Lab 6C)
- Demonstrate your understanding of safe lab practices (Labs 6B, 6C)
- Select and use scientific equipment appropriately (Labs 6B, 6C)
- Compile and organize data, using data tables and graphs (Labs 6B, 6C)
- Select and use appropriate scientific units and symbols (Labs 6B, 6C)
- Communicate the results of lab activities (Labs 6B, 6C)

Words to Know

algal bloom
antibiotic
antiseptic
carbon
carbon cycle
compost
composting
decomposition
disease
disinfectant
food poisoning
irradiated
mutation
nitrogen
nitrogen cycle
nitrogen fixation
organic matter
photosynthesis
preservatives
protein
resistant
respiration
vaccine
vaccination

A puzzle piece indicates knowledge or a skill that you will need for your project, Micro-organisms at Work, at the end of Unit 3.

6.1 Micro-organisms and the Environment

> You will need to know the benefits and costs of micro-organisms to the environment, for your project, Micro-organisms at Work.

Almost every organism on Earth, including humans, depends on the actions of micro-organisms. Many micro-organisms feed on **organic matter**, which is any matter derived from living organisms. Some of this is waste (excrement), and some is the bodies of dead plants and animals. Micro-organisms recycle the chemicals in this organic matter, which makes them available to be used again by other living organisms.

Micro-organisms in the Carbon Cycle

Carbon is a chemical used to make substances that provide energy for many organisms, including humans. The **carbon cycle** is the process by which carbon is used again and again by organisms in the environment (Figure 6.2). Micro-organisms are involved in 2 parts of the carbon cycle. They help to bring carbon into the carbon cycle and they help to recycle carbon from dead organisms and animal waste.

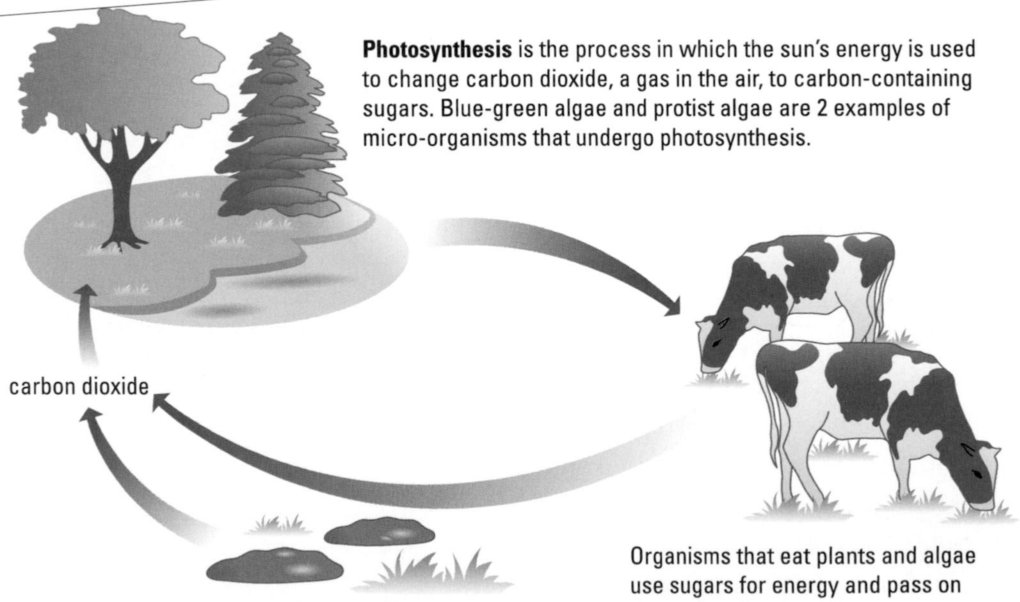

Photosynthesis is the process in which the sun's energy is used to change carbon dioxide, a gas in the air, to carbon-containing sugars. Blue-green algae and protist algae are 2 examples of micro-organisms that undergo photosynthesis.

Organisms that eat plants and algae use sugars for energy and pass on the carbon they contain.
Respiration is the process in which carbon-containing substances such as sugars are broken down to release energy and carbon dioxide gas.

Decomposition is the process by which substances are broken down, or decomposed. Most of the organic matter in the world is decomposed by micro-organisms, especially bacteria and fungi. These micro-organisms use waste and dead tissue as a food supply.

FIGURE 6.2
The carbon cycle.

The carbon cycle benefits all the organisms on Earth, including humans, by keeping enough carbon available to make the carbon-rich substances that supply the energy required for life.

Micro-organisms and the Nitrogen Cycle

Nitrogen is a chemical used to make **protein**, an important building block for the cells of most living things. Most living things, including humans, get the nitrogen they need from the protein in other organisms. For example, humans get the nitrogen they need from the protein found in meat and in protein-rich plants like beans. The **nitrogen cycle** is the process that allows nitrogen to be reused. Figure 6.3 shows the stages of the nitrogen cycle.

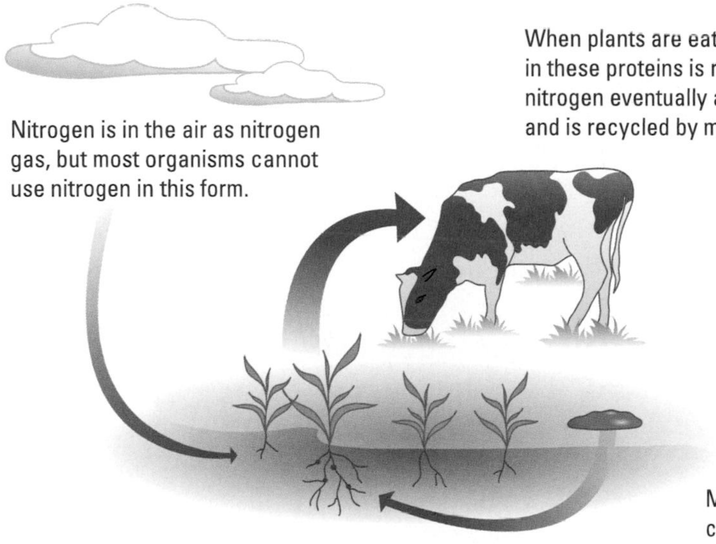

Nitrogen is in the air as nitrogen gas, but most organisms cannot use nitrogen in this form.
When plants are eaten by other organisms, the nitrogen in these proteins is reused to make new proteins. This nitrogen eventually again becomes waste or dead cells, and is recycled by micro-organisms.
Most of the nitrogen that plants use comes from decomposition of organic matter by micro-organisms such as bacteria and fungi in the soil. These micro-organisms produce nitrogen-containing substances that dissolve in water and can be taken up by the roots of plants.
Nitrogen fixation is the process of converting nitrogen gas in the air into other nitrogen-containing substances. Certain species of bacteria are capable of nitrogen fixation, and produce nitrogen-containing substances that plants can use to make protein.

FIGURE 6.3 The nitrogen cycle. Why is this cycle important to all living things?

Micro-organisms Can Harm the Environment

Under some conditions, the number of micro-organisms can become so high that they harm other organisms. You can find out more about the relationships between organisms in the environment in Section 9.1. Large numbers of micro-organisms can consume so much food and other resources that other organisms may no longer be able to survive. Some species of micro-organisms can cause illness in other living things, including humans.

Algal Blooms

Algae are usually a beneficial part of the environment. However, if the number of algae cells becomes too high, algae can be very harmful. An **algal bloom** is a very high concentration of algae cells that is harmful to the environment.

Algal blooms occur when a body of water, such as a pond or stream, contains very high levels of nutrients (Figure 6.4). Algae get nutrients from decomposing plants and animals, and from human and animal waste (excrement). If large amounts of human sewage or farm waste are dumped into the water, the level of nutrients will be so high that the algae will produce an algal bloom. The thick patches of algae that form as a result prevent oxygen from mixing with the water and block out light. An algal bloom can be so severe that nothing else will be able to live in the area.

An algal bloom called a red tide can affect seawater. These blooms are caused by red protist algae. During a red tide, there are so many red algae cells that the water looks red. The algae that cause red tides produce a substance that is poisonous to some other organisms, including humans. If a person eats shellfish that have fed on the algae in a red tide, he or she will become very ill and may even die.

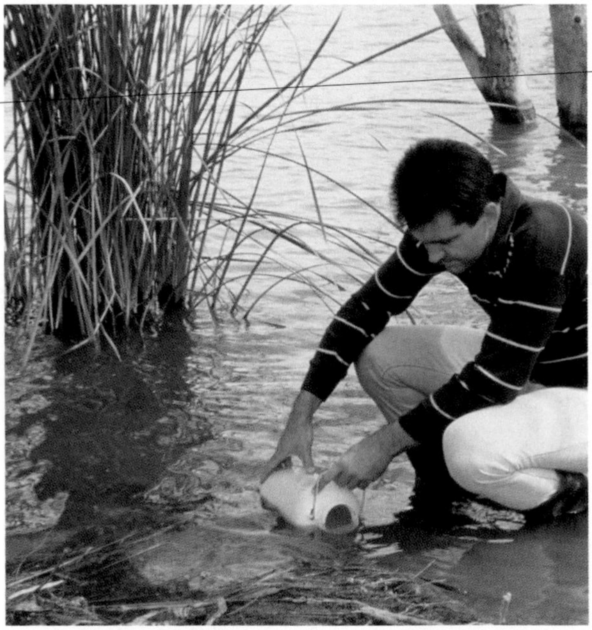

FIGURE 6.4 Why are algal blooms harmful to the other organisms in the environment?

Micro-organisms and Water Pollution

Animal waste, especially our own sewage, can contain micro-organisms that cause disease in humans. A **disease** is any change in the way the body of an organism functions, that causes harm to the organism. Micro-organisms cause disease in 2 ways, as shown in Figure 6.5.

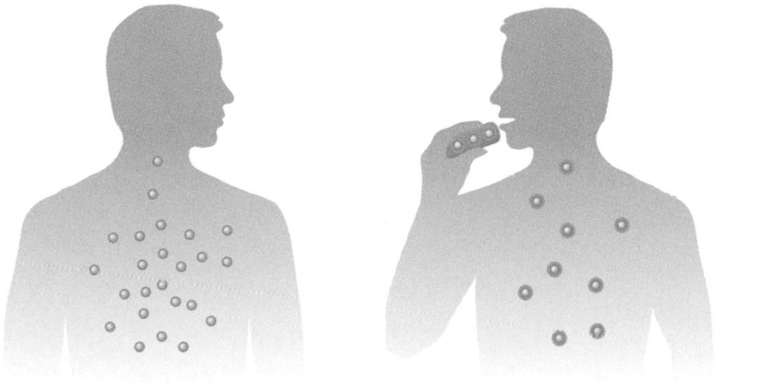

A micro-organism can cause disease when it invades the body, and uses the cells of the body to supply it with food.

A micro-organism can cause disease when it enters the body and releases a poison, or when a person eats or drinks something that contains a poison from a micro-organism.

FIGURE 6.5 How micro-organisms cause disease.

FIGURE 6.6 Polluted water can contain harmful micro-organisms.

When water is polluted by untreated sewage or by animal waste from farms, the levels of harmful micro-organisms can become so high that the water becomes unsafe to drink.

Using Micro-organisms to Improve the Environment

FIGURE 6.7 By using micro-organisms to clean up this spill on site, these workers could avoid handling the waste.

Our society produces some substances that can be hazardous to our health and the health of the environment. For example, the fuels we use for our vehicles are poisonous. Some micro-organisms can break down some of these substances into harmless chemicals.

Scientists have found ways to use micro-organisms to degrade dangerous chemicals that pollute the environment. Using micro-organisms in this way can save money, and does not add harmful chemicals to the environment. Since workers bring the micro-organisms to the site, there is no need to transport the hazardous chemicals.

ACTIVITY 6A Farming Practices and *E. coli* Bacteria

The bacteria *E. coli* O157:H7 caused 7 deaths and 2300 cases of serious disease when it got into the drinking water in Walkerton, Ontario, in the year 2000. Pollution of drinking water and *E. coli* O157:H7 has been connected to certain farming practices.

In this activity, you will conduct research about different farming practices and their links to the *E. coli* O157:H7 contamination of drinking water.

What You Will Need

- pen or pencil
- markers or coloured pencils
- paper or Bristol board
- Internet, reference books or articles

What You Will Do

1. Get into groups of 4. Give each person in your group a number from 1 to 4.
2. Depending on the number you are given, conduct research to answer the corresponding question below. Make sure you use a number of different reference sources in your research.
   - If you have the number 1: What farming practices have been linked to the *E. coli* O157:H7 pollution in drinking water?
   - If you have number 2: How is water tested for the presence of *E. coli* bacteria?
   - If you have number 3: What are the effects of drinking water that contains *E. coli* O157:H7?
   - If you have number 4: How can the pollution of drinking water by *E. coli* be prevented?
3. After research is complete, meet with the others who investigated the same question as you. Discuss what you discovered. Make any changes or additions to your research that you think are necessary based on your discussion.
4. Return to your original group and share your information.
5. As a group, decide on a method to display the information you found.

What Did You Find Out?

1. Do you think the pollution of drinking water with *E. coli* bacteria is a serious problem? Explain your answer in 2 or 3 sentences.

Making Connections

2. Do you think that some farmers should change their farming practices to prevent *E. coli* pollution of drinking water? Give reasons for your answer.

Review and Apply

1. List ways that micro-organisms are involved in nutrient recycling. Make a chart of your ideas.
2. In a series of labelled diagrams, show the development and effects of an algal bloom on the environment.
3. Provincial parks allow us to be close to nature by camping, hiking and picnicking. One of the responsibilities of people who work in provincial parks is to look for harmful micro-organisms in the lakes and streams. Suggest at least 2 ways that harmful micro-organisms might get into the water of a provincial park.
4. Imagine you are the owner of a company that specializes in using bacteria to clean up hazardous waste. You are preparing a bid for a contract to clean up a hazardous waste spill. In a paragraph, explain the advantages of your company's procedures over other methods.
5. Organize the concepts you have learned in this section in a graphic organizer.

6. **Giardiasis**

Giardiasis is a disease caused by the protist *Giardia lamblia*. This micro-organism can be found in soil, food, water, or on surfaces that have been contaminated with the waste of an infected organism. You can get giardiasis by getting *Giardia lamblia* in your mouth after you have picked up a contaminated object, such as toys, bathroom fixtures or diaper pails, or by drinking contaminated water. Giardiasis can give you fever, stomach cramps, nausea and severe diarrhea.

FIGURE 6.8 *Giardia* is often present in lakes with high numbers of beavers.

a) Suggest 2 or 3 ways that you might avoid getting giardiasis.
b) What role do you think cleanliness plays in preventing giardiasis?
c) Interview someone who works in a daycare facility. Ask them if they have ever experienced an outbreak of giardiasis and what they do to prevent this situation. Report your findings to your class either as a 10-minute talk, or as a poster.

6.2 Micro-organisms in Agriculture

FIGURE 6.9 What roles do micro-organisms play in this workplace?

Micro-organisms are extremely important in agriculture. Through the carbon cycle and the nitrogen cycle, the micro-organisms found in the soil recycle material from plants and animals into nutrient-rich soil. Successful agriculture depends on healthy soil. An important component of soil consists of partially broken-down matter from plants and animals. Micro-organisms are, in part, responsible for making this part of soil.

To get a good yield from crops, agricultural workers must ensure that sufficient nutrients are available in the soil. Micro-organisms enrich the soil through their roles in the carbon and nitrogen cycles. The process of nitrogen fixation by certain species of micro-organisms, such as the bacteria *Rhizobium*, supply some crop plants with additional nitrogen (Figure 6.10). Agricultural workers often add this bacteria to the soil to promote this process.

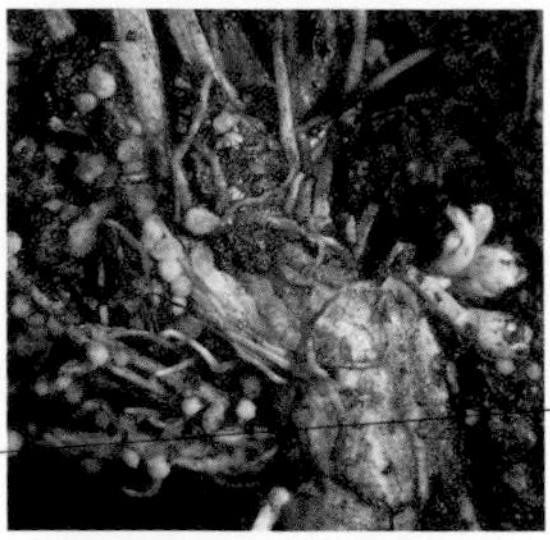

FIGURE 6.10 The nodules (bumps) on the roots of this plant are filled with bacteria that supply the plant with nitrogen, through the process of nitrogen fixation.

Micro-organisms can also be used to keep harmful insects under control. For example, the bacterial species *Bacillus thuringiensis*, or Bt, produces a poison that kills many harmful insects but leaves animals, birds, plants and humans unaffected. You will learn more about agricultural practices that also protect the environment in Section 10.1.

Micro-organisms also help to keep farm animals, or livestock, healthy. All animals, including humans, rely on helpful bacteria to digest food. Animals that chew their cud, such as cattle, cannot break down their food without these helpful micro-organisms (Figure 6.11).

FIGURE 6.11 Without certain bacteria, these cows could not get any energy or nutrients, no matter how much they ate.

Plant Diseases

Plant diseases can be caused by fungi, viruses and bacteria. Plant diseases can kill or damage an entire crop. For example, when wheat is infected by the fungus *Fusarium*, the stem of the wheat plant becomes so weak that it can no longer support the top of the plant. When the plant falls over, the wheat grain rots on the ground.

Micro-organisms can attack an agricultural crop at any time during production. Figure 6.12 shows some examples of disease on crops caused by micro-organisms. If a crop becomes diseased, a farmer may not be able to harvest anything and will be left without income.

You will need to know the benefits and costs of micro-organisms in agriculture for your project, Micro-organisms at Work.

A) 

B) 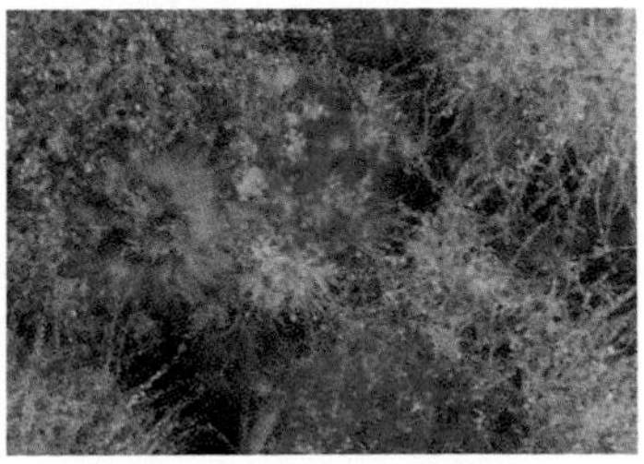

C) 

FIGURE 6.12 A) Fungus on corn; B) Mould on strawberry plants; C) Fungus on harvested pears. Micro-organisms can attack at any stage of crop production.

Animal Diseases

Diseases in farm animals can be caused by viruses, bacteria, fungi and protozoa. Some diseases, such as the skin disease ringworm, are not serious and can be treated easily. However, some micro-organisms cause serious diseases that can spread throughout an entire herd of animals. For example, foot-and-mouth disease is caused by a virus that spreads so easily that the only treatment is to destroy all the animals that may be infected (Figure 6.13). Other diseases in farm animals can also spread to humans. There are about 150 diseases that are known to have affected humans who worked with diseased animals.

FIGURE 6.13 In 2001, large herds of sheep were killed in Britain in order to control an outbreak of foot-and-mouth disease.

Controlling Harmful Micro-organisms

When harmful micro-organisms arise in the farm workplace, they can wipe out entire crops and herds. Therefore, it is extremely important to control these micro-organisms before they cause problems.

Controlling Micro-organisms that Cause Plant Disease

Micro-organisms can usually grow on just a few species of plants. By changing the type of crop that is grown (crop rotation), the numbers of micro-organisms can be kept low (Figure 6.14).

Other ways to control micro-organisms that cause plant diseases include:

- immediately destroy infected plants;
- plant varieties of plants that are resistant to, or able to withstand, the micro-organisms. For example, seed companies sell wheat that is resistant to the fungus that causes wheat rust;
- spray chemicals on crops.

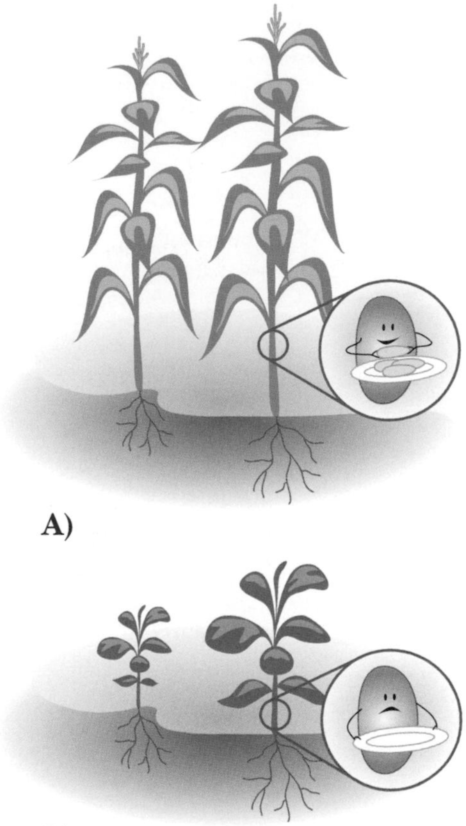

A)

B)

FIGURE 6.14 A) The micro-organism represented in this cartoon feeds on corn. If only corn is grown, the micro-organism will have a food supply year after year. B) When the crop is changed to beans, the micro-organism no longer has a food supply.

Controlling Micro-organisms that Cause Animal Disease

The best way to control the micro-organisms that cause animal disease is to keep conditions clean and dry. Micro-organisms can reproduce very quickly in manure and other animal waste. Other ways to control micro-organisms that cause animal diseases include:

- keep barns and stalls clean, dry and free of animal waste;
- keep animals well-fed;
- do not overcrowd the animals;
- provide regular veterinary care.

FIGURE 6.15 How might the micro-organisms that cause disease be controlled here?

Even well-kept animals will occasionally become ill. Sick animals should be treated with medications, to prevent disease from spreading to other animals. If a disease cannot be treated, then all the diseased animals must immediately be destroyed.

Challenges to Controlling Micro-organisms in Agriculture

Keeping animals under clean and healthy conditions is the best defence against disease-causing micro-organisms. Similarly, rotating crops and destroying diseased plants is the best defence against micro-organisms that attack plants. Some other ways of controlling harmful micro-organisms in agriculture can be challenging. For example, planting disease-resistant crops is not always possible. They may not exist, or they may be very expensive.

Spraying chemicals to control micro-organisms is expensive and can be dangerous. These chemicals can be poisonous to other organisms, including humans and farm animals. Micro-organisms can also become **resistant** to a chemical that is used to control them. When this happens, that chemical can no longer be used and new chemicals must be developed. This is true for chemicals that are sprayed on crops, and for chemicals that are used as medicines to treat disease in animals.

Surf the Web

Go to www.science.nelson.com and follow the links for ScienceWise Grade 11, Chapter 6, Section 6.2. Look at the information on other ways to control the micro-organisms that cause disease in agriculture.

FIGURE 6.16 What types of safety procedures would this farmer have to follow?

LAB 6B

Micro-organisms and Composting

Be Safe!

- Wash your hands thoroughly before leaving the lab.
- When using the utility knife, always cut away from your body.

Composting is the process of turning kitchen and garden waste into nutrient-rich soil, or **compost**. Micro-organisms play an important role in the process of composting. Anyone can make compost, using a ready-made composter from the store, or one you make yourself.

Purpose

In this lab, you will make a simple composter and use it to compost vegetable scraps.

Materials

- 2 2-L plastic pop bottles with caps
- utility knife or sharp scissors
- waterproof marker
- yogourt cup
- foam plate
- clear tape
- large nail
- thermometer or temperature probe
- terry-cloth towelling or other insulating material
- chopped vegetable scraps
- small pieces of newspaper

FIGURE 6.17 Materials for composting unit.

Procedure

1. With the waterproof marker, label the two 2-L bottles "1" and "2."

2. Using the utility knife, cut off the top of bottle 1 just *below* the shoulder, as shown in Figure 6.18A. Cut the top of bottle 2 just *above* the shoulder (Figure 6.18B). The top from bottle 1 should be able to sit on the bottom of bottle 2 as in Figure 6.18C.

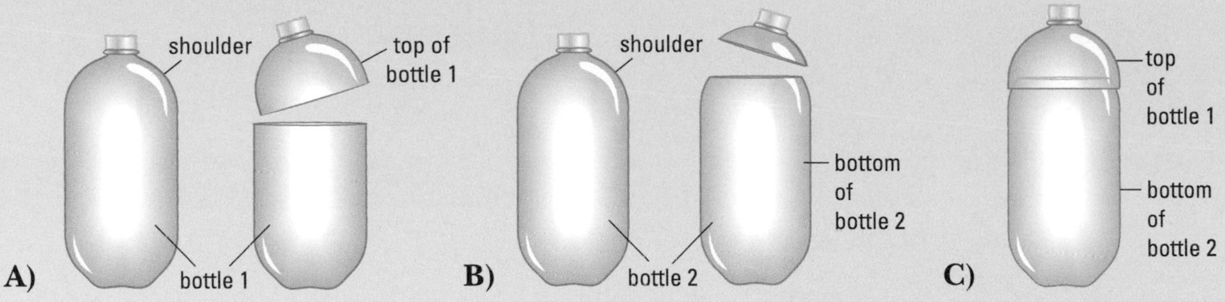

FIGURE 6.18 A) Cut bottle 1 just below the shoulder. B) Cut bottle 2 just above the shoulder. C) Place top 1 on bottom 2.

3. Remove top 1 from bottom 2. Place bottom 2 cut-edge down on a foam plate and trace its diameter. Cut a foam disc of this diameter. Use the nail to punch air holes through the foam disc.

4. Place the yogourt cup upside down in the bottom of bottle 2, to create a stand to support the foam disc. Place the foam disc on the stand.

5. On the outside of bottom 2, draw a line marking the edge of the foam disc. Cut air holes around the side of the bottle so that all the holes are underneath this line.

6. Place the cap on top 1. Place top 1 back on bottom 2. Your completed composter should look like the example in Figure 6.19.

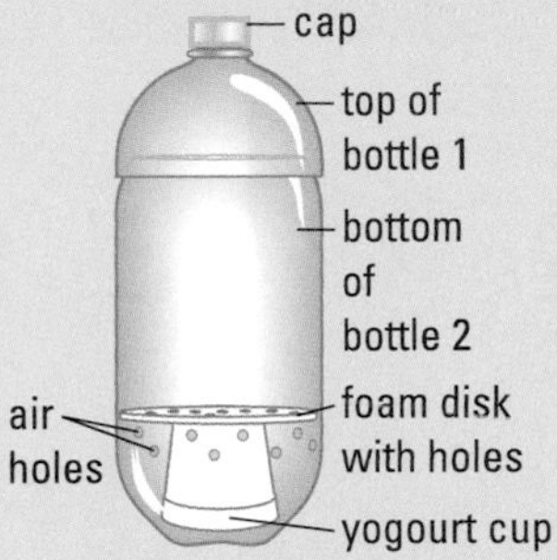

FIGURE 6.19 The completed composter.

7. Cut your vegetable scraps into 1-cm to 2-cm pieces. Cut an equal amount of newspaper pieces into the same size. Soak the newspaper pieces thoroughly in water, drain them, then mix them with the scraps.

8. Fill your composter with the mixed scraps and newspaper. Do not pack down the mixture. Wrap your composter in terry-cloth towelling.

9. Set your composter somewhere warm, where it will not be disturbed. Do not place it on a heating vent or in direct sunlight.

CONTINUED

10 In your notebook, create a data table using the headings in Figure 6.20. You will need sufficent space to enter data for at least 14 days.

Day	Observations	Temperature (°C)

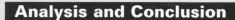

FIGURE 6.20

11 Every day, unwrap your composter and record any changes you see in your data chart. Look for changes such as the presence of odours, colour changes, or changes in the texture of the material. Check and record the temperature of the composting material, by removing the cap from the composter and carefully inserting a thermometer or temperature probe (Figure 6.21). Wrap the towelling around your composter again when you finish.

FIGURE 6.21 Place the bulb of the thermometer below the surface of the composting material.

Analysis and Conclusion

1 Did your kitchen scraps turn into compost? Give evidence to support your answer.

2 Create a bar graph showing the temperature of your compost over time.

3 When you exercise, your metabolism speeds up and so you heat up. Compost also heats up when micro-organisms are metabolizing. From your bar graph, describe how the temperature of the compost changed over time. When do you think the micro-organisms were metabolizing the most?

Extension and Connection

4 Green waste is kitchen and yard waste that comes only from plants. Explain why only green waste should be used in a composter.

5 When towns and cities organize large-scale composting programs, they ask that people separate green waste from other garbage. Do you think people in your school would be willing to separate garbage for composting? Why or why not?

Review and Apply

1. Create a chart listing ways micro-organisms can be helpful and be harmful in agriculture.
2. Explain how crop rotation can control harmful micro-organisms. You can include a diagram in your answer.
3. In 1 or 2 sentences, state 2 reasons why controlling micro-organisms that cause disease in farm animals is important.
4. Create a poster that could be hung in a large cattle barn, which would explain to workers why manure must be removed quickly.
5. Write a letter to the owner of a vegetable farm, explaining the benefits of using *Bacillus thuringiensis* to control insects.
6. Add the new concepts from this section to the graphic organizer you started in Section 6.1.

Job Link

Landscape Worker

Landscape workers plant and care for plants.

Responsibilities of a Landscape Worker

- applying mulch, fertilizers and other chemicals
- general lawn care, planting and maintaining gardens
- may operate and make minor repairs on equipment

Where do they Work?

- landscaping and chemical lawn-service companies
- athletic fields, golf courses, cemetery grounds, parks, and recreation facilities

Skills for the Job

- ability to work with little supervision
- good physical stamina, since heavy lifting is often required

Education

- high school diploma may be required
- many companies require additional training

FIGURE 6.22 A landscape worker must control the micro-organisms that cause diseases in plants.

6.3 Micro-organisms in the Kitchen

FIGURE 6.23 Micro-organisms are involved in the production of each of these foods.

When was the last time you had some cheese? How about some yogourt or chocolate? Certain micro-organisms help us to make these and many other foods we eat. For example, one species of yeast is used to make bread. The yeast feeds on the sugar in bread dough and produces carbon dioxide gas (and a little alcohol). Little bubbles of this carbon dioxide fill the dough and make it expand, or rise.

Some types of cheese, such as blue cheese (Roquefort) and Gorgonzola, are produced by adding a beneficial mould. Yogourt, sour cream and buttermilk are made from milk to which certain species of bacteria are added.

Food poisoning is caused by eating food that contains harmful micro-organisms. Food poisoning can give you severe stomach cramps, diarrhea and vomiting. If very young or very old people get food poisoning, they can end up in the hospital and may even die. Some causes of food poisoning are shown in Figure 6.24.

Common Causes of Food Poisoning

- Storing food in a way that allows micro-organisms to grow quickly.

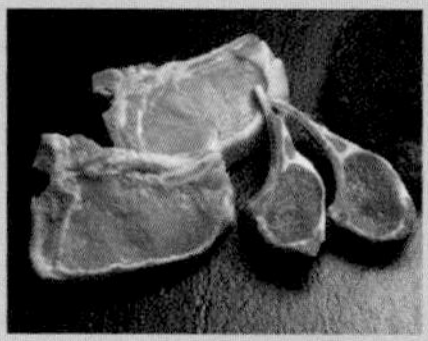

- Transferring micro-organisms from your unwashed hands, utensils, surfaces, or from other foods.

- Under-cooking food. Thorough cooking kills any harmful micro-organisms that might be present.

- Handling of food by someone who is sick.

FIGURE 6.24 Keeping food safe is a matter of keeping harmful micro-organisms under control.

Controlling Micro-organisms that Cause Disease

You will need to know how to control micro-organisms in the kitchen to complete your project, Micro-organisms at Work.

Harmful micro-organisms in the kitchen can be controlled quite easily by paying attention to how food is prepared and stored. Anything that might touch food, including your hands, must be kept very clean. Every workplace that handles food has its own specific ways of controlling harmful micro-organisms, but the following guidelines will apply to most:

- Surfaces where foods are prepared, such as countertops, should be cleaned regularly using hot, soapy water or bleach.
- All items used to prepare or serve food, such as cutlery, should be kept very clean.
- Anyone involved in food handling or preparation must be very careful about personal cleanliness. Hands should be washed regularly with hot water and soap, and loose hair should be tied back or covered.
- Food should always be cooked at a temperature high enough to kill micro-organisms. This is especially important for ground meats or chicken.
- Food that is to be stored in a can, bottle, or at room temperature must be placed into a sterilized container while it is still hot so that micro-organisms cannot grow.
- Foods that can spoil must be stored in a refrigerator or freezer. Since the cold temperatures only slow down the growth of micro-organisms, all foods in cold storage must be labelled with the date they were prepared, and removed if they are stored too long. Health Canada produces guidelines to determine the maximum time foods may be stored frozen.

FIGURE 6.25 Why are hairnets required in this workplace?

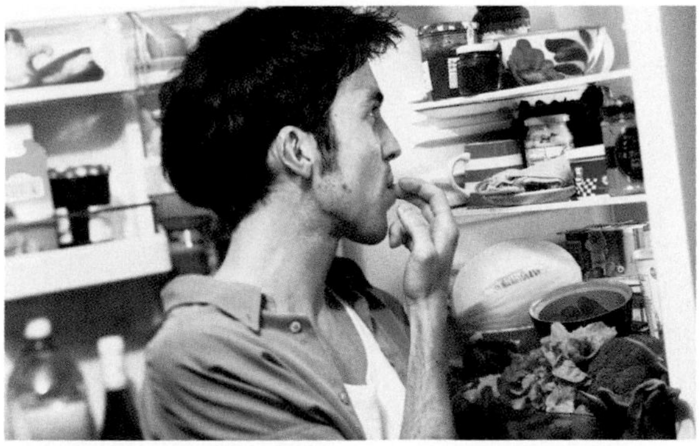

FIGURE 6.26 Why is it important to know how long something has been stored in the fridge?

FIGURE 6.27 How does drying food control the growth of micro-organisms?

Using Technology to Control Micro-organisms

Food producers have found ways to prepare foods that control the growth of micro-organisms. Canning seals foods into a sterile container before micro-organisms can grow. Drying foods removes most of the moisture from food, killing many micro-organisms and stopping them from reproducing.

Preservatives are chemicals that are added to food to control the growth of micro-organisms (Figure 6.28). Most packaged foods contain these chemicals.

Common Food Preservatives

Preservative	Purpose	Example
Nitrates	Prevent the growth of the bacteria that causes botulism, a deadly form of food poisoning.	
Sulphates	Slow the growth of harmful bacteria.	
Sodium propionate	Prevents the growth of certain bacteria and moulds.	

FIGURE 6.28 Some chemicals are added to packaged foods to prevent the growth of micro-organisms.

Some foods are **irradiated**, or exposed to high-energy beams, to control harmful micro-organisms. The high-energy beams are applied when the food is very fresh and tightly wrapped. Any micro-organisms in the food are killed. Since the food is wrapped during irradiation, no other micro-organisms can get on the food, and it stays free of micro-organisms until it is opened.

LAB 6C

Making Yogourt

Helpful bacteria are used in the production of yogourt. To make yogourt at home, milk and an active (living) yogourt culture is needed.

FIGURE 6.29 You will use commercial yogourt as a source of bacteria.

Purpose

In this lab, you will prepare a sample of yogourt.

Materials

- hot plate
- safety goggles
- oven mitts
- pH paper or pH meter
- two 500-mL beakers
- 100-mL graduated cylinder
- 250 mL milk
- 60 mL cream
- stirring rod or spoon
- masking tape
- thermometer
- lab coats
- plastic wrap
- terry-cloth towelling
- 250-mL graduated cylinder or measuring cup
- 250 mL of commercial yogourt with live bacteria
- waterproof marker

Be Safe!

- Do not eat these products.
- Wash your hands thoroughly before you leave the lab.
- Do not touch your mouth, eyes, nose, or ears when working with micro-organisms.
- Dispose of the yogourt according to your teacher's instructions.

Procedure

Part One: Making Yogourt

1. Measure and combine 250 mL of milk and 60 mL of cream in the 500-mL beaker.
2. Place the beaker on a hot plate. Set the hot plate to medium. Bring the milk and cream mixture to a boil.
3. Let the milk and cream boil for 1 minute and then use the oven mitts to remove the beaker from the hot plate.
4. Using the waterproof marker, write your name on a clean 500-mL beaker.
5. Transfer the mixture to the labelled 500-mL beaker. Carefully place the thermometer in the beaker. Allow the contents to cool to 40 to 45°C.

CONTINUED

FIGURE 6.30 Make sure you label your yogourt mixture.

6. Add 4 mL of plain yogourt to the cooled mixture. The yogourt adds live bacteria to the cream and milk mixture. Stir well.
7. Cover the beaker with plastic wrap, and wrap it with the terry-cloth towelling. Be careful not to spill the contents of the beaker. Wrap masking tape around the towelling, then write your name on the tape.
8. Place the beaker in a warm place where it will not be disturbed. Let it sit overnight.

Part Two: Comparing Commercial Yogourt to Your Yogourt

1. On a clean sheet in your notebook, prepare a data table like the example in Figure 6.31.

Characteristic	Commercial yogourt	My yogourt
Colour		
Texture		
pH		
Mass of empty 100-mL cylinder		
Mass of 100-mL cylinder + 100 mL yogourt		
Mass of 100 mL yogourt		
Density (mass/100 mL)		

FIGURE 6.31 Sample data table.

2. The next day, carefully take your yogourt to your workstation and unwrap it.
3. Observe the colour and texture of the yogourt. Record your observations in your data table.
4. Measure the pH of the commercial yogourt and your yogourt. Record your observations.
5. Measure an empty, clean 100-mL graduated cylinder using a balance. Record your data.

6. Transfer 100 mL of the commercial yogourt into the cylinder. Determine the mass of the cylinder + yogourt. Record your observations.

7. Pour the yogourt back into the beaker. Wash the graduated cylinder.

8. Repeat steps 5 to 7 using your yogourt.

9. For both the commercial yogourt and your yogourt, substract the mass of the empty cylinder from the mass of the cylinder + yogourt. This gives you the mass of the yogourt alone. Record your answers in the data table.

10. For both the commercial yogourt and your yogourt, divide the mass of the yogourt by its volume (100 mL). This is the density of the yogourt. Record your answers in the data table.

Analysis and Conclusion

1. Using the information in your data table, make point-form notes to summarize the similarities and differences between your yogourt and the commercial yogourt.

2. To maintain the quality of their product, yogourt manufacturers ensure that their yogourt always has the same density and pH. Based on your data, was your yogourt the same quality as the commercial yogourt? Explain your answer.

3. Share your data table with another group. What are the similarities and differences? As a group, brainstorm reasons that might explain the differences. In 2 or 3 sentences, identify the reasons you think are the cause of these differences.

Extension and Connection

4. Explain why the yogourt in this experiment may not be safe to eat.

5. Describe what you could do to make yogourt at home that you could be sure was safe to eat.

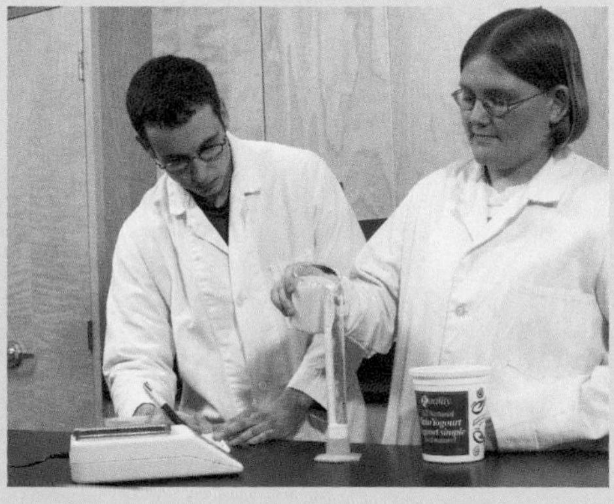

FIGURE 6.32 What happens to the bacteria in yogourt when it is left in a warm place overnight?

Review and Apply

1. List 3 examples of how micro-organisms are used to produce food.

2. Create a safety poster that explains food poisoning, and identifies at least 3 ways that food poisoning can be avoided at home.

3. You are the manager of a fast-food restaurant. Prepare a brief 10-minute talk that you might give to your staff to explain why it is important for them to keep the kitchen clean. Remember, your staff may not know a lot about micro-organisms.

4. You are a home-care provider working with elderly people. One of your clients has asked you to take something out of the freezer. When you look in, you find that none of the food is labelled. Describe the actions you would take to protect the health of your client. Your suggestions must show respect for your client's property.

5. Add the new concepts from this section to the graphic organizer you started in Section 6.1.

Surf the Web

Health Canada provides Canadians with information on the safe handling and storage of foods. Find out what micro-organisms are most likely to cause problems and what you can do at home and at work to protect your health and the health of others. You can find links to this information at **www.science.nelson.com**. Follow the links for ScienceWise Grade 11, Chapter 6, Section 6.3. Prepare a point-form summary of the information you find.

■

Job Link

Food Service Worker

FIGURE 6.33 Colin Francis works part-time in a grocery store bakery.

ScienceWise: How did you get this after-school job?

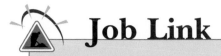

Colin Francis: I had experience in food preparation. I also had taken cooking and baking classes.

ScienceWise: What do you like most about your job?

Colin Francis: I like the short hours. I work 2 shifts a week from 3:00 until 7:00. I also enjoy baking and working with the public.

ScienceWise: What role do micro-organisms play in your work?

Colin Francis: Since the customer is eating our food, we have to make sure that no harmful micro-organisms are transferred to our baked goods. We also use yeast, to make our breads and cakes rise.

ScienceWise: How do you ensure the safety of your customers?

Colin Francis: I follow proper food sanitation procedures. I wear a clean uniform, hat and apron. I also wash my hands a lot to prevent the spread of harmful bacteria. We also make sure the baked goods are stored in the refrigerator so that micro-organisms will not grow. We always maintain a clean work surface by using a disinfectant and all the equipment is sterilized in a high-temperature dishwasher.

ScienceWise: What advice would you give others who may be interested in this field of work?

Colin Francis: Take courses if they are available at your school. If you are going to work with food and the public, you must learn about proper hygiene. You will learn this in food courses. Try to get part-time job at a restaurant, even if it is only a few hours a week.

Imagine you are applying for a job at a local pizza place. Write a cover letter to this business that shows you understand food safety issues.

6.4 Micro-organisms and Medicine

You will need to know the benefits and costs of micro-organisms in medicine for your project, Micro-organisms at Work.

Medicine is concerned with treating and curing diseases, as well as maintaining health. Since micro-organisms can cause disease, many of the things that medical workers do are concerned with controlling harmful micro-organisms. Other micro-organisms make products that benefit medicine and human life. You can read more about the micro-organisms that cause disease in Section 7.1.

FIGURE 6.34 Many medical treatments depend on micro-organisms.

Using Micro-organisms in Medicine

Many of the medicines we use to treat diseases caused by micro-organisms are produced by other micro-organisms. Doctors also can use micro-organisms to prevent us from getting sick.

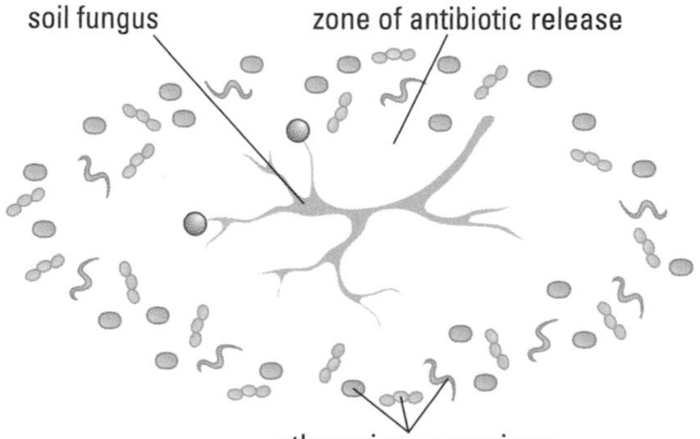

FIGURE 6.35 Antibiotics are produced by soil micro-organisms to help them to compete with other micro-organisms for space and food.

Antibiotics

Antibiotics are chemicals that kill or slow down (inhibit) the reproduction of micro-organisms. Most antibiotics are chemicals produced by micro-organisms, such as fungi, that live in the soil. These micro-organisms produce antibiotics to prevent other species of micro-organisms from living in the same area, which ensures they have enough food, water and space (Figure 6.35).

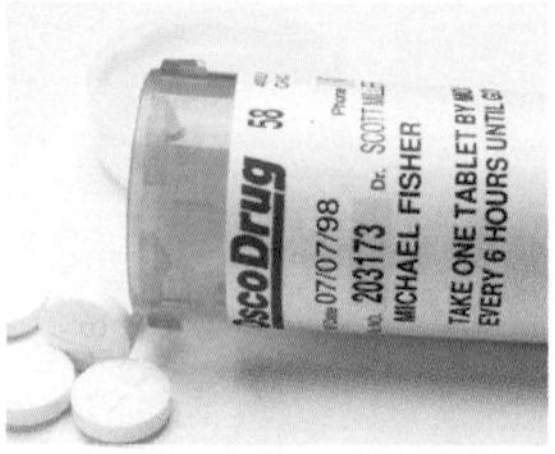

FIGURE 6.36 Antibiotics are usually provided as pills that are swallowed.

Doctors use antibiotics to kill bacteria cells that have entered a patient's body and are causing disease. These chemicals kill only the bacteria, but are usually harmless to us. Antibiotics can treat many diseases, including acne, ear infections and throat infections.

Vaccines

A **vaccination** is an injection that protects a person from getting a particular disease. For example, children may receive a vaccination to protect them from getting measles. A **vaccine** is the substance that is injected into the body.

Vaccines against a particular disease are usually prepared using the same micro-organisms that cause that disease. For example, the virus that causes measles is used to prepare the measles vaccine. The micro-organisms in the vaccine are either dead or extremely weak, so they will not be able to cause disease. You will learn more about how vaccines work in Section 7.3.

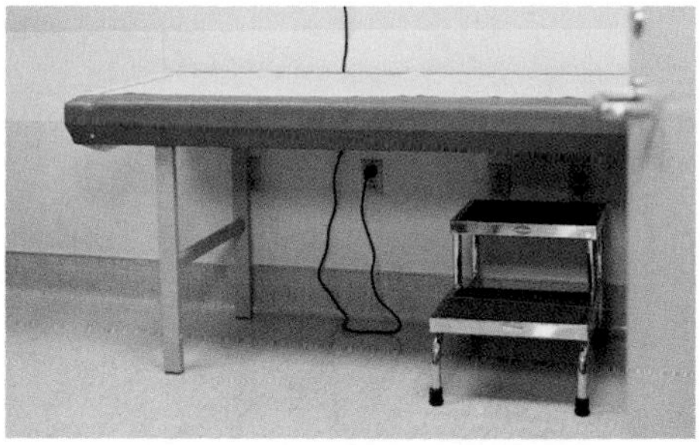

FIGURE 6.37 Using paper to cover surfaces helps to prevent harmful micro-organisms from passing from patient to patient.

Controlling Micro-organisms in Medicine

Because micro-organisms can cause disease, it is very important to control micro-organisms in medicine. Using antibiotics and vaccines is one way to control micro-organisms in medicine. Paying close attention to hygiene is also extremely important in controlling harmful micro-organisms. Everyone in a medical workplace must take special care to regularly wash their hands, to keep their hair clean and tidy and to wear clean clothing. Many items used in medicine are disposable, so that micro-organisms are less likely to be passed from person to person.

Hospitals, clinics and doctors' offices are visited every day by people who are likely to be carrying disease-causing micro-organisms. Therefore, these workplaces are cleaned regularly with a type of chemical called a disinfectant. A **disinfectant** is a chemical that can kill micro-organisms on surfaces (Figure 6.38).

Antiseptics are chemicals that slow down the growth of micro-organisms and can be applied to the skin. Antiseptics prevent micro-organisms from entering wounds, such as you might get when you cut yourself or when you have an operation.

FIGURE 6.38 Why is it important for medical workplaces to use disinfectants every day?

Challenges to Controlling Micro-organisms in Medicine

Every living thing has genetic material that determines many of the characteristics that individual will have. For example, your genetic material determines the colour of your hair and whether you are male or female. **Mutations** are changes in the genetic material of an organism.

Micro-organisms can undergo mutation (mutate) very quickly. Sometimes mutations change a micro-organism in a way that affects our ability to control it.

For example, bacteria can undergo mutations that make them able to withstand treatment with an antibiotic. When this happens, the antibiotic can no longer be used to treat a disease caused by the bacteria. You will learn more about this kind of mutation in Section 8.3.

Mutations can also make vaccines useless. Vaccines only work if they are made with micro-organisms that are very similar to the ones that cause a particular disease. For example, the flu vaccine will only work if it is prepared using the correct mutated form (mutant) of the flu virus. This virus mutates so quickly that scientists usually put 3 or more different mutants in one vaccine, and change which mutants they include every year. However, sometimes, despite these efforts, a particular vaccine is not able to prevent the flu in everyone.

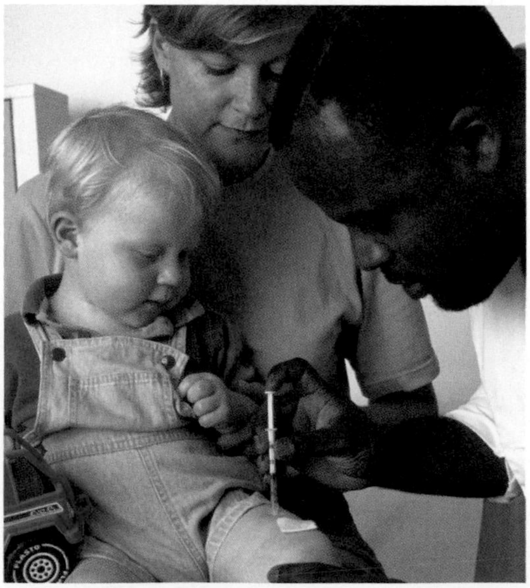

FIGURE 6.39 Because micro-organisms mutate, some vaccines may not always work.

ACTIVITY 6D

Micro-organisms in Medicine

Different micro-organisms can both cause and cure diseases in humans, so it is important for everyone to learn about these organisms. In this activity, you will work in a group to research and present information about 1 aspect of micro-organisms in medicine.

What You Will Need

- coloured markers, paper, and Bristol board
- Internet access (if available)
- reference books, magazines and newspapers

What You Will Do

1. As a group, choose 1 of the following topics to research:
   - micro-organisms and hospital hygiene;
   - costs and benefits of vaccines;
   - "super bugs," or multi-drug resistant bacteria.
2. Brainstorm ideas relating to the topic you have chosen. Make a list of your ideas.
3. Using your list, assign each person in your group at least 1 area to research. Everyone in the group must find and collect information on the area they are assigned.
4. Working individually on the area you were assigned, use Internet and print resource material to collect information.
5. When research is complete, meet with the other group members to discuss your findings. Decide if you have all the information you need. If not, complete any additional research.

What Did You Find Out?

1. As a group, review all the collected information. Decide on the most effective way of presenting your findings to the rest of your class. Some ideas are: a newsletter, a multi-media presentation, a poster, or a Web page.
2. Prepare and make your presentation.

Making Connections

3. Micro-organisms that have costs and benefits to medicine can affect workplaces other than hospitals and clinics. Make a list of at least 3 other workplaces that are likely to be affected by micro-organisms that cause or help to cure disease. For each of the workplaces, explain the connection to micro-organisms in medicine.

Review and Apply

1. State 2 ways that micro-organisms are useful in medicine.
2. Explain why medical workplaces must be very clean and use disinfectants regularly.
3. Imagine you have a job in a medical clinic. Are you more likely, less likely, or as likely to be affected by disease-causing bacteria than people who do not work in a medical workplace? Give reasons for your answer.
4. Why are vaccines not always able to prevent disease?
5. What is a vaccine? Describe how micro-organisms are used to make vaccines.
6. Explain how mutation reduces the effectiveness of some vaccines.
7. In hospitals, re-usable medical instruments are wrapped in foil and subjected to extremely high heat. Explain why this procedure is necessary, referring to micro-organisms.
8. Add the new concepts from this section to the graphic organizer you started in Section 6.1.

6.5 Chapter Summary

Now You Can...

- Describe some of the costs and benefits of micro-organisms to the environment (6.1)
- Describe some of the costs and benefits of micro-organisms in agriculture (6.2)
- Describe some of the costs and benefits of micro-organisms in food preparation (6.3)
- Describe some of the costs and benefits of micro-organisms in medicine (6.4)
- Describe some of the challenges to developing and using technologies that control micro-organisms (6.2, 6.3, 6.4)
- Describe how micro-organisms are used to make vaccines and antibiotics, and some of the challenges to using vaccines and antibiotics (6.4)

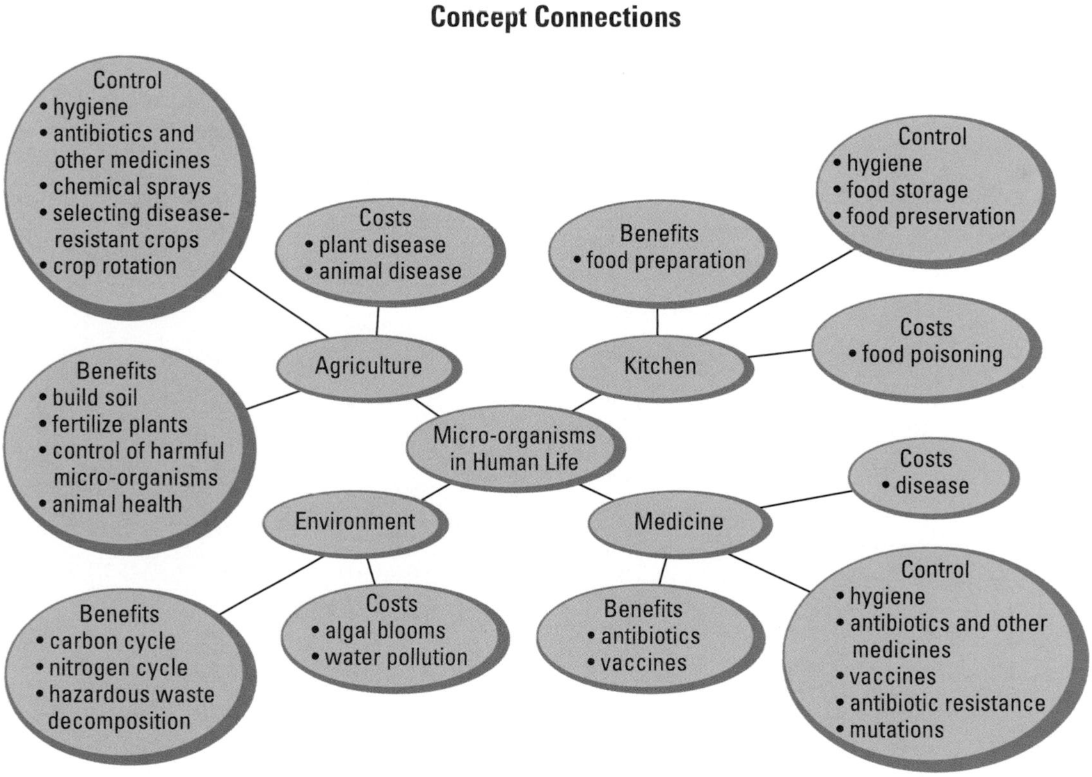

FIGURE 6.40 Compare your completed graphic organizer to the one on this page. How did you do? Can you add any new links to your organizer?

CHAPTER 6 *review*

Knowledge and Understanding

1. In 2 sentences, state 1 way that micro-organisms can benefit the environment and 1 way that micro-organisms can harm the environment.

2. Copy each of the following words in your notebook. From the 2 choices given, match each word with its correct definition. Write only the correct definition in your notebook.
   a) algal bloom:
      i) a very high concentration of algae cells that is harmful to the environment
      ii) a very high concentration of algae cells that benefits the environment
   b) composting:
      i) the process of turning kitchen and garden wastes into nutrient-rich soil
      ii) the process of breaking down hazardous wastes such as gasoline
   c) yogourt:
      i) a milk product made with yeast
      ii) a milk product made with bacteria
   d) antiseptics:
      i) chemicals used to slow down the growth of micro-organisms, that can be applied to the skin
      ii) chemicals produced by certain micro-organisms that can kill, or stop, the growth of other micro-organisms

3. In point form, describe 2 things that an agricultural worker, on a farm that raises cattle, can do to help control micro-organisms that can cause disease in cattle.

4. Identify at least 3 different foods that are made using micro-organisms.

5. Identify 3 general ways that harmful micro-organisms can be controlled in a kitchen.

Inquiry

6. During an experiment with a small-scale composter, a student collects the data in Figure 6.41.

Day	Temperature (°C)
1	24
3	25
6	29
9	24

FIGURE 6.41

Based on this data, on which day were the micro-organisms in the compost most active? Give reasons for your choice.

7. You are an entrepreneur with a home-based business making yogourt. Identify 2 characteristics you could use to check the quality of your yogourt.

Making Connections

8. Imagine you have a friend who is planning to work for a company that sprays chemicals on crops to control disease-causing organisms. Write a short paragraph describing how you would explain to your friend the importance of learning how to use these chemicals safely.

9. You are a supervisor in a large food processing plant. Ten new workers are starting at your plant today, and you are responsible for informing them about the control of micro-organisms in this workplace. In point form, list the things that these new workers must know to keep harmful micro-organisms under control in this workplace.

10. You are a member of the housekeeping staff of a large hospital. In a short paragraph, discuss the challenges to controlling harmful micro-organisms in this workplace.

Communication

11. Using cookbooks or other reference books, find at least 3 foods that are prepared using micro-organisms. Prepare a set of recipe cards that explains how to prepare these foods. Your recipe cards should identify the specific micro-organisms that are used and what they do.

12. Work with a partner. Write a script for a public service announcement that could be presented on the radio or television, which describes at least 2 ways harmful micro-organisms can be controlled in crop fields. Your announcement should take no more than 10 minutes to read, and should identify some of the costs and benefits of the control methods you describe.

13. On index cards, draw pictures of actions that would allow harmful micro-organisms to grow in a kitchen. You may not put any words on your cards. Make at least 5 cards. When you have finished, exchange cards with a partner. Take turns explaining why the actions on the cards can allow harmful micro-organisms to grow. Suggest ways the actions could be corrected to make the kitchen a safe workplace.

PUTTING IT ALL TOGETHER

Micro-organisms at Work

In this unit, you have learned something about different classes of micro-organisms, their life-cycles and the conditions under which they grow. You have also found out how micro-organisms can benefit human life, and how they can sometimes cause problems. You will now use all this information to design a safe workplace: your own home-based catering business.

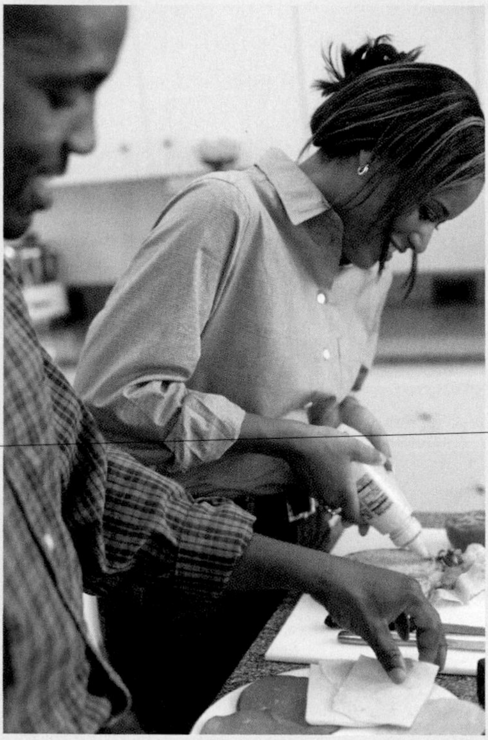

The Plan

Imagine you and several of your classmates have decided to start a home-based catering business. You will be running the business out of the kitchen of one of your group member's home. Before you start your business, you will make a plan to ensure that your business is carried out in a way that will ensure that harmful micro-organisms are controlled. You will also make note of any micro-organisms that will help your business.

What You May Need

- paper, pencils and pens
- reference sources such as magazines, books, or Internet access

FIGURE C1 What role would micro-organisms play in the design of a kitchen for a home-based catering business?

What You Will Do

1. As a group, decide the services you will offer and who will be your primary clients. Be as specific as possible. For example, you might prepare lunches for delivery to local businesses, or prepare snacks and other items for children's birthday parties.

2. Based on the services and clientele you chose in step 1, prepare a menu of the foods you will offer. You should have a minimum of 10 different foods on your menu.

3. Find recipes for each of the foods on your menu, and prepare a master list of the ingredients. These are the items you must always keep at hand to run your business. Note any items that involve helpful micro-organisms.

4. Sketch a floor plan of the kitchen that you will be using for your business. If possible, take measurements of the actual kitchen, and mark them on your floor plan. Include any appliances in the kitchen that you will use in your business.

5. Look over the floor plan of the kitchen. As a group, brainstorm the areas in the kitchen that are most likely to support the growth of harmful micro-organisms. Mark these areas on the floor-plan, using a different letter for each area. On a separate sheet of paper, prepare a legend, describing the risk from micro-organisms in each area. For example, you might put an "A" over the kitchen sink and state, "Harmful micro-organisms can grow in the sink if it is not kept clean."

6. Food handling and storage is an important part of controlling harmful micro-organisms in this workplace. As a group, prepare a list of workplace safety guidelines for everyone to follow, to ensure that your workplace is safe for you and for your clients. Keep in mind the following points:
   - You will be handling different types of food.
   - You will need to store prepared and unprepared foods for various periods of time.
   - You will need to ensure that everyone in the workplace practices good personal hygiene.
   - You will need to ensure that harmful micro-organisms are controlled every day.
   - Kitchen workplaces have safety hazards other than harmful micro-organisms, such as kitchen fires. You must consider all these risks in your guidelines as well.

7. Prepare a presentation portfolio summarizing your work. Your portfolio should include your menu, your ingredient list with helpful micro-organisms noted, your kitchen plan and legend, and your workplace safety guidelines.

CONTINUED

What Did You Find Out?

1. Identify the classes of micro-organisms that could impact your home-based catering business. Describe how these could be either harmful or helpful to your business.

2. If you had a business loan to redesign your kitchen, what additional steps could you take to control harmful micro-organisms?

Assessment

3. Place your portfolio in the place designated by your teacher. Compare your portfolio with those prepared by other groups. Make a note of things you particularly liked about other portfolios, and anything you think your group did particularly well.

4. In a paragraph, comment on what you think was done well in other groups' presentations. What did you like best about your own group's project? What improvements could you make to your kitchen design, without spending too much money?

The Immune System and Human Health

UNIT
4

CHAPTER 7: Disease and Your Body's Defences
CHAPTER 8: Reducing the Incidence of Disease
PUTTING IT ALL TOGETHER: Creating a Public Health Awareness Campaign

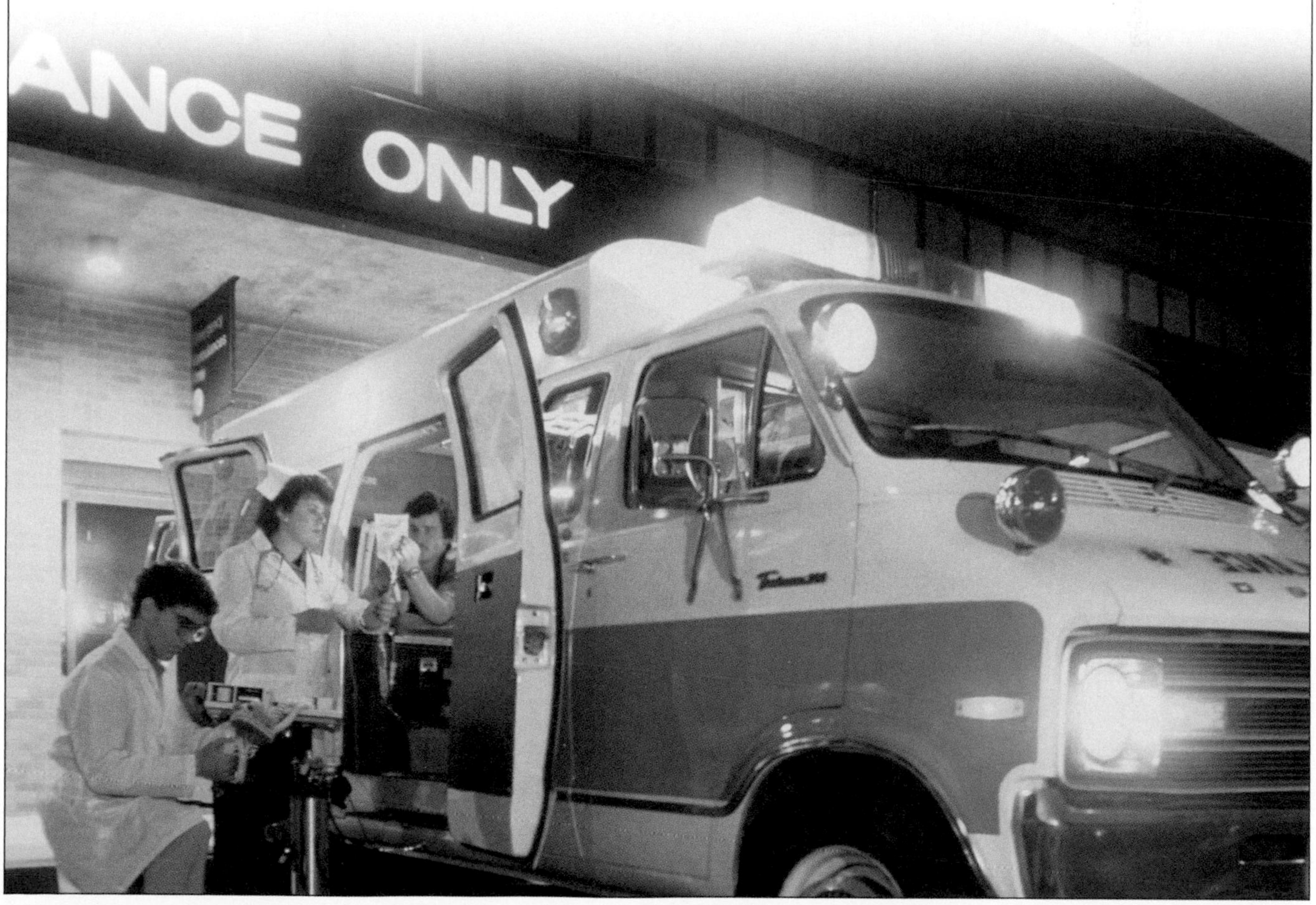

CHAPTER 7

Disease and Your Body's Defences

Have you ever wondered why you become ill? Do you find that when people around you have colds or the flu, you do not catch it? Or are you someone who seems to catch everything that is going around? Look at the photographs below. Is the person in the first photograph sneezing from a cold, or from an allergy? Can you catch allergies like you can catch a cold? Can sharing food spread disease? How about holding hands?

FIGURE 7.1

What You Will Learn

After completing this chapter, you will be able to:

- Explain the difference between communicable and non-communicable diseases (7.1)
- Describe the causes of disease (7.1, Lab 7B)
- Describe how communicable diseases are spread (7.1, Lab 7A)
- Describe 3 different ways that the human body fights disease (7.2, 7.3)
- Identify and describe some components of the human body that fight disease (7.2, 7.3)
- Identify and describe some components of the human body that protect us from disease (7.2, 7.3)

What You Will Do

- Collect and interpret data on the spread of a mock disease (Lab 7A)
- Communicate the results of a lab investigation by using a data table (Lab 7A)
- Observe and make drawings of microbes that cause disease (Lab 7B)
- Use a microscope appropriately and safely (Lab 7B)
- Work safely by wearing appropriate protective equipment in a lab (Lab 7A)

Words to Know

antibody
antigen
carrier
cellular membrane
communicable disease
contagious disease
disease
general defence
immune
immune response
infected
infectious disease
macrophage
mucus
non-communicable disease
pathogen
specific defence
symptom
vaccination
vector

A puzzle piece indicates knowledge or a skill that you will need for your project, Creating a Public Health Awareness Campaign, at the end of Unit 4.

7.1 What Is Disease?

Everyone gets sick now and then. We all know just how awful having a disease can feel. But what exactly is a disease? Is a cold a disease? How about cancer? Although they are very different, in fact both colds and cancer are diseases. A **disease** is a change in the normal way a body functions that causes harm to the body.

Different diseases have different symptoms. **Symptoms** are the changes in our bodies that occur when we get a disease. For example, the symptoms of a cold may be sneezing, runny nose, coughing, and aching. Figure 7.2 shows examples of some products that are used to treat symptoms of some diseases.

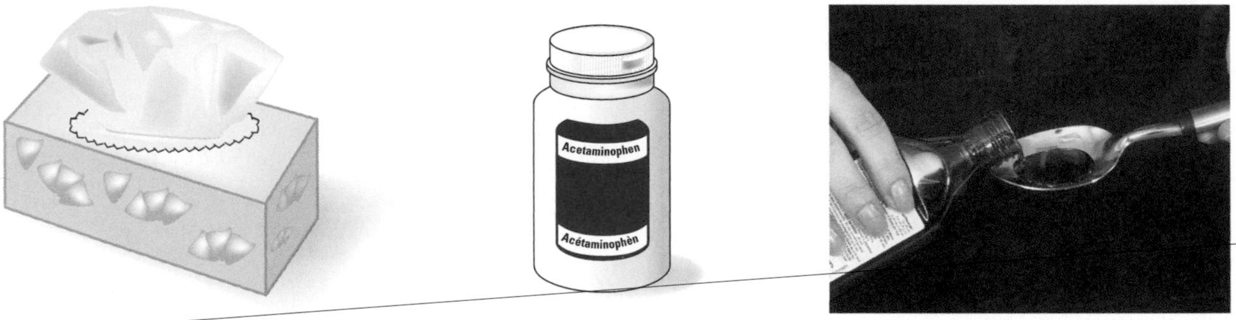

FIGURE 7.2 Each of these products is used to treat particular symptoms. What kinds of precautions do you need to take when you use over-the-counter medicines?

You would never catch a cold from someone who only has athlete's foot, because each of these 2 diseases has a different cause. In fact, every different disease has its own specific cause. Diseases can be classified into 2 groups based on their causes. The first group is diseases that can spread from person to person, and the second group is diseases that never spread. Figure 7.3 shows an example of a disease from each of these groups.

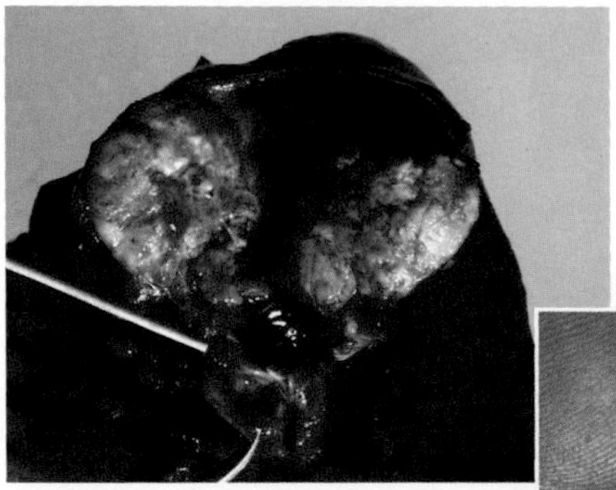

FIGURE 7.3A The lung of someone who had cancer.

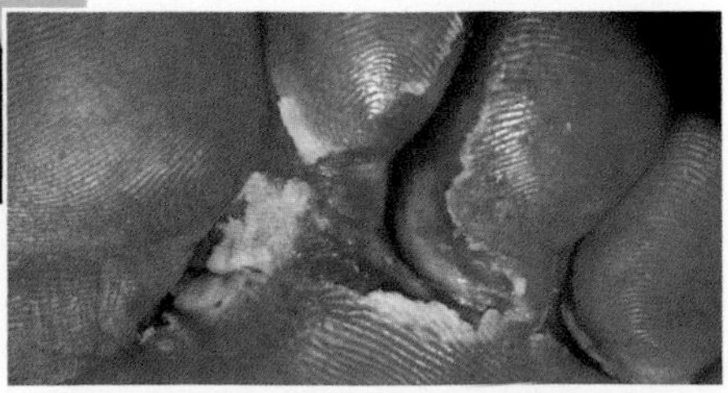

FIGURE 7.3B The foot of someone with athlete's foot. Which of these diseases can you catch from someone else?

Communicable Diseases

A **communicable disease** is a disease that can spread from person to person. A communicable disease can also be called an **infectious disease** or a **contagious disease**. Communicable diseases are always caused by something that enters your body, called a pathogen. For example, rubella is a communicable disease that many people get during childhood (Figure 7.4).

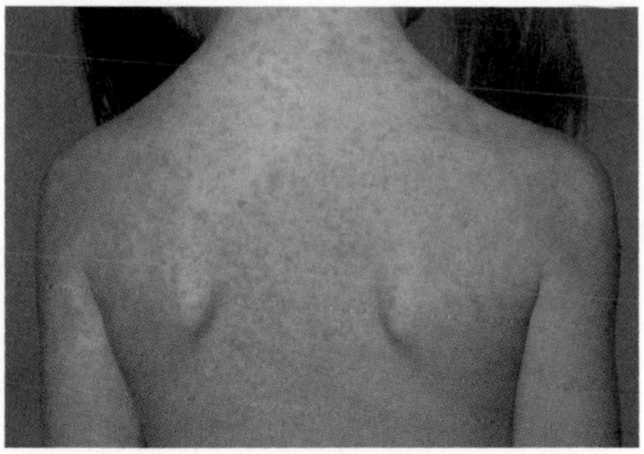

FIGURE 7.4 Person with rubella, or German measles. Rubella is caused by bacteria. Have you ever had rubella? What symptoms did you have?

Pathogens

A **pathogen** is something that enters your body, reproduces (makes more copies of itself), and causes you to become sick. A pathogen transmits, or passes on, the disease. Most people call pathogens "germs" in everyday life. Most pathogens are micro-organisms such as bacteria, viruses, fungi, or protists. You can find out more about micro-organisms in Unit 3 of this textbook.

You catch a communicable disease by being exposed to a pathogen, and then becoming infected by that pathogen. When you are **infected**, a pathogen has entered your body.

But why do pathogens enter our bodies in the first place? The human body is warm, temperature-controlled, moist and dark—exactly the conditions that many pathogens need to live. Our bodies also provide food for pathogens.

You will need to know about pathogens and communicable diseases to complete your project, Creating a Public Health Awareness Campaign.

ScienceWise Fact

Even when it looks clean, water can contain harmful pathogens. When you are hiking or camping, you should always boil or treat water from lakes and streams before you drink it to protect yourself from these pathogens. There is more information about water safety in Section 10.3.

The Spread of Disease

In order to transmit, or spread, a disease, the pathogen must get from one person's body to someone else's. What are some ways that this might happen?

You will need to know how disease is spread for your project, Creating a Public Health Awareness Campaign.

FIGURE 7.5 Even indirect contact can spread pathogens.

Pathogens are transmitted in 3 general ways:

1. *Through contact with a person infected with a disease.* Disease can be spread by direct contact with a sick person, such as when someone touches, kisses, or is involved in sexual activity with that person. Disease can also spread through indirect contact with a sick person, such as if someone else shares a bite of their food, uses an object he or she touched, or is close by when he or she sneezes or coughs. Look at Figure 7.5. How could a pathogen spread between these 2 people?

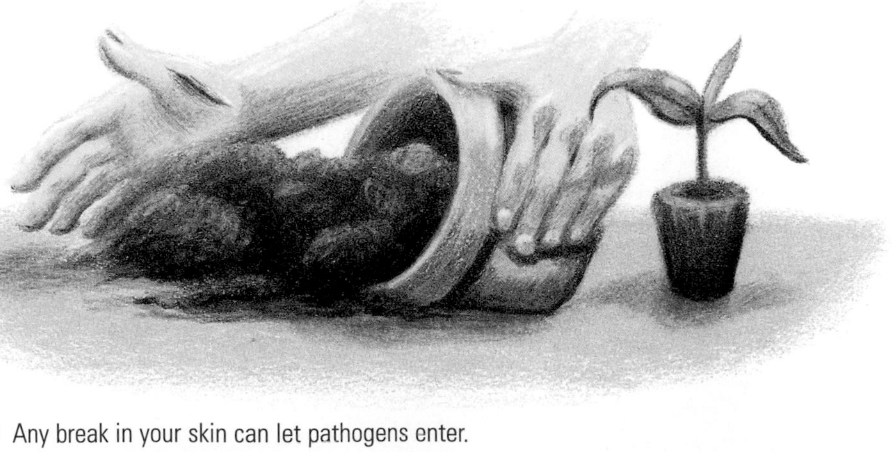

FIGURE 7.6 Any break in your skin can let pathogens enter.

2. *Through an uncovered cut or wound.* Some pathogens live in the air and soil and on objects around us and are usually quite harmless. However, if they enter our bodies through an uncovered break in the skin, these pathogens can then cause disease. For example, the person in Figure 7.6 has an uncovered cut on one hand, which could allow pathogens in the soil to cause infection.

3. *Through infected people, animals and insects without a disease.* Sometimes a pathogen can live inside an organism but not cause disease. However, these pathogens can sometimes be passed on and cause a person to become sick. An organism that is infected by a pathogen but is not sick is called a **carrier**, or a **vector** of a disease. The organism can be an animal, an insect, or another person. Figure 7.7 shows a human example of a disease carrier, and Figure 7.8 shows an insect example.

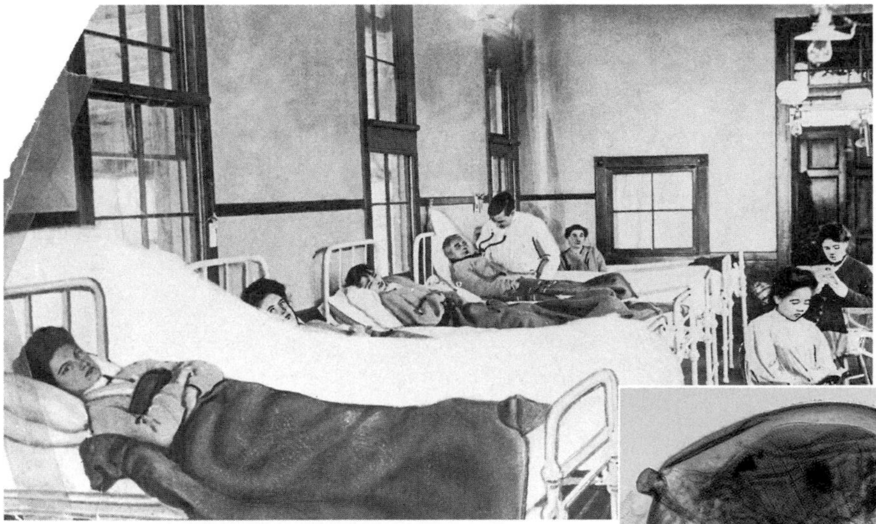

FIGURE 7.7 Mary Mallon, or Typhoid Mary, was a carrier of typhoid fever. Mary was a cook who handled food for many people, which spread typhoid fever to thousands of people in New York City in 1904.

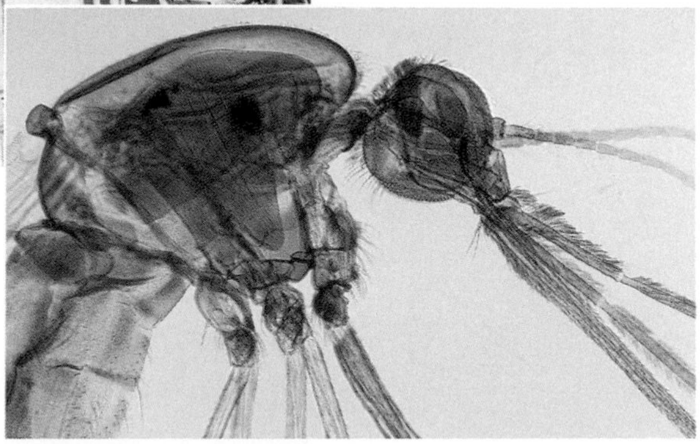

FIGURE 7.8 In many parts of the world, the mosquito is a vector of the deadly disease malaria, which kills many people every year.

Some Communicable Diseases and Their Symptoms

Disease	Pathogen	How do you catch the disease?	Disease symptoms
Strep throat 	*Streptococcus* bacteria	The pathogen enters the body through any breaks in our skin.	Very sore throat, fever and thick yellow mucus in throat.
Influenza 	*Influenza* virus	Any contact with a person with the pathogen in their body.	Coughing, sneezing, severe body aches, high fever and nausea.
Ringworm 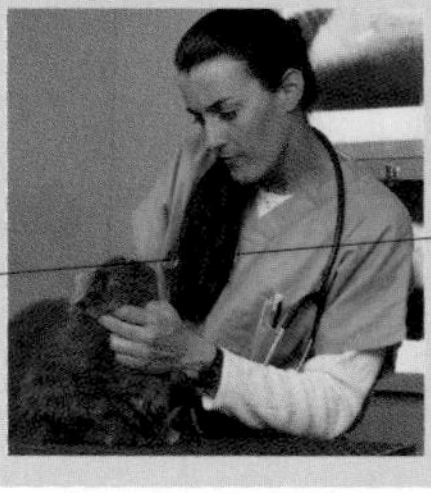	*Trichophyton* fungus	Skin-to-skin contact with an infected person or pet, or contact with something that an infected person, or pet, has touched.	Scaly, itchy, sometimes painful patches on the skin that look like red rings.

FIGURE 7.9 Many disease symptoms can be treated with over-the-counter medicines. Why is it important to see a doctor if your symptoms do not improve in a few days?

Non-communicable Diseases

A **non-communicable disease** is any disease that cannot be spread from one person to another. People with a non-communicable disease have something in their body that does not work properly. Sometimes people are born with a non-communicable disease. For example, sickle-cell anemia is a blood disease that some people have right from birth. Other non-communicable diseases develop over time. For example, people can develop heart disease as they get older.

You cannot catch a non-communicable disease. People with non-communicable diseases simply have something wrong in the way their body works.

Some Non-communicable Diseases and Their Symptoms

	Disease	Symptoms
	Multiple sclerosis	Numbness, muscle weakness and blurred vision.
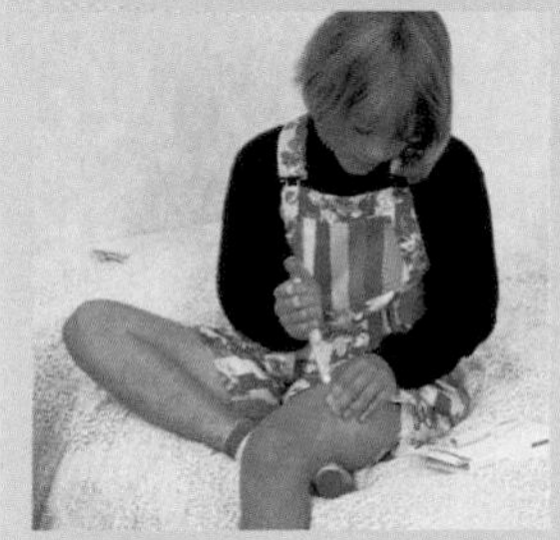	Diabetes	Symptoms of diabetes vary, and include frequent urination, excessive thirst, rapid weight loss, fatigue and high amounts of sugar in the blood or urine.
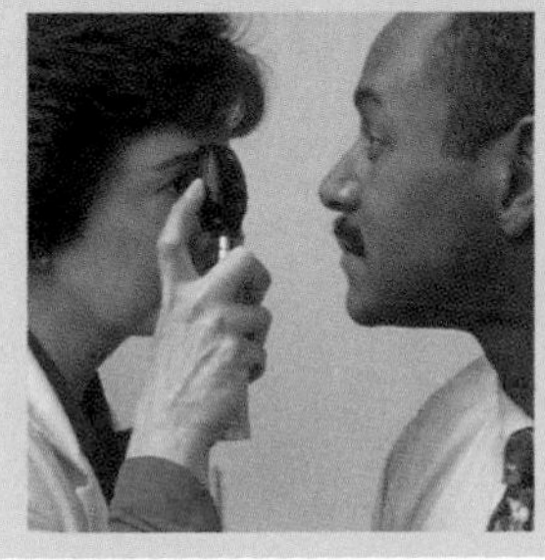	Glaucoma	Loss of vision or tunnel vision.

FIGURE 7.10 Why are you not able to catch these non-communicable diseases?

Surf the Web

Brainstorm some other non-communicable diseases and their symptoms. When you have finished, do some research and check your ideas. You can begin by using the information on the symptoms of other non-communicable diseases found at **www.science.nelson.com**. Follow the links for ScienceWise Grade 11, Chapter 7, Section 7.1.

LAB 7A

The Spread of Disease

Your teacher has filled a class set of test tubes with water, except for 1. This 1 tube contains a harmless mock, or pretend, pathogen. The mock pathogen can "infect" the other test tubes and can be identified by the indicator solution. You are going to follow the spread of the mock pathogen through your class.

Be Safe!

- Wash your hands before leaving the lab.
- Wear gloves and goggles throughout the lab. You can check the procedures for safe handling of chemicals in Section 1.2.

Purpose

In this lab, you will simulate how disease spreads in a group of people through direct contact.

Materials

- gloves and goggles
- phenolphthalein indicator solution
- a numbered test tube containing a clear liquid
- tracking sheet

Procedure

1. Obtain your materials. On your tracking sheet, record your name and the number of your test tube.
2. Circulate among your classmates, carrying your tracking sheet and test tube with you. Choose 1 person with whom to make direct contact.
3. Working with the person you have chosen, 1 of you must empty the contents of your test tube into the test tube of the other person. This will leave 1 of you with a full test tube and the other with an empty test tube, as shown in Figure 7.11.
4. Pour all the liquid in the full test tube into the empty test tube, to make sure the liquids are well mixed. You should have 1 full test tube and 1 empty test tube, as shown in Figure 7.12.
5. Pour half of the liquid in the full test tube back into the empty test tube. Both you and the other person should now have a half-filled test tube again, as shown in Figure 7.13.

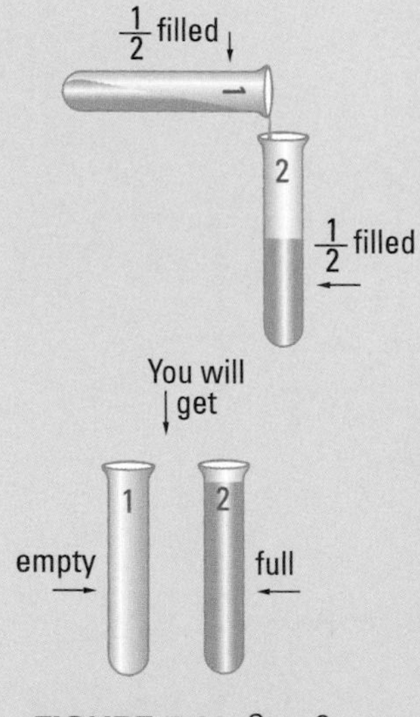

FIGURE 7.11 Step 3.

6. Record the person's name and the number of their test tube in the first row of your tracking sheet.

7. Repeat steps 2 to 6 with at least 3 other people.

8. Return to your station. Add 1 drop of phenolphthalein solution to your test tube.

9. If the liquid in your test tube turned pink when you added the phenolphthalein indicator, it means that you were "infected" by the mock pathogen (Figure 7.14). Record whether or not you were "infected."

10. When directed by your teacher, raise your hand if you were "infected." Count and record the number of people in your class who were "infected."

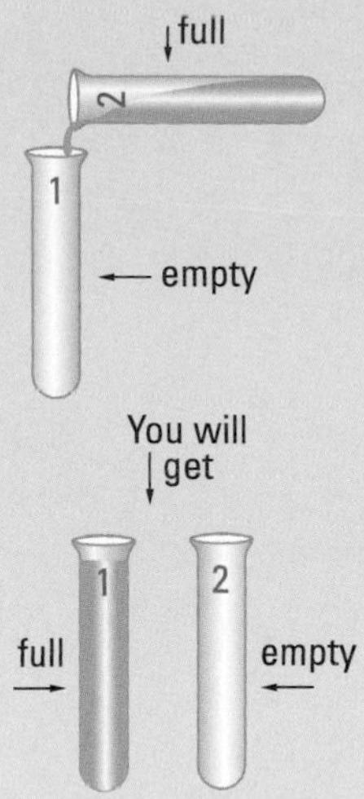

FIGURE 7.12 Step 4.

Analysis and Conclusion

1. Your teacher will tell you the number of the test tube that contained the mock pathogen. As a class, use this information and the information on your tracking sheet to trace the spread of the mock pathogen through the class.

2. Make a flow chart with arrows to illustrate your route through the class. Mark the point at which you first became "infected."

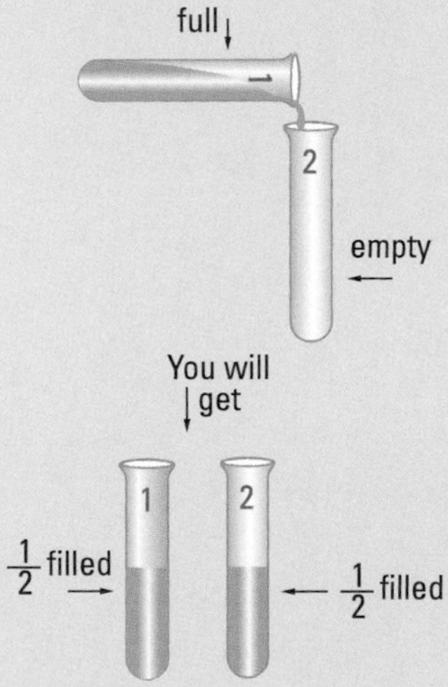

FIGURE 7.13 Step 5.

Extension and Connection

3. Imagine that you worked in an office where people usually greet one another by shaking hands. Someone in your office has a cold. As a group, discuss how the social habits of this office might cause other people to catch the cold. Can you think of a way to prevent the cold from spreading that will not offend anyone?

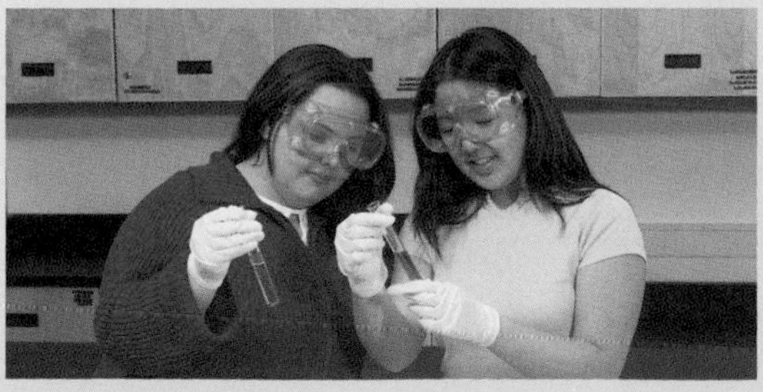

FIGURE 7.14 One of these students was "infected" with the mock pathogen.

LAB 7B

A Look at Bacterial Pathogens

An important step in determining the type of disease a person has is to identify the pathogen. One characteristic that can distinguish one type of bacteria from another is its shape. Scientists divide bacteria into 3 groups based on their shape: cocci, bacilli and spirilla (Figure 7.15).

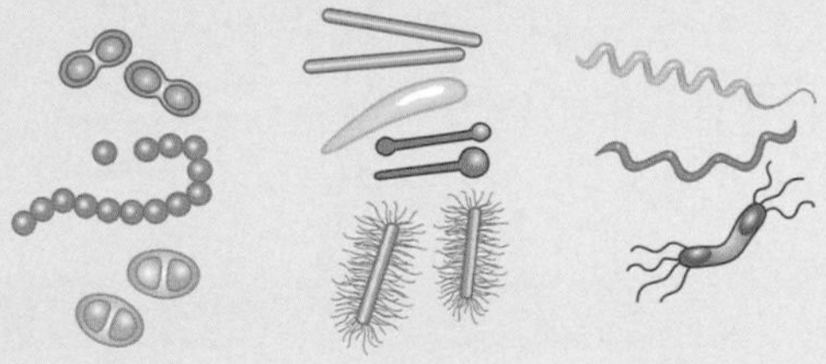

FIGURE 7.15 Some examples of cocci, bacilli and spirilla bacteria cells.

Purpose

In this lab, you will examine several species of bacteria, using prepared slides and a microscope, and make labelled scientific diagrams.

Materials

- microscope
- prepared slides of cocci, bacilli and spirilla bacteria

Procedure

1. With a partner, review the proper procedure for using the microscope.
2. Obtain 1 of the prepared slides of bacteria cells and place it on the stage of your microscope. Focus the slide under the 10× lens. When the image is in focus, turn to the 40× lens. See Figure 7.16.

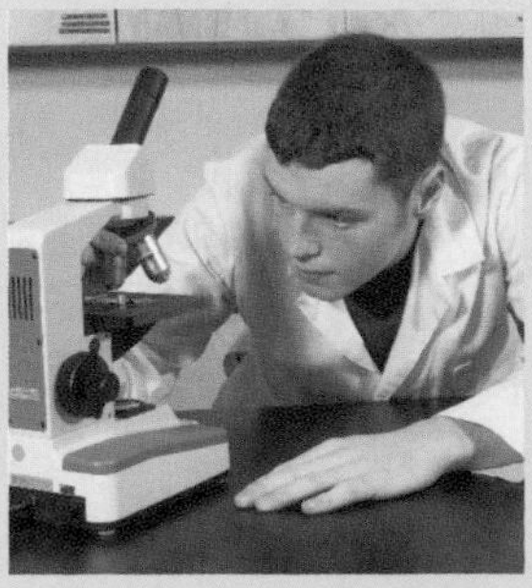

FIGURE 7.16 Watch from the side as you change lenses to be sure that the lens does not hit the slide.

3 If you need to, adjust the focus slightly. Remember, always focus by moving the lens up, away from the slide (Figure 7.17).

4 On a clean sheet of paper, draw a simple scientific diagram of what you observe through the microscope.

5 The slide is labelled with the name of the bacteria. Record this name on your diagram.

6 Repeat steps 2 to 5 for at least 2 other species of bacteria.

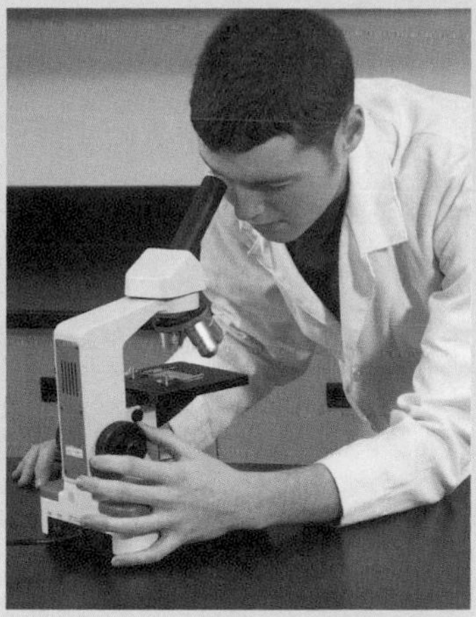

FIGURE 7.17 Always focus AWAY from the slide to avoid hitting the slide and damaging the lens.

Analysis and Conclusion

1 In your notebook, create a data table using the headings in Figure 7.18. From your drawings, fill in the table.

Specific name of bacteria	Shape

FIGURE 7.18

2 The endings on the scientific names for bacteria are Latin words for a specific shape. Look at the table you created in step 1. The name of each bacteria ends in *-cocci*, *-bacilli*, or *-spirilla*. What do these words mean in English?

Extension and Connection

3 Working with at least 1 other person, use books or the Internet to find out more about 1 of the species of bacteria you observed. Does this bacteria cause a disease? What conditions does it need to live? Present your findings as a 10-minute talk to your class, a poster, or a half-page report.

4 In a short paragraph, explain why someone working at a water treatment plant might need to determine the shape of bacteria in the water.

Review and Apply

1. Copy the following 2 columns into your notebook. Match the terms in the first column with the ideas in the second column by connecting them with lines.

1) Non-communicable disease	**a)** causes communicable disease
2) Communicable disease	**b)** body changes, such as fever
3) Symptom	**c)** contagious disease
4) Pathogen	**d)** diseases you cannot catch

2. Write a sentence that explains the meaning of the word "pathogen."

3. In 2 or 3 sentences, explain what is meant by the phrase "symptoms of a disease." Include the symptoms of a common disease such as a cold or the measles in your answer.

4. Create a table or Venn diagram that explains the similarities and differences between communicable diseases and non-communicable diseases.

5. Imagine that you work in a fast-food restaurant. A fellow employee comes to work with a cold. In point form, list at least 3 ways that this person could spread the cold pathogen to others in this workplace.

6. Organize the concepts you have learned in this section in a graphic organizer.

7. **Health and Personal Habits**

   Spitting on the ground can be dangerous to the health of others around you. Write a sentence to explain why this statement is true. With at least 1 other person, brainstorm alternatives to spitting.

   Discuss ways that you might convince another person to change this habit, in a way that would not hurt that person's feelings. Present your work to your classmates as a 10-minute skit, or some other creative way of your own choosing.

Try This at Home

Reducing the Spread of Disease at Home

Communicable diseases can be spread from person to person by direct contact with someone who is ill, by touching something that a person with a disease has been handling, or from a disease carrier. When someone where you live first brings a disease home, it makes sense to conclude that they were exposed to a pathogen somewhere other than at home. However, you have probably found that once 1 person gets sick, at least 1 other person in your home will get sick as well.

Think about the last time that someone at your house brought home a cold or the flu and passed it on to others. Answer the following questions.

1. Who else became ill? Make a list of everyone else who became ill. Arrange their names in order of first to last to fall ill.

2. From your list, suggest ways that this disease might have been passed from person to person. The order in which each person became ill might help you come up with some ideas. For example, if a small child was the first to become ill, the person who is most involved in changing and feeding the child would be likely to encounter the pathogen most often.

3. Think about ways that the spread of this disease might have been prevented. Consider all the ways that disease is transmitted. Prepare a list of suggestions as to how people in your home might behave differently and have a better chance of avoiding disease the next time someone becomes ill.

4. Make a small poster that you could put up somewhere to remind people in your home of your suggestions.

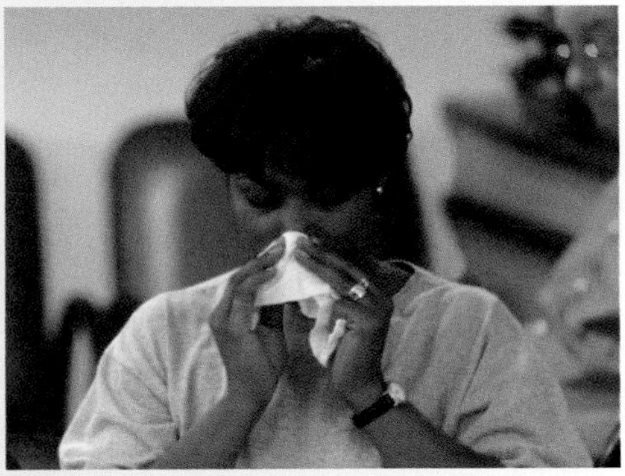

FIGURE 7.19 What can you do to prevent the spread of disease in your home?

7.2 Defending Against Pathogens

Pathogens are all around us. In any single day, you are exposed to many different pathogens. Of course, you do not get ill every day. Why not? The reason is that your body has built-in defences against the invasion of the pathogens.

The First Line of Defence

In order to make you ill, a pathogen must first get inside your body. Your first line of defence is to stop pathogens from ever doing this. Figure 7.20 shows the main barriers against pathogens of the human body.

Your skin is actually a very good barrier against many pathogens. Your whole body is covered by skin, even in places that you usually think of as being inside your body. For example, you have skin inside your mouth, ears and nose. Your skin seals you up, something like the plastic wrapping on a sandwich.

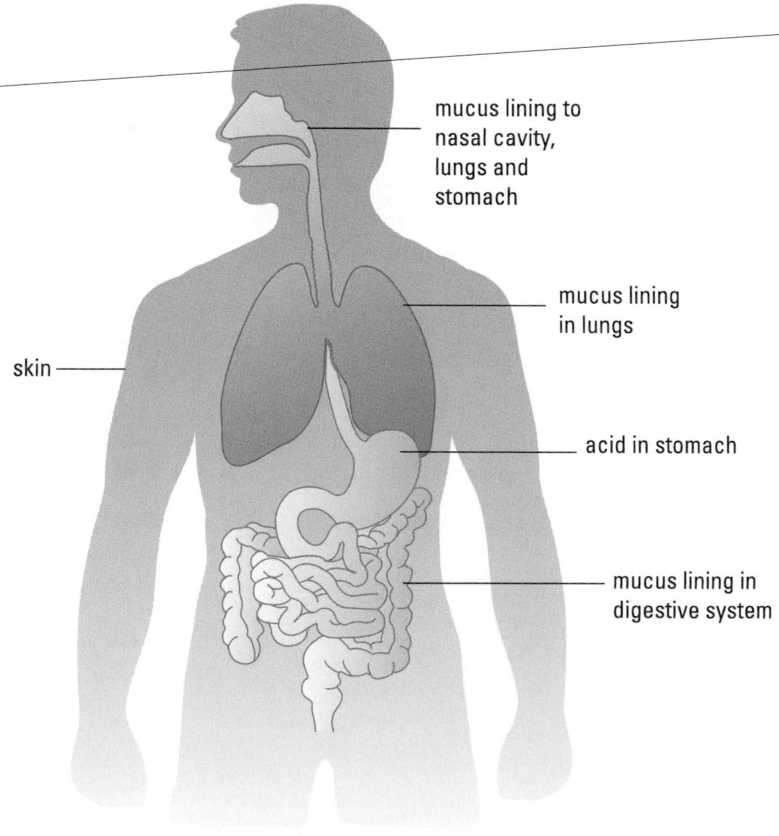

FIGURE 7.20 The first line of defence is to prevent pathogens from entering the body.

Some areas of your body, such as your nose, lungs and the inside of your intestines, are lined with a mucus membrane. **Mucus** is a thick, sticky fluid; you expel mucus when you sneeze. This mucus helps to keep pathogens out by trapping them and preventing them from moving inside. In fact, one of the reasons you sneeze is to expel pathogens that have become trapped in the mucus layer inside your nose and throat. If a pathogen should reach your stomach, it will likely be destroyed by your stomach acid.

When the First Line Fails

Your skin can only defend you if it is unbroken. If you have an uncovered cut or a scrape, pathogens have a direct route to the inside of your body. You may not even know that you have a break in your skin. For example, the skin inside your nose is quite thin and easily broken, especially when the air is dry. Whenever someone with a cold sneezes next to you and does not cover his or her mouth and nose, you are likely to breathe in the cold pathogen that they sneeze out. If you have a break in the skin inside your nose, the cold pathogen has a way to get inside your body, and you end up becoming ill as well.

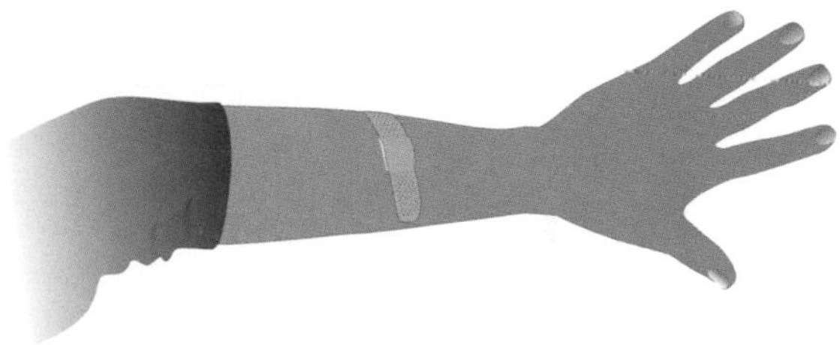

FIGURE 7.21 Why is it important to cover a cut in your skin?

The Second Line of Defence

When a pathogen gets past the first line of defence and enters your body, it is faced with your second line of defence. You have seen this second line of defence in action if you have ever had an infected cut, such as the one shown in Figure 7.22.

When a pathogen first enters your body, it encounters a cell called a macrophage. **Macrophages** are cells in your blood that fight infection.

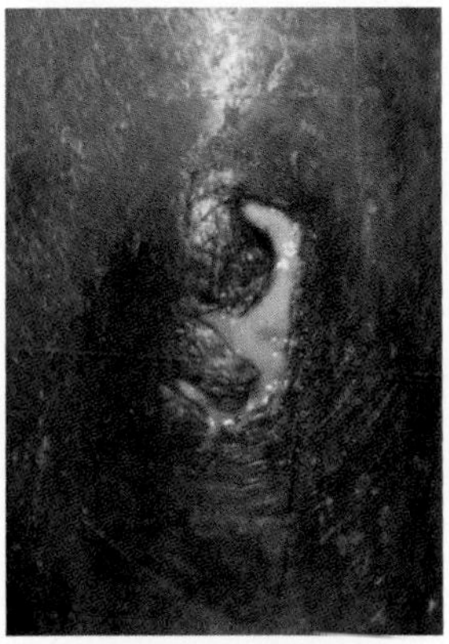

FIGURE 7.22 What is the yellowish fluid that we see in infected cuts? What does it do?

Macrophages to the Rescue!

Macrophages are white blood cells that have only 1 job: they destroy pathogens. Like most cells, macrophages are surrounded by a cellular membrane. The **cellular membrane** is the thin layer that surrounds a cell; it acts something like a plastic bag holding the jelly-like cell contents together. Figure 7.23 shows the main cell structures of a macrophage.

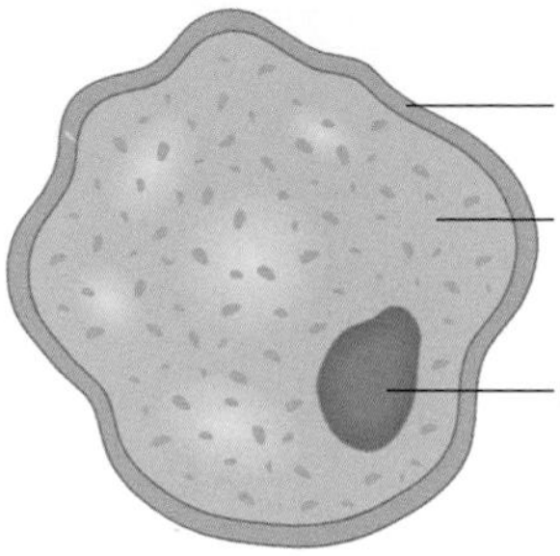

FIGURE 7.23 The cellular membrane of the macrophage has an important role in defending against pathogens.

A macrophage will attack any type of pathogen that enters your body and try to destroy it. If they kill the pathogens quickly enough, macrophages can prevent you from getting sick. Macrophages also help you to recover from a disease, because they keep working until all the invading pathogens are destroyed.

When a macrophage encounters a pathogen, the cellular membrane of the macrophage starts to move around the entire pathogen. This process is shown in Figure 7.24. When the pathogen is completely encircled by the cellular membrane, that part of the cellular membrane containing the pathogen breaks off. This forms a structure similar to a little bag inside the macrophage, which now contains the pathogen. The macrophage then releases chemicals to digest the pathogen. These chemicals kill off the pathogen and the macrophage that attacked it. Therefore, your body can use each macrophage only once. The pus around an infected cut is made up of macrophages that died after killing a pathogen.

ScienceWise Fact

Fever? A fever is your body's way of fighting an infection. A low fever makes your body a less welcoming home for bacteria and can even kill them. However, a very high fever is dangerous, because as well as killing bacteria, it kills your body's cells too, especially those in your brain.

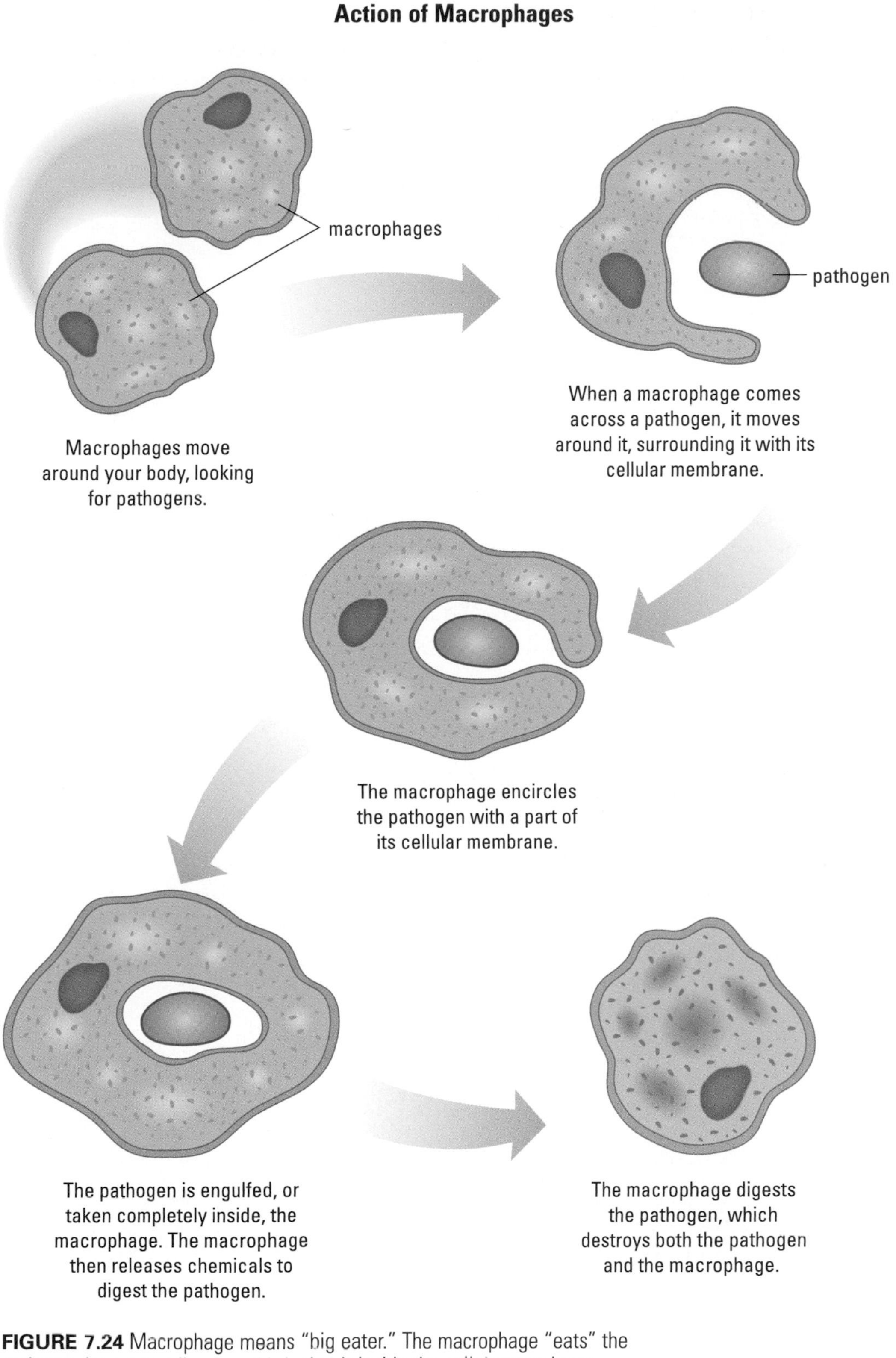

Action of Macrophages
macrophages
pathogen
Macrophages move around your body, looking for pathogens.
When a macrophage comes across a pathogen, it moves around it, surrounding it with its cellular membrane.
The macrophage encircles the pathogen with a part of its cellular membrane.
The pathogen is engulfed, or taken completely inside, the macrophage. The macrophage then releases chemicals to digest the pathogen.
The macrophage digests the pathogen, which destroys both the pathogen and the macrophage.

FIGURE 7.24 Macrophage means "big eater." The macrophage "eats" the pathogen by surrounding it and bringing it inside the cellular membrane.

When the Second Line Fails

Remember that when a pathogen gets inside your body, the first thing it does is begin to reproduce. Some pathogens can produce thousands of copies of themselves very quickly. Sometimes, your body cannot produce enough new macrophages to keep up with the increasing number of invading pathogens. When this happens, your body depends on the third line of defence.

The Third Line of Defence

The third line of defence is made up of special chemicals in your blood called antibodies. **Antibodies** are chemicals that can determine if there is anything in your body that is foreign, or not really a part of you. Scientists call this distinguishing between self and non-self. Pathogens are non-self.

An **antigen** is anything in your body that an antibody has determined to be non-self. Each different antibody in your body has only 1 antigen, so each antibody will "recognize" only 1 antigen (see Figure 7.25). This is very different from the case of macrophages, which will attack any invader they find. An antigen can be a whole pathogen or just a part of it (Figure 7.26).

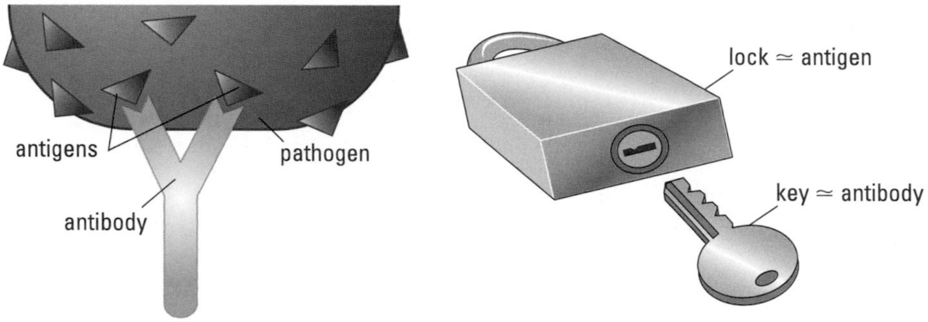

FIGURE 7.25 Each antibody is "tailor-made" for a specific antigen. It will work with no other antigen, just as a key will only work with 1 lock. In this example, the antigen is only a part of the pathogen.

When an antibody encounters its antigen, it attaches to it tightly. The antibody then sends out a signal telling your body to start making millions of more copies of that particular antibody. Your body can make antibodies much more quickly than it can make macrophages, so the number of antibodies keeps up with the numbers of pathogens much more easily. These new antibodies then bind to any other copies of the antigen that are in your body.

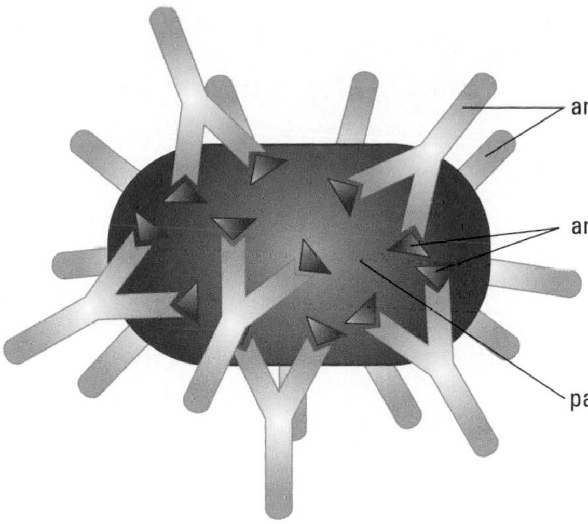

FIGURE 7.26 When an antigen is a part of a whole pathogen, then many antibodies can bind to a single pathogen.

When antibodies bind to a pathogen, as shown in Figure 7.26, that pathogen is no longer able to do many of the things that make you ill. It cannot move, so it is much easier for it to be "caught" by white blood cells and destroyed. It cannot reproduce, so it cannot replace the destroyed pathogens.

All of the 3 lines of defence are important to your health. In fact, your first, second and third lines of defence act together so well that you usually do not even know when a pathogen has invaded.

General and Specific Defences

In the fight against disease, your body has to face hundreds of different pathogens every day. Your skin provides a barrier against pathogens that try to enter your body. Your macrophages attack and try to destroy any pathogens that they find in your body. **General defences** are defences that act against any pathogen. The first and second lines of defence (your skin and your macrophages) are general defences.

An antibody will only attack those pathogens that contain (or are) its antigen. If an antibody encounters something that is not its antigen, it does not attack it. Instead, it carries on looking for pathogens that contain or are its antigen. **Specific defences** are defences that act against only 1 type of pathogen. Antibodies are a specific defence.

Review and Apply

1. In 1 or 2 sentences, explain how your skin helps you to avoid disease.
2. Imagine you are the supervisor of a landscaping company. Write a notice to post in the workplace that explains why it is important to cover any cuts or scrapes with a bandage.
3. Draw a diagram of a macrophage. Label the part, or parts, of the cell that are important in defending against disease.
4. Create a flip book or cartoon strip that shows the action of a macrophage in 7 or more steps.
5. Explain the relationship between an antibody and an antigen.
6. Imagine that a meteor is a pathogen and your body is a planet. The meteor is about to hit the planet! Using the information in this chapter, draw a newspaper-style cartoon of 3 or more panels that tells the story of how the planet protects itself against the meteor. Your story must end with the destruction of the meteor.
7. Add the new concepts from this section to the graphic organizer you started in Section 7.1.

8. **Presenting Disease Defences**

In a small group, brainstorm how you might explain to Grade 9 students how the 3 lines of defence protect us from disease. Your explanation should include answers to the following questions:

a) How does your body keep pathogens out?
b) What is a macrophage and what does it do?
c) What is an antibody? What is an antigen? How do antibodies help to keep us healthy?

Choose a creative way to present your answer. For example, you could write a song or a skit, or make a video presentation. Ensure that your choice allows you to present all the information clearly.

7.3 The Immune Response

Did you have chicken pox when you were a child? If you did, you are unlikely ever to get chicken pox again, even if you are in direct contact with someone else suffering with the itchy red spots of that disease. Once you have had certain diseases, you are immune to that disease. When you are **immune** to a particular disease, your body can resist infection by the pathogen that causes that disease. Another way of saying this is that you have an immunity against the disease. How does getting a disease make you immune?

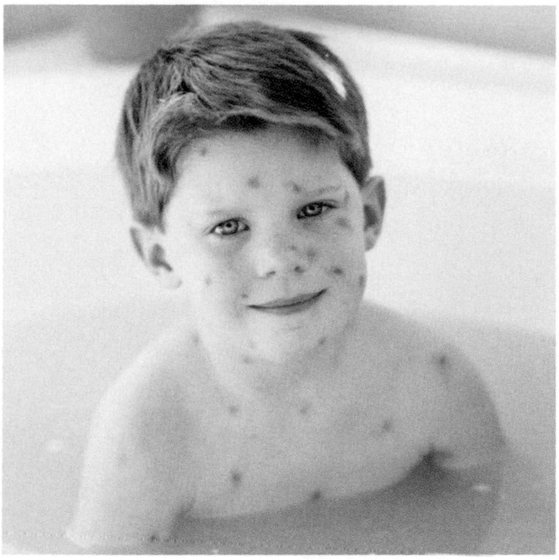

FIGURE 7.27 You will be immune to the chicken pox pathogen if you had this disease as a child.

Immunity and Antibodies

We become immune to a disease when our body makes antibodies against the pathogen that causes the disease. Recall from Section 7.2 that antibodies form the third line of defence against disease. Each antibody will attack only those pathogens that are (or contain) its antigen.

Recall that an antigen can be a whole pathogen or just a part of it. When a pathogen enters your body for the first time, it will not be an antigen for most of the antibodies it encounters. Your body produces millions of different kinds of antibodies. Eventually, an antibody that recognizes the antigen will encounter and bind to it. Every time an antibody binds to an antigen, your body begins a process called the immune response. The **immune response** is the human body's response to an antigen that it recognizes.

You will need to know how we become immune to disease for your project, Creating a Public Health Awareness Campaign.

ScienceWise Fact

Chicken pox is usually a relatively mild disease in healthy children under the age of 13. Compare this to adults, who are 25 times more likely to die as a result of this disease.

The Immune Response

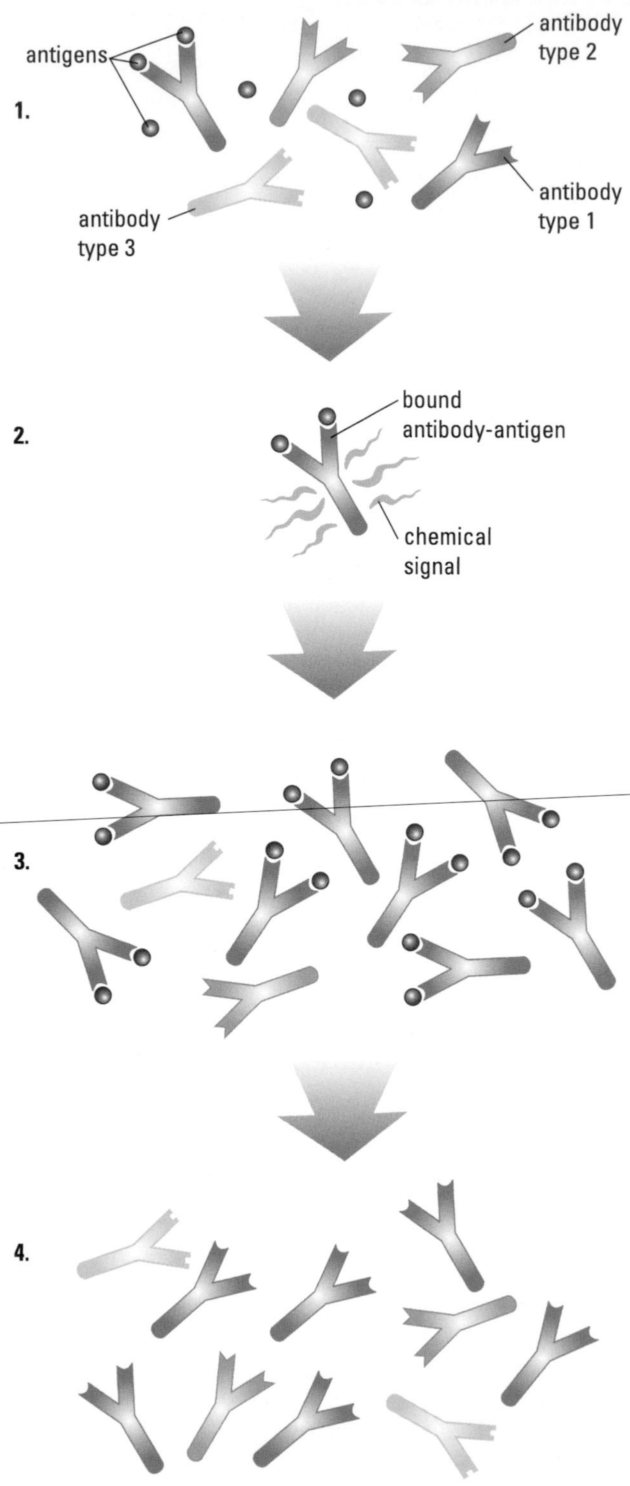

1. The body has thousands of types of antibodies. One specific type of antibody recognizes the new antigen that has invaded the body. Recall that the antigen may be a whole pathogen or just part of the pathogen. In this example, the antigen is the whole pathogen.

2. When an antibody binds to its antigen (in this case antibody type 1), the antibody sends out a chemical signal that tells the body to make more copies of that antibody. The chemical signal is represented by wavy lines in this diagram.

3. In response to the chemical signal, the body begins to make thousands of copies of the antibody that recognized the antigen. In this example, the body has made more copies of antibody type 1. The new copies of the antibody bind to all the remaining antigens in the body, which can then be destroyed by macrophages.

4. Even when all the antigens have been destroyed and it is no longer infected, the body continues to make a higher number of the antibody that encountered its antigen. In this example, the body continues to make a higher number of antibody type 1. Therefore, the body is "stocked up" with antibodies against that antigen, so it can fight it more quickly should it invade the body again. For example, if the antigen were the measles pathogen, your body would be able to fight off invasion more easily, protecting you from getting this disease.

FIGURE 7.28 The immune response produces many copies of antibodies against 1 particular antigen.

Figure 7.28 shows you the steps in the immune response. The first 3 steps should be familiar to you, because they are also stages in the third line of defence against a pathogen that has entered your body. Look again at the fourth step. After your body has encountered a pathogen once, *it always has a high number of antibodies against that pathogen.* What do you think the advantage of this might be?

The advantage is that your body is now prepared to fight the pathogen should it ever invade your body again. This is like having antiseptic ointment and bandages in a first-aid kit, so that you, are prepared should you get injured. This would ensure that you were prepared and could cover up a cut when it first happened.

If you do not clean and cover a cut right away, pathogens have an easy way into your body, so waiting to apply first aid can make any cut more serious and even make you ill. In the same way, if your body cannot start fighting pathogens that have invaded your body right away, the number of those pathogens continues to grow, which could make it more difficult for you to recover. The immune response is your body's way of "stocking up" on just the right kind of antibodies. These antibodies are ready to begin fighting immediately the next time the pathogen enters your body.

Surf the Web

To protect workers, the *Occupational Health and Safety Act* requires all employers to have a first-aid kit on their premises. You can find more information about this act in Section 1.1. First-aid kits help to make sure that all workers can receive first-aid treatment right away. Different workplaces must have different items in their first-aid kits, depending on the hazards present in the workplace. Go to **www.science.nelson.com** and follow the links for ScienceWise Grade 11, Chapter 7, Section 7.3, to find the first-aid kit requirements for some examples of workplaces. How is preparing specific first-aid kits similar to the specific defences of the body's immune system?

Becoming Immune by Disease

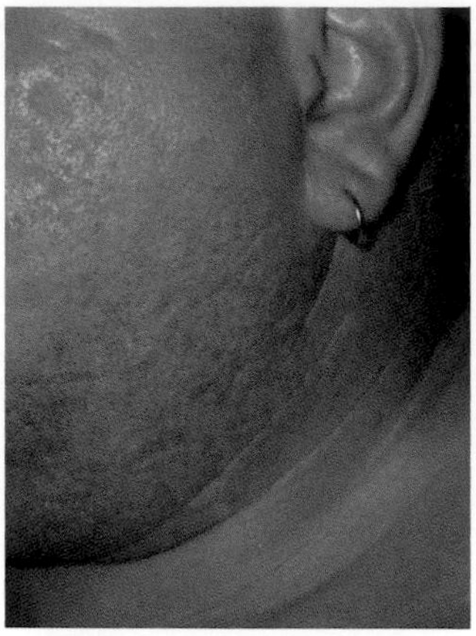

FIGURE 7.29 This person will be immune to another infection by the pathogen that causes the mumps because of the immune response.

There are 2 ways that you can become immune to a disease. You read about the first way in the preceding paragraphs; you become infected with a pathogen and your body then produces antibodies against that pathogen. This method is quite effective the second time you become infected with the pathogen; but what about that first time? The first time you will probably become quite ill.

The person in Figure 7.29 has a disease called the mumps. The mumps pathogen causes the glands in the neck to become extremely swollen, which is very painful. Once someone has had the mumps, they will be immune and be protected from another infection by the mumps pathogen. Unfortunately, many diseases cause such serious symptoms that people can become disabled or even die from their effects. For example, polio is a disease that was once common in Canada. Polio can cause severe paralysis, leaving people unable to walk and, in severe cases, unable to breathe without assistance from a machine.

Becoming Immune by Vaccination

Although the body has to be exposed to a pathogen for it to become immune to that pathogen, scientists have found ways to make this happen without causing disease. When a person receives a **vaccination**, or an injection against a disease, the doctor is injecting a dead, or a very weak, form of a particular pathogen into the body. For example, many people are vaccinated against common childhood illnesses like the measles. The body will mount the immune response to a pathogen whether that pathogen is alive or dead. An antibody will recognize and bind to the pathogen, and then send out a signal for the body to make many more antibody copies. Therefore, a person can be stocked up on antibodies against a pathogen even though he or she has never had the actual disease.

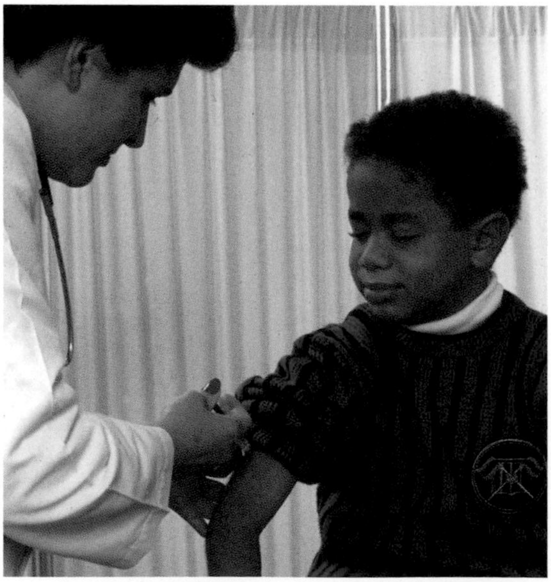

FIGURE 7.30 Vaccination causes a child's body to produce antibodies against specific diseases. Once a child has produced antibodies against a disease, the child will either never get that disease, or will get only a mild case.

Knowledge to the Rescue

Throughout history, as scientists and doctors learned more about pathogens and the way our bodies fight disease, they have used this knowledge to find ways to help us avoid becoming sick. For example, at one time people did not know that pathogens existed, because they are so small. Doctors would operate on people without washing their hands, because they did not know better! By learning about the immune response, we are now able to protect ourselves from getting many diseases. Figure 7.31 shows you some of the most important advances in understanding the role of the immune system in fighting diseases.

Timeline of Scientific Knowledge

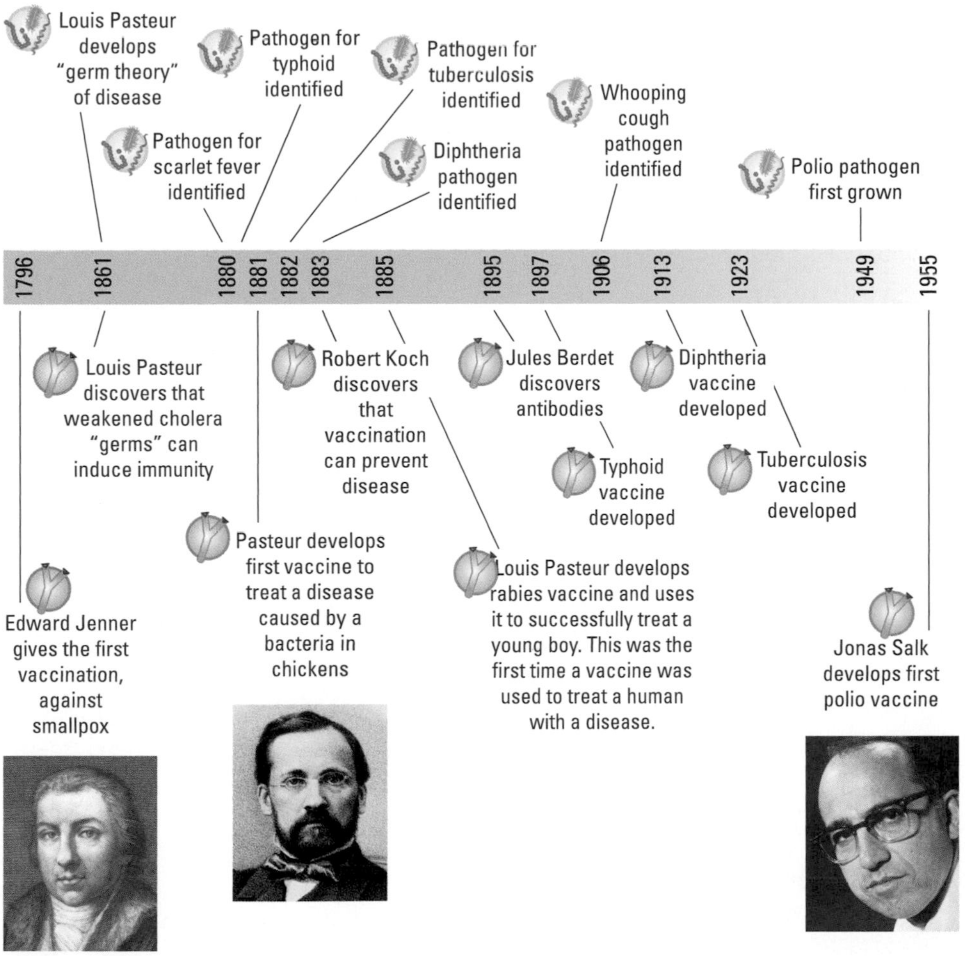

FIGURE 7.31 Learning about the causes of disease and about the immune response has changed life for the better for everyone.

Review and Apply

1. What is the immune response?

2. Make a chart of the differences and similarities between the 2 ways that a person can become immune to a disease. Your answer must describe the details of how the body becomes immune for both of the 2 ways.

3. Many medical workers, such as nurses and paramedics, are required by their employers to receive vaccinations against influenza. Explain why an employer might make this requirement.

4. Every year, doctors recommend that everyone get a flu shot, but many people do not. Create a plus/minus chart outlining the positive and negative factors involved in getting the flu shot. Based on your chart, do you think a flu shot is necessary? Defend your answer using an example.

5. Agree or disagree with the following statement: Knowledge is the most important part of preventing disease. In groups, or as a class, debate your opinion. You must be prepared to defend your opinion with facts.

---

6. Add the new concepts in this section to the graphic organizer you started in Section 7.1.

7. **Science and Human Health**
   Working with at least 1 other person, choose 1 of the milestones on the timeline in Figure 7.31. Use the library and the Internet to find out more information about the scientist. Use the following questions to guide your research.

   a) Where did the scientist work?
   b) What kind of educational background did the scientist have?
   c) Did the scientist make any other discoveries?
   d) How did the work of the scientist help to improve the health of other people?

   When you have found enough information to answer all these questions, prepare a poster or use presentation software to create a visually pleasing summary of what you found. Your presentation should make it easy for someone looking at your work to understand the importance of the work of the scientist.

7.4 Chapter Summary

Now You Can…

- Explain the terms communicable and non-communicable disease (7.1)
- Identify and describe some causes of disease (7.1, Lab 7B)
- Identify and describe activities that spread disease at home, at school and in the workplace (7.1, Lab 7A)
- Apply your knowledge of disease to reducing your risk of becoming ill (7.1, 7.2, 7.3)
- Describe the 3 ways that your body fights infection by a pathogen (7.2)
- Describe the chemicals in your body that help to protect you from disease (7.3)
- Understand and communicate the importance of the immune response to human health (7.3)

Concept Connections

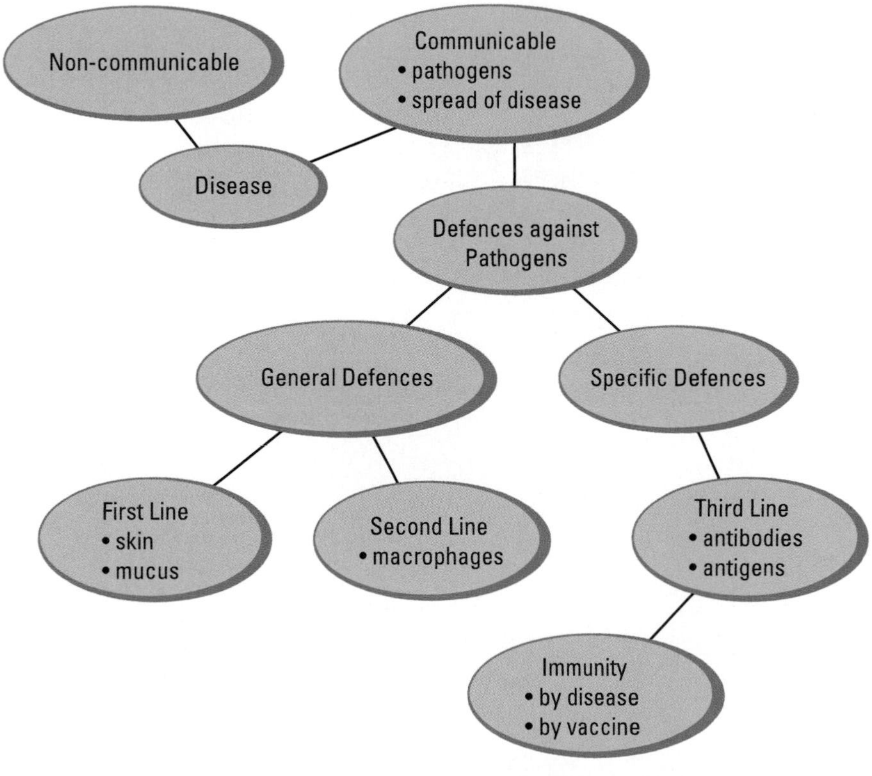

FIGURE 7.32 Compare your completed graphic organizer to the one on this page. How did you do? Can you add any new links to your organizer?

CHAPTER 7 *review*

Knowledge and Understanding

1. Identify whether each of the following diseases is communicable or non-communicable:
   - **a)** measles
   - **b)** arthritis
   - **c)** ringworm
   - **d)** flu (influenza)
   - **e)** multiple sclerosis
   - **f)** diabetes

2. For each of the situations below, describe how the actions described can cause disease to spread:
   - **a)** A mother brings her little girl to daycare when she has the measles.
   - **b)** A waiter does not wash his hands after using the toilet.
   - **c)** A hospital orderly leaves sheets from a sick person's bed sitting in a hall where visitors pass.

3. Create a flow chart that shows the action of macrophages fighting a pathogen that has entered a wound in your skin. You can use words, drawings, or a combination of both.

4. Describe the first, second and third lines of defence against pathogens of the human body.

5. Working in a group of 3 or 4 classmates, create a script for a skit that explains what happens when a person is vaccinated against a disease. Make your skit entertaining, but be sure it contains all the information about this process. If there is time, present your skit to the rest of your class.

6. Explain how the immune response helps the human body to prepare against infection by a pathogen.

Inquiry

7. Draw a macrophage and label the part or parts that are important in fighting pathogens.

8. Explain why it is important always to focus the microscope lens up, away from the slide.

9. You have a job as a veterinarian's assistant. You have been asked to clean up the lab bench where the veterinarian was viewing a slide with some living bacteria on it. These bacteria could cause a mild, but unpleasant, illness in humans. You use gloves and are careful not to touch the slide as you work. Is there anything else you should do to make sure you do not become infected? If your answer is "yes," describe what additional action you should take.

Making Connections

10. You and a friend are going camping for a weekend. Since you will only be gone for 2 days, your friend does not think you need to bring bandages along. Do you agree with your friend? Explain your answer.

11. Some daycare providers will only look after children who have had all the recommended vaccinations. Explain why a daycare might have such a policy.

12. Your friend tells you that he will not get the measles because his little sister had them. What would you tell your friend to explain the error in his understanding of immunity?

13. Hospitals always wash sheets in very hot water with detergent and bleach. This can make the sheets quite rough and uncomfortable. Explain why hospitals always wash sheets in this way.

Communication

14. With a partner, write a script for a school announcement that explains the importance of washing your hands before you eat. Your announcement can only be 1 minute long.

15. With a partner, or in a small group, create a game or a song that a preschool teacher could use to inform the students why it is important to use a tissue to cover a sneeze.

CHAPTER 8

Reducing the Incidence of Disease

As scientists and medical professionals have learned more about pathogens and disease, they have been able to use this information to help keep us healthy. They have found ways to control pathogens both before and after they infect us. They have discovered how our actions can increase, or decrease, our chances of encountering pathogens. They have also found that the parts of the human body that usually protect us from disease can become diseased themselves. Look at the pictures in Figure 8.1. How do vaccines prevent disease? Why should you wear something on your feet in public change rooms? How do the laws and inspectors we have—especially for restaurants and for people who work with food—help to prevent disease?

FIGURE 8.1

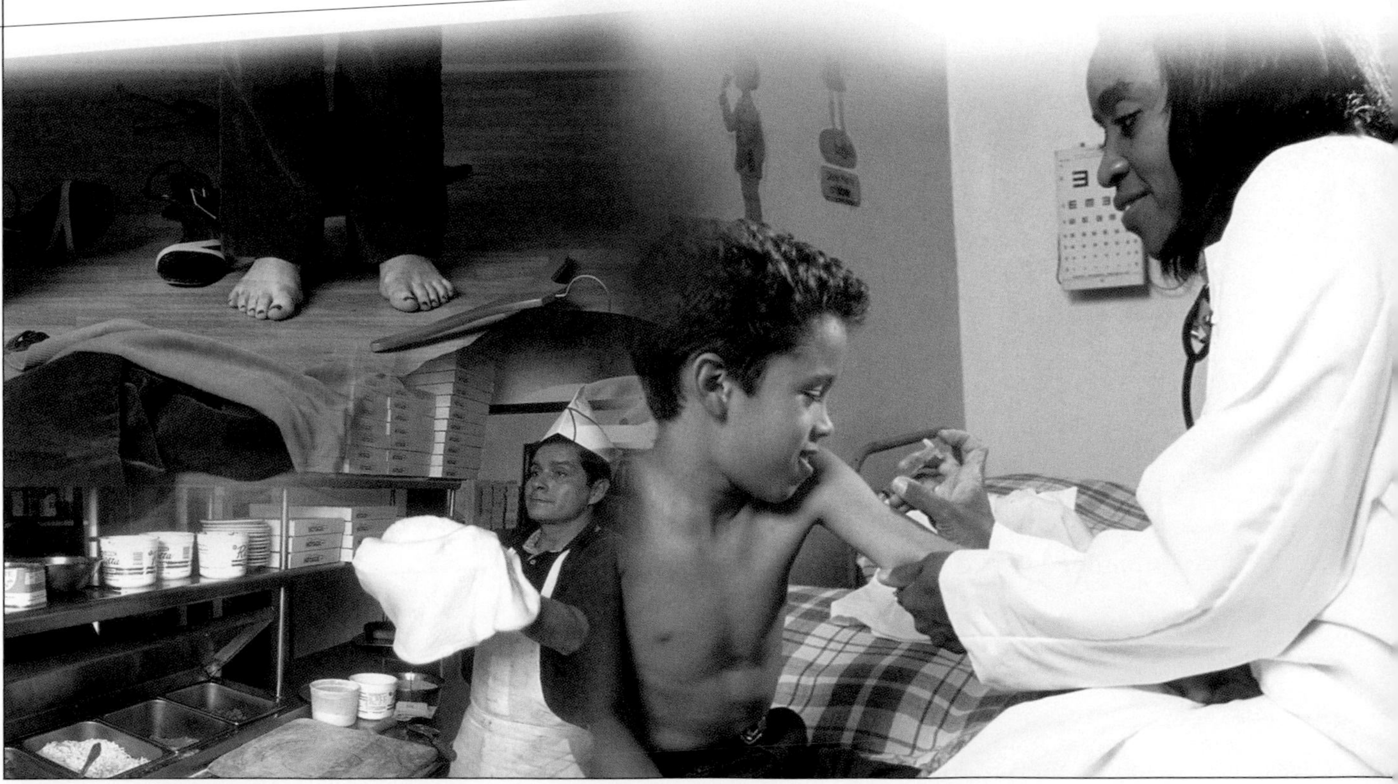

What You Will Learn

After completing this chapter, you will be able to:

- Describe the components of the human immune system (8.1)
- Describe how the components of blood are related to the human immune system (8.1)
- Describe common diseases of the human immune system and how they can be treated and prevented (8.2)
- Describe how antibiotics are used to treat disease and how their misuse can make antibiotics less useful (8.3)
- Analyze how our knowledge of the causes of disease has enabled us to develop new ways of treating and preventing disease (8.3)
- Identify careers related to the treatment and prevention of disease (8.1, 8.3)

What You Will Do

- Use a microscope and prepared slides to observe, identify and draw the components of blood (Lab 8A)
- Carry out a lab to determine the effectiveness of household cleaners on the growth of bacteria (Lab 8B)
- Use appropriate safety procedures when working with micro-organisms (Lab 8B)
- Collect and analyse data, using tables and diagrams (Labs 8A, 8B)
- Communicate the results of lab investigations (Labs 8A, 8B)

Words to Know

allergen
allergy
antibiotic
antibiotic resistant
antibiotic susceptible
auto-immune disease
immune system
lymph
lymph node
mutation
plasma
platelets
public health standards
red blood cells
spleen
tonsils
white blood cells

A puzzle piece indicates knowledge or a skill that you will need for your project, Creating a Public Health Awareness Campaign, at the end of Unit 4.

8.1 Fighting Pathogens: The Battlefield

In Chapter 7, you discovered how your body fights against disease. Your skin keeps pathogens from entering your body. Macrophages and antibodies work to destroy any pathogens that do make it inside the body. But where does this action take place? What parts of your body are involved? There is not just one answer to these questions. Some of the action takes place in your blood and some of it takes place in the parts of your body that make up the human immune system.

The Parts of the Blood

You probably already know that your blood carries oxygen to your cells as it travels through the blood vessels of the circulatory system. Your blood also has many other jobs, one of which is to work with the immune system. Blood is like a soup of different cells and chemicals that your body needs. Blood carries out many functions. Your blood:

- carries the oxygen you breathe in from your lungs to all the cells in your body;
- carries carbon dioxide from the cells of your body to your lungs, where it is breathed out;
- keeps your body temperature around 37°C;
- delivers necessary food and other chemicals to your cells;
- takes waste products away from all your cells, so they can be broken down and removed from your body;
- seals any cuts you get, to prevent your blood from flowing out;
- makes your antibodies;
- brings antibodies and macrophages to where they are needed.

These different roles are carried out by 4 different parts, or components, in the blood. (Figure 8.2).

Components of the Blood

Component	Description
Plasma	**Plasma** is a yellowish liquid composed of water and dissolved chemicals, such as food. Waste products are also carried away from cells by plasma. All the cells of the blood float in the plasma.
Red blood cells	**Red blood cells** carry oxygen to and take carbon dioxide away from all the cells of the body.
White blood cells	**White blood cells** are a group of cells that perform different functions in the body. Macrophages are a type of white blood cell. Another type of white blood cell makes antibodies.
Platelets	**Platelets** are cells that form blood clots, which seal wounds and stop your blood from leaving your body.

FIGURE 8.2 The 3 cell types (red blood cells, white blood cells, and platelets) float in the liquid plasma.

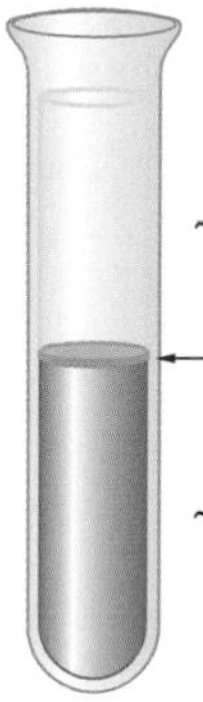

FIGURE 8.3 Plasma can be separated from blood cells by spinning it very fast in an instrument called a centrifuge.

The Immune System

Figure 8.4, on the next page, shows you the tissues and organs that are part of the **immune system.** The immune system is made up of lymph fluid, lymph vessels and nodes, the thymus, the spleen, and the tonsils. The macrophages and antibodies that protect against pathogens are produced by these tissues and organs. The immune system uses **lymph,** a watery fluid similar to blood plasma, to carry white blood cells and antibodies to where they are needed. In this way, the immune system is similar to the circulatory system, which uses the blood to carry oxygen and nutrients to where they are needed. The **spleen** is a large organ that produces white blood cells and destroys foreign particles, such as pathogens. The **tonsils** and **lymph nodes** are smaller structures in the immune system that also produce white blood cells and destroy foreign particles.

You will need to know how the immune system fights pathogens for your project, Creating a Public Health Awareness Campaign.

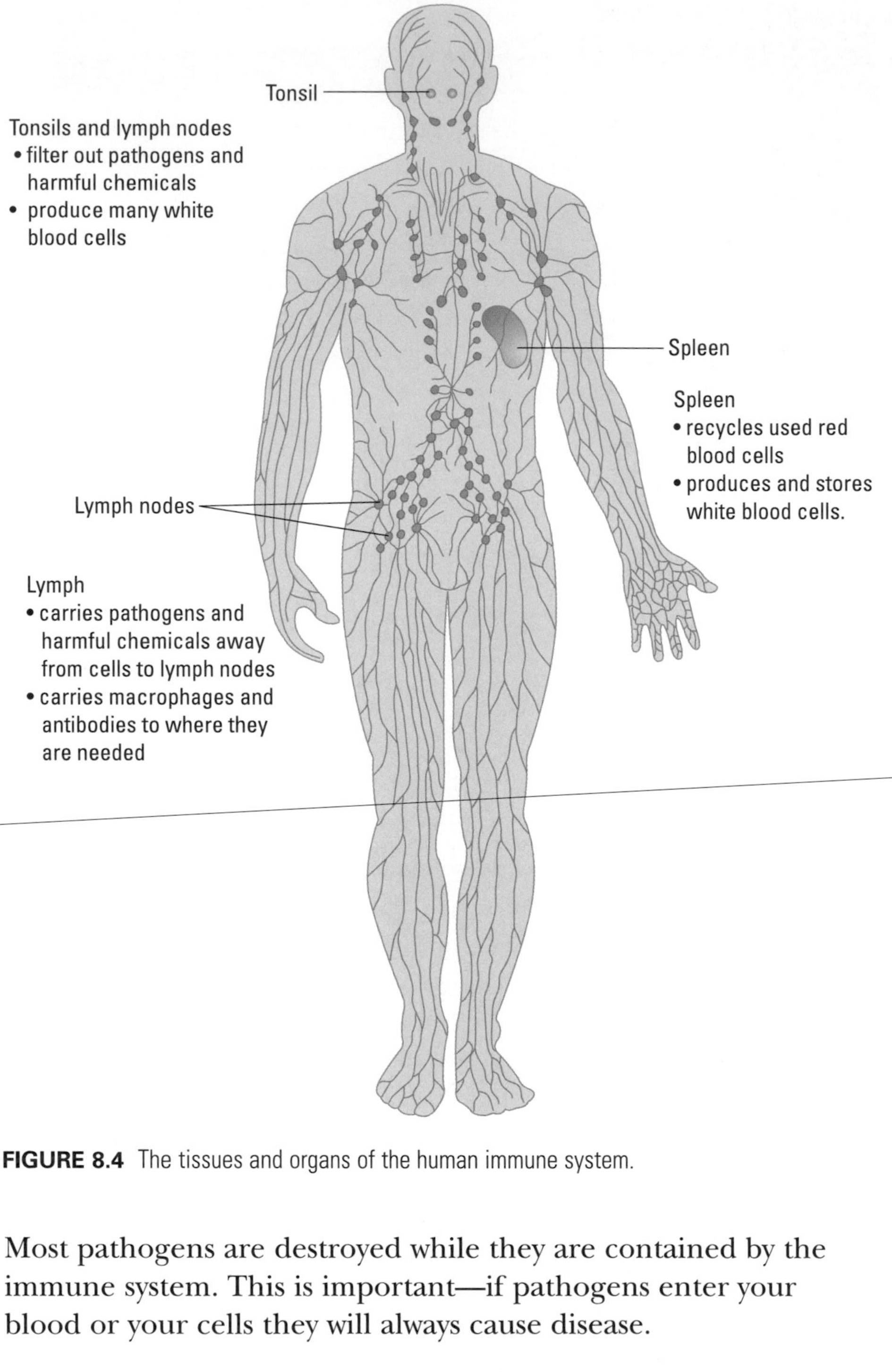
Tonsil
Tonsils and lymph nodes
• filter out pathogens and harmful chemicals
• produce many white blood cells
Spleen
Spleen
• recycles used red blood cells
• produces and stores white blood cells.
Lymph nodes
Lymph
• carries pathogens and harmful chemicals away from cells to lymph nodes
• carries macrophages and antibodies to where they are needed

FIGURE 8.4 The tissues and organs of the human immune system.

Most pathogens are destroyed while they are contained by the immune system. This is important—if pathogens enter your blood or your cells they will always cause disease.

Review and Apply

1. In your notebook, identify whether the following statements are true or false. Correct any false statements to make them true.
   a) Red blood cells are part of the human immune system.
   b) Antibodies are made in your blood.
   c) Plasma is a yellowish liquid that carries macrophages and antibodies to where they are needed.
   d) Platelets form blood clots and seal wounds, which prevents your blood from leaving your body.

2. Your blood can be thought of as a highway that transports materials to and from your cells. Create a comic-book-style story, a skit, or a poster that shows all the items that are carried by your blood "highway."

3. List the components of blood that are also part of the human immune system.

4. In 1 or 2 sentences, explain what lymph fluid is and what it does.

5. Are white blood cells a part of the immune system or a part of the blood? Explain your answer.

6. In a graphic organizer, organize the concepts you have learned about in this section.

Surf the Web

Medical clinic assistants work with doctors, nurses and medical technicians in hospitals, laboratories, or in other patient-care facilities. Research the responsibilities, skills, and educational requirements for a career as a medical clinic assistant. You can begin by looking at the information on medical clinic assistants found at **www.science.nelson.com**. Follow the links for ScienceWise Grade 11, Chapter 8, Section 8.1.

FIGURE 8.5 Medical assistants can perform many different tasks, depending on where they are employed.

LAB 8A

A Close Look at Blood

To understand the relationship between blood cells and the immune system, scientists first had to find out about the different kinds of cells contained in the blood. What are the characteristics of these cells?

Purpose

In this lab, you will identify and observe the composition, appearance and percentage of red and white blood cells in human blood.

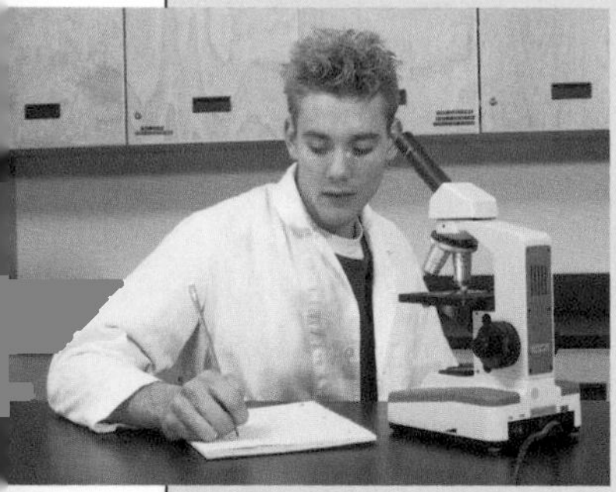

FIGURE 8.6 A scientific drawing is a labelled diagram that shows the important features of what you are observing.

Materials

- prepared slide of human blood
- compound microscope

Procedure

1. Obtain a prepared slide and a compound microscope. Carry the microscope to your workstation in the correct manner.
2. Design and construct a data table that you will use to record your observations about the cell types in blood. What kinds of cells do you need to observe to meet the purpose of this lab? Write these cell types at the top of the columns in your data table. Add rows to your table. You will need to have enough room in the rows to draw a sketch of the different cell types and to write notes about them.
3. Look at the photograph of white blood cells in Figure 8.7A, and compare these cells to the red blood cells in Figure 8.7B. In your data table, write down anything that you think will help you tell these 2 types of cells apart.
4. Place a prepared slide of human blood on the stage of your microscope. Focus the slide under 40× magnification, using the proper procedure. Remember: NEVER adjust the focus down towards the slide while you are looking through the eyepiece.

A)

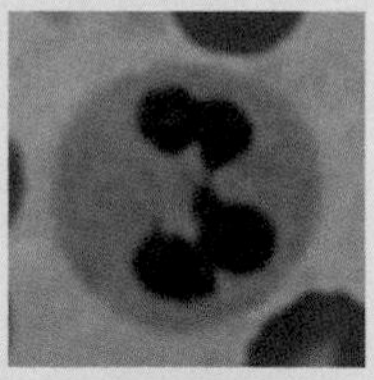

B)

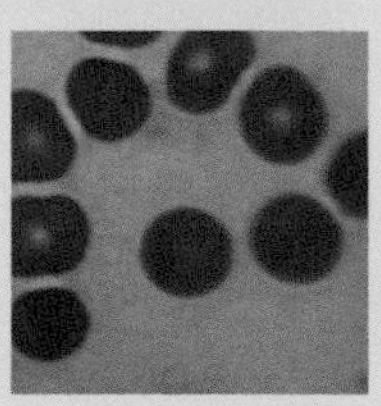

FIGURE 8.7 A) White blood cells; B) Red blood cells.

5. Examine the slide under 100× magnification. Identify the red blood cells and the white blood cells.
6. Compare the size of the red blood cells to the size of the white blood cells. Record your observations.
7. Compare the number of red blood cells to white blood cells on your slide. How many red blood cells can you see for every white blood cell? Record your estimate of the difference in the number of these 2 cell types in your data table.
8. Figure 8.8 shows you how to divide the field of view (the circle of light you see in your microscope) into 4 sections. Count the number of red blood cells in one quarter of the field of view. Record this number in your data table.
9. Count the number of white blood cells in the same quarter of the field of view that you just used. Record this number in your data table.
10. Sketch a red blood cell. In your diagram, label those parts of the cell that you can identify.
11. Sketch at least 2 white blood cells, choosing cells that look different from one another. In your diagrams, label all the parts of the cell that you can identify.

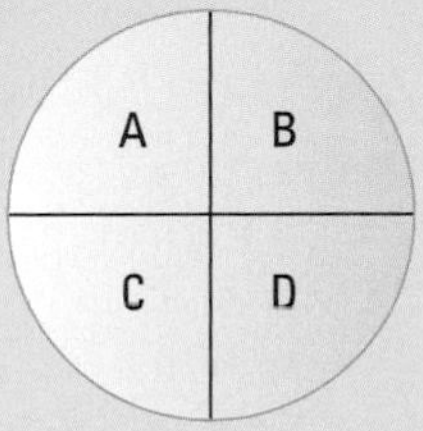

FIGURE 8.8 Divide the circle in your field of view into quarters.

Analysis and Conclusions

1. Do both red blood cells and white blood cells have a nucleus? If not, identify which of these cells does not have a nucleus.
2. Are there more red blood cells or white blood cells in human blood? Suggest a reason why this is true, referring to the role of each type of cell in the human body.
3. Explain why all white blood cells do not look the same.

Extension and Connection

4. Some drug treatments cause the number of white blood cells in a patient's blood to decrease. Explain why this side effect of drug treatments can cause a patient to become more likely to be infected by a pathogen.

8.2 Diseases of the Human Immune System

Like any other part of the human body, the immune system can be affected by either non-communicable diseases, or by communicable diseases.

Knowing about non-communicable diseases is useful for your project, Creating a Public Health Awareness Campaign.

Non-communicable Diseases of the Immune System

In Section 7.3, you learned about the immune response. Recall that the immune response is the process by which your body makes many antibodies against an antigen. An antigen is usually a pathogen or a part of a pathogen. The immune response helps your body to prepare to fight off the invasion of a pathogen. Sometimes, however, the body makes a mistake and prepares antbodies against particles that are harmless. These particles can be things in the environment such as plant pollen, or substances from cats and dogs, or they can be parts of your own body. People whose immune system makes these mistakes will have a non-communicable disease of the immune system.

Allergies

Do you, or someone you know, have allergies? Allergies are very common, so chances are the answer is yes. An **allergy** is an immune response, by the body, to something that is not usually harmful. Some of the more common allergies are allergies to certain animals, certain plants, or certain foods (Figure 8.9). People who have allergies may develop symptoms such as itchy eyes, runny noses and sneezing whenever they encounter the allergen. An **allergen** is anything that causes an allergy.

FIGURE 8.9 Many people are allergic to the pollen in flowers.

Why is it that one person can be allergic to cats and not to dogs or ragweed, while someone else can be allergic to ragweed but not to cats or dogs? This is because allergies are caused by the production of antibodies against specific allergens. If someone is allergic to ragweed, their body has made antibodies against a part of that plant, usually the pollen. Once your body has made antibodies against a substance, every time you encounter that substance, your body will try to destroy it.

How is an allergen different from an antigen? All allergens are also antigens, because an antigen is anything that is recognized by an antibody. But allergens do not usually do any harm to the human body. For example, people who are allergic to cats react to a particle produced by cats called dander. Dander is not poisonous and is not a pathogen, so for people without cat allergies, it is not dangerous. For people with cat allergies, dander is both an allergen and an antigen. In comparison, the measles pathogen is harmful to the human body. Therefore, the measles pathogen is only an antigen.

FIGURE 8.10 One of these can cause a serious and deadly allergy in some people. Which one do you think it is?

ScienceWise Fact

Asthma is a serious, chronic disease of the respiratory system (the breathing apparatus of the human body). People who have asthma suffer periods in which they have great difficulty breathing. Scientists are not sure what causes asthma, but for many people episodes are triggered by an allergy.

The symptoms of an allergy are caused by the changes in your body that occur during the immune response. Most people with allergies develop minor symptoms such as a runny nose and sneezing. Some people can have more severe reactions caused by the swelling of parts of the body. This swelling can be relatively harmless, such as swollen eyes or itchy bumps called hives, or it can be life-threatening, such as severe swelling of the throat that blocks breathing. Minor allergy symptoms can be treated with non-prescription medicines such as those in Figure 8.11, but people with severe allergies must use prescription medicines, or visit the emergency room to treat their symptoms.

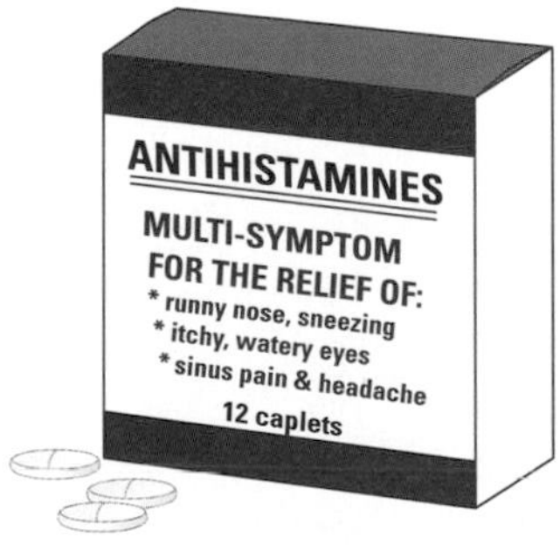

FIGURE 8.11 The symptoms of some allergies can be treated with a group of medicines called antihistamines.

Auto-immune Diseases

Auto-immune diseases are diseases in which a person's immune system attacks cells in his or her own body. When someone has an auto-immune disease, his or her immune system mistakes some of the cells of the person's own body for a foreign substance. As a result, the immune system responds to the cells, or parts of the cells, of the body as if the person were under attack by a pathogen.

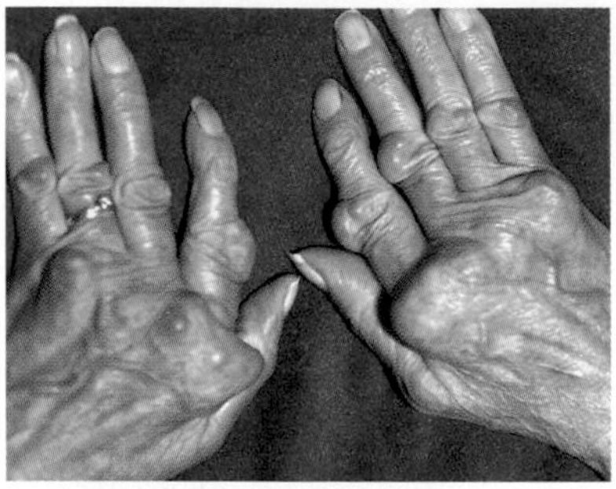

FIGURE 8.12 Rheumatoid arthritis is an example of an auto-immune disease.

Auto-immune diseases are usually very serious, because the immune system will slowly destroy part of the body, as shown in Figure 8.12. Some auto-immune diseases you may have heard of are: multiple sclerosis, in which the immune system attacks part of the nervous system; Crohn's disease, in which the digestive system is attacked; and psoriasis, in which cells in the skin are attacked. Although prescription drugs are available to treat the symptoms, these diseases cannot yet be cured.

Communicable Disease of the Immune System: AIDS

Until 1987, no pathogens were known to attack the immune system itself. This changed with the first case of Acquired Immune Deficiency Syndrome, or AIDS. Since then, AIDS has become a household word. Thousands of lives have been lost worldwide to this disease and the number of cases continues to grow.

AIDS is caused by the human immunodeficiency virus, or HIV. HIV attacks and destroys the white blood cells that make antibodies. People with AIDS, therefore, have low levels of antibodies and are unable to fight off infection by pathogens that would normally be easily destroyed (Figure 8.13). AIDS victims usually die of other diseases because their immune system is no longer able to fight off infection.

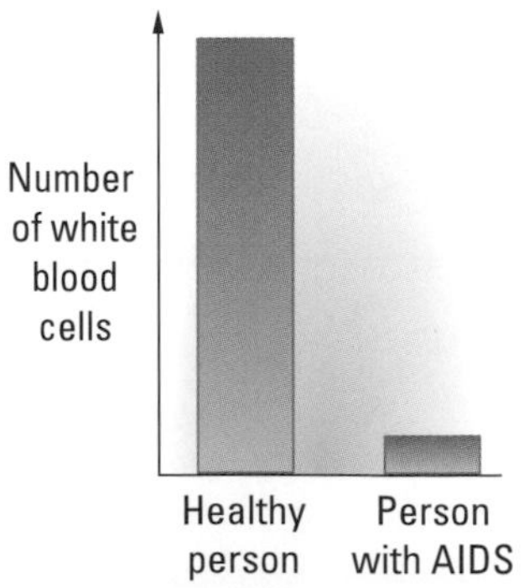

FIGURE 8.13 AIDS reduces the number of white blood cells that a person produces. Why would this affect a person's health?

Since 1995, medicines have been made available that can prevent the AIDS virus from reproducing and destroying white blood cells. These medicines increase the expected life span of people with AIDS. Although AIDS is no longer a death sentence, people infected with HIV must take many different and expensive medicines every day. These medicines can also have severe side effects including rashes, nausea, diarrhea, anemia, headaches, painful or numb feet, hepatitis and possibly diabetes. However, the medicines do not kill off the virus that is already in the body, so if a person stops taking the medicines for any reason, the virus will start to reproduce and destroy white blood cells again.

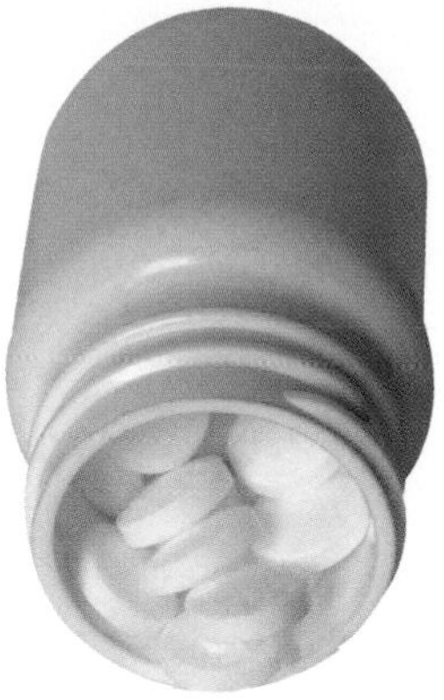

FIGURE 8.14 Although there are medicines to treat AIDS, they are expensive and can have very unpleasant side effects.

HIV Testing

When a person first becomes infected with HIV, he or she is unlikely to have any symptoms at all. It can take years for symptoms to develop. However, anyone who is infected with HIV can pass the virus on to other people by certain kinds of contact. Therefore, anyone who thinks they may have become infected with HIV should see a doctor and be tested for the virus. A person who has been infected by HIV is said to be HIV-positive. Someone who has not been infected by HIV is said to be HIV-negative.

Avoiding Transmission of HIV

Many viruses, such as the influenza virus, can travel through the air from one person to another. However, HIV can only survive within body fluids such as blood, saliva, or semen. Because of this, AIDS can only be transmitted by direct contact with the body fluids of another person. Because AIDS is such a serious disease, governments around the world have launched AIDS education programs to teach people how to avoid spreading HIV.

Knowing how communicable diseases affect the immune system will be helpful for your project, Creating a Public Health Awareness Campaign.

Review and Apply

1. In 2 or 3 sentences, explain the relationship between the immune system and allergies. Use a specific example in your answer.
2. Can diseases of the immune system be cured? In your answer, explain the difference between curing a disease and treating a disease.
3. In your own words, explain the difference between an allergen and an antigen.
4. Imagine you are a server in a restaurant. A customer tells you that she is allergic to wheat and asks you to make sure that wheat is not used to make the soup she has ordered. When you ask the cook, you are told that only a very small amount of wheat flour is used to thicken the soup. Would it be safe to serve this dish to the customer? Give reasons for your answer.
5. List 3 auto-immune diseases.
6. Choose 1 of the following jobs: police officer, hospital orderly, or ambulance attendant. Given that HIV is only transmitted by direct contact with body fluids, write a short paragraph describing how people in the job you choose might come into contact with HIV when they are at work.
7. Add the concepts you have learned in this section to the graphic organizer you started in Section 8.1.
8. **Allergies in the Workplace**

   People must be exposed to allergens before they develop an allergy to it. Because they are exposed almost every day, people sometimes develop allergies to materials they encounter regularly in their workplace.

   Working with at least 1 other person, choose 1 of the following workplaces: a riding stable, a candy factory, or a landscape company. For the workplace you choose, brainstorm a list of substances that would be likely to cause allergies. Use the Internet and the library to find out about common types of allergies in order to complete your list. When you have finished, choose 1 of the substances on your list and describe at least 2 ways that people in that workplace could reduce their exposure to that allergen. Present your work as a memo that would be suitable to pass out to employees in the workplace.

8.3 Treating and Preventing Disease

When you become ill, you might go to see a doctor. Based on your symptoms, your doctor will determine what is causing your illness and decide what treatment to give you. Your doctor depends on scientific knowledge to make these decisions. In fact, we all depend on scientific knowledge to get the correct treatment and to find new ways of treating and preventing disease.

Treating Communicable Diseases

Recall that communicable diseases are caused by pathogens. When a patient is ill because he or she is infected by a pathogen, doctors choose a treatment method that will kill or inhibit the growth of that particular kind of pathogen. The treatment is often a chemical medicine. These chemicals will help your body fight an infection by reducing the number of pathogen cells that your immune system has to remove from your body. When you take a medicine against a pathogen, you will not get as ill, or will be ill for a shorter time, than if you let your immune system fight the infection without help.

Diseases that are caused by bacteria, such as strep throat, are treated by antibiotics. **Antibiotics** are medicines that kill or inhibit the growth of bacteria only. Fungal infections must be treated with anti-fungal medication. These are chemicals that will kill or inhibit the growth of fungus cells only. For example, athlete's foot can be treated only with an anti-fungal medication. Diseases that are caused by protists, such as giardiasis, must be treated with chemicals that will affect this type of micro-organism.

FIGURE 8.15 These products can be used to treat the common cold, which is caused by a virus. Do these treatments affect the cold pathogen?

Diseases that are caused by viruses, such as influenza and colds, are more difficult to treat because we do not yet have many medicines that will affect this type of pathogen. For viruses that cause non-life-threatening diseases, such as colds, doctors can only treat the symptoms, leaving your immune system to fight the pathogen unaided. However, for some serious diseases caused by viruses, such as AIDS, scientists have been able to find some medicines that can affect the virus.

The Discovery of Antibiotics

Antibiotics are very important in treating diseases that are caused by bacteria. Most antibiotics are chemicals that are produced naturally by soil micro-organisms. You can review this information in Section 6.4. How did scientists and doctors learn that chemicals produced by micro-organisms in the soil could be used to treat diseases in humans?

Until the 1800s, no one knew about the existence of micro-organisms or understood the causes of disease. The first step towards discovering antibiotics was taken by Louis Pasteur, who proposed that tiny microscopic particles, or "germs," were the cause of disease. Scientists then began to look for the micro-organisms that caused disease. The first micro-organisms shown to cause disease in humans were bacteria.

With this new knowledge, scientists then began to look for ways to treat disease by attacking the bacteria. The hope was to find substances that could kill the bacteria and not harm people. The most important discovery was made almost accidentally by Sir Alexander Fleming (Figure 8.16).

FIGURE 8.16 Sir Alexander Fleming (1881–1955) turned a lucky observation into a major scientific achievement, for which he was awarded the Nobel Prize in 1945.

In 1928, Fleming was working with *Staphylococcus*, a type of bacteria that causes many diseases in humans. One day, he noticed some mould in a Petri dish in which he was growing *Staphylococcus* bacteria. To his surprise, there were no bacteria growing near the mould. Figure 8.17 shows what Sir Fleming might have seen.

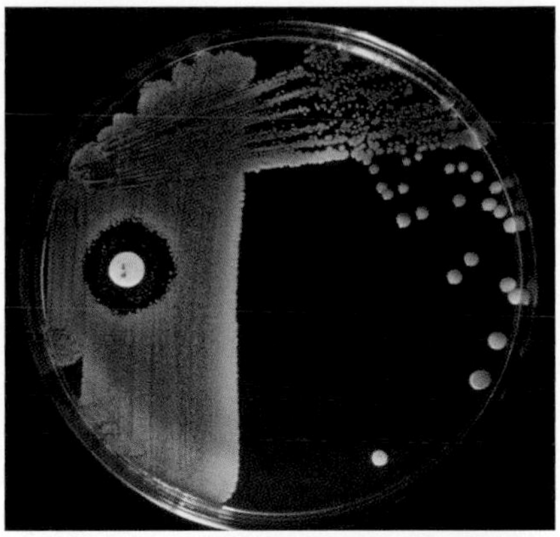

FIGURE 8.17 Fleming observed a reaction similar to this, on a Petri dish that accidentally had both mould and bacteria growing on it. Would the treatment of disease be different if he had just thrown the plates away?

The mould was the species *Penicillium notatum,* a common mould found in soil. Fleming wondered if the mould was killing the bacteria cells. He carried out some experiments to test this idea and discovered that, in fact, the mould could kill many different species of bacteria, because *Penicillium notatum* produces the antibiotic penicillin. Since Fleming's discovery, penicillin has saved many lives, and is still used to treat disease today.

Since the discovery of penicillin, many other antibiotics have been found. For each new discovery, scientists first had to identify the bacteria that caused a particular disease, then hunt for an antibiotic that would affect that bacteria. Some of these discoveries are shown in the timeline in Figure 8.18.

You may need to know about the development of antibiotics for your project, Creating a Public Health Awareness Campaign.

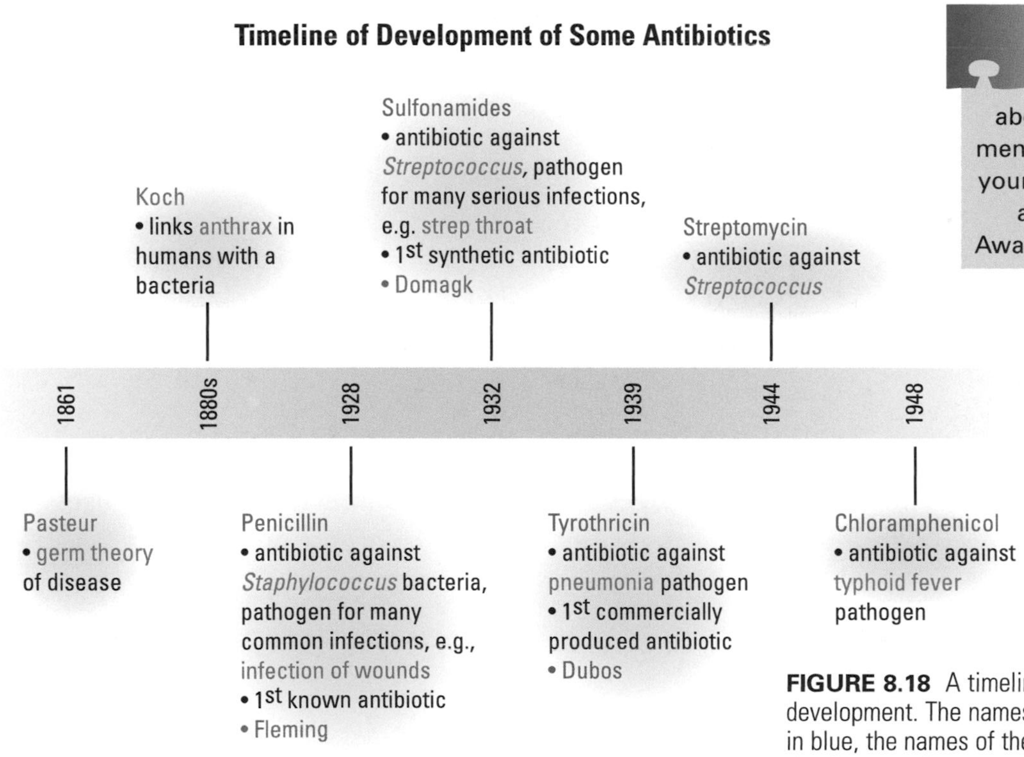
Timeline of Development of Some Antibiotics
1861
Pasteur
• germ theory of disease
1880s
Koch
• links anthrax in humans with a bacteria
1928
Penicillin
• antibiotic against *Staphylococcus* bacteria, pathogen for many common infections, e.g., infection of wounds
• 1st known antibiotic
• Fleming
1932
Sulfonamides
• antibiotic against *Streptococcus*, pathogen for many serious infections, e.g. strep throat
• 1st synthetic antibiotic
• Domagk
1939
Tyrothricin
• antibiotic against pneumonia pathogen
• 1st commercially produced antibiotic
• Dubos
1944
Streptomycin
• antibiotic against *Streptococcus*
1948
Chloramphenicol
• antibiotic against typhoid fever pathogen

FIGURE 8.18 A timeline showing antibiotic development. The names of the antibiotics are in blue, the names of the micro-organisms and the diseases they cause are in green, and the names of the scientists who made the discoveries are in purple.

Antibiotic Resistance

FIGURE 8.19 Worried parents sometimes ask for antibiotics for diseases that are not caused by bacteria.

Some people, especially those with young children, think that taking antibiotics for any infection is a good idea. Other people do not take all of the antibiotics a doctor prescribes so they can save the "extra" pills for the next time they feel sick. Still others stop taking their antibiotics as soon as they feel better, instead of taking the full amount they were prescribed. These behaviours are all examples of improper use of antibiotics.

Unfortunately, improper use of antibiotics has led to the development of bacteria that are no longer affected by antibiotics. A bacterial cell is **antibiotic resistant** when it is not affected by an antibiotic that should kill it or inhibit its growth. How can using an antibiotic improperly make bacteria antibiotic resistant? To answer that question, you must first understand what happens to the bacteria in your body when you take an antibiotic.

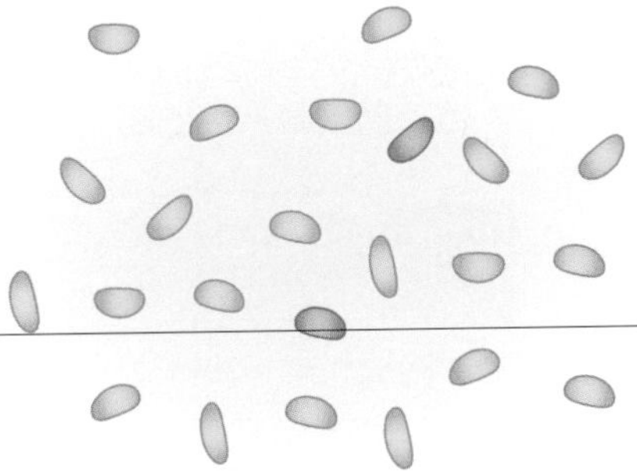

FIGURE 8.20 A small number of the cells of any species of bacteria will be antibiotic resistant.

When you are infected by a species of bacteria, there are many different individual cells of that bacterial species in your body (Figure 8.20). Most of these bacteria will die or stop reproducing when you take an antibiotic. Bacterial cells that are killed or stop reproducing in the presence of an antibiotic are **antibiotic susceptible.** However, there will always be some bacterial cells that are antibiotic resistant in your body. If there are only a few, your immune system can easily kill off these resistant bacteria cells.

Using antibiotics can increase the number of individual bacterial cells that are antibiotic resistant by 2 different processes: mutation of genetic material, and exchange of genetic material.

Mutation of Genetic Material

Mutations are changes in the genetic material of an organism. Mutations occur naturally in all living organisms. In bacteria, mutations can cause some of the bacteria cells to become resistant to an antibiotic.

Mutations only happen to 1 individual bacterial cell at a time, not to a whole species. When a person takes antibiotics, any bacteria cells that have mutated and become antibiotic resistant will continue to reproduce. The antibiotic-susceptible bacteria will be killed or stop reproducing (Figure 8.21).

When a patient takes antibiotic medicine exactly as the doctor prescribed, their immune system is able to destroy the antibiotic-resistant bacterial cells. However, if a patient stops taking the antibiotic early or does not take it properly, the immune system does not have enough time to destroy all the antibiotic-resistant bacterial cells. If this person passes on the infection, there will be a higher number of antibiotic-resistant cells to infect the next person (Figure 8.21B).

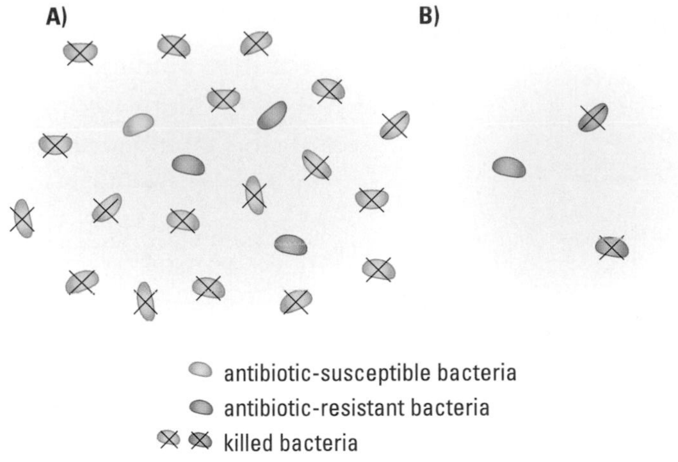

FIGURE 8.21 A) When you take an antibiotic, antibiotic-resistant bacterial cells are not affected. B) If you do not take all of the antibiotic, your immune system will not have enough time to kill all the resistant bacterial cells.

Exchange of Genetic Material

Although bacteria do not undergo true sexual reproduction, they can exchange some of their genetic material. You can review information about reproduction of bacteria in Section 5.2. When antibiotics are present, antibiotic-resistant bacteria exchange the genetic information for antibiotic resistance with the antibiotic-susceptible bacterial cells around them. In other words, antibiotic-resistant bacterial cells can share their mutation with antibiotic-susceptible bacterial cells (Figure 8.22).

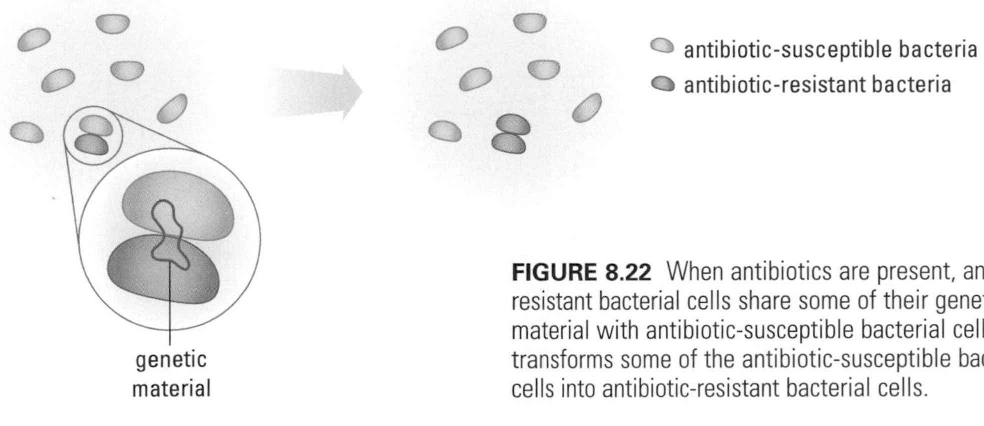

FIGURE 8.22 When antibiotics are present, antibiotic-resistant bacterial cells share some of their genetic material with antibiotic-susceptible bacterial cells. This transforms some of the antibiotic-susceptible bacterial cells into antibiotic-resistant bacterial cells.

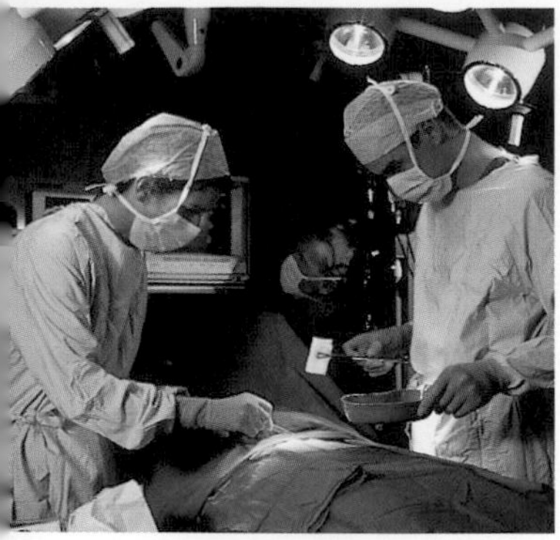

FIGURE 8.23
Because hospitals use a lot of antibiotics, antibiotic-resistant bacteria often show up there first.

Today, we use a lot of antibiotics. Until recently, some doctors prescribed antibiotics before they were sure a patient had a bacterial infection. Many people do not follow their doctor's instructions and stop taking an antibiotic when they first begin to feel better. As a result, there are many more antibiotic-resistant bacteria around today. Many older antibiotics, such as penicillin, can no longer be used to combat many diseases they once could. Some scientists believe that we might someday be unable to treat any disease with antibiotics because of antibiotic-resistance. Therefore, it is very important that everyone use antibiotics properly so the rate at which antibiotic-resistant bacteria appear is as slow as possible.

Treatment of Non-communicable Diseases

Non-communicable diseases are not caused by a pathogen, which can make them more difficult to treat. As scientists learn more about how the body works, they are more able to determine what is wrong in the body of those with a non-communicable disease, which can help to find new ways to treat these diseases. We can now treat the symptoms of many non-communicable diseases, such as epilepsy, diabetes and depression, allowing many people to lead a more normal life. Even more exciting, scientists can sometimes cure non-communicable diseases that were once a death sentence, such as many cancers.

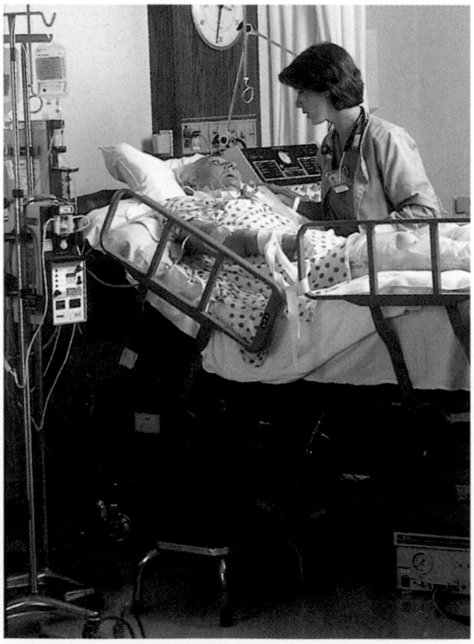

FIGURE 8.24 Many non-communicable diseases, such as heart disease, can now be treated by surgery. Doctors can even transplant a healthy heart into a patient, giving them additional healthier years of life.

Prevention of Communicable Diseases

Learning about the causes of disease has also allowed doctors and scientists to find ways to prevent many communicable diseases. For example, knowledge about how the immune system functions to fight pathogens allows for the treatment and prevention of disease through vaccines.

FIGURE 8.25 Development and use of the smallpox vaccine means that today, no one is at risk of getting smallpox.

Scientific knowledge about pathogens has also taught us how to prevent disease in our everyday life by practising good hygiene. Before the existence of micro-organisms was known, people did not understand the importance of hygiene in disease prevention. Now we know how to prevent harmful pathogens from spreading: by practising good personal hygiene, by handling and storing food safely and by avoiding creating areas where pathogens can grow in our homes and workplaces. You will find more information about these ways of preventing disease in Sections 6.3 and 6.4.

Hygiene is so important to preventing disease that our society enforces certain hygiene standards in all public places. Whether you are buying food in a grocery store, getting your hair cut, or visiting a hospital, you are protected from many pathogens by public health standards. **Public health standards** are guidelines and laws that are prepared by government groups at the federal (Canada-wide), provincial, and municipal (city and town) level. Every different type of business has both general and specific rules it must follow in order to be allowed to operate. Examples of these rules are shown in Figure 8.27 and Figure 8.28 on the next page.

FIGURE 8.26 Why are these people required to wear gloves when handling food?

Examples of Food Safety Guidelines in Canada

Less specific → More specific

Level of regulation	Example
Government of Canada	The government writes and enforces Canada-wide public health guidelines, such as "The Canadian Food and Drugs Act" and "The Canadian Food and Drug Regulations."
Public health inspectors	These people inspect organizations that produce, prepare, transport and sell food. For example, inspectors check that meatpacking facilities are clean and use methods that do not allow pathogens to grow.
Provincial governments	Provincial regulations are specific to each province, and provincial inspectors check to ensure the regulations are followed. For example, the provinces set their own safety regulations about washing dishes by hand.
Municipal governments	Different cities have regulations dealing with food safety in the particular businesses in their city. For example, a municipal regulation might state that food must be handled only with utensils or clean gloves.

FIGURE 8.27 By having regulations and inspectors, we ensure that everyone in Canada is protected from unnecessary exposure to pathogens.

B.22.016: No person shall sell directly to the public any poultry, poultry meat, or poultry meat by-product that has been barbecued, roasted, or broiled on his premises and intended to be ready for consumption unless that poultry, poultry meat, or poultry meat by-product (a) has, at all times prior to sale, been stored at a temperature of 4 degrees Celsius or lower or 60 degrees Celsius or higher.

FIGURE 8.28 Laws that protect public health are very specific. There are many different regulations to ensure all the different types of foods and situations are covered.

You will need to know about the food safety guuidelines in Canada to complete your project, Creating a Public Health Awareness Campaign.

Prevention of Non-communicable Diseases

Advances in scientific knowledge have also allowed doctors and scientists to find ways to prevent some non-communicable diseases. For example, we now know that smoking is a leading cause of lung cancer. Because of this information, many people choose not to start smoking. Governments have also created laws that protect people from this cause of disease. Many cities have laws that restrict smoking in restaurants and other public places. Throughout Canada, it is illegal to sell tobacco to people under the age of 18. Figure 8.29 provides some other examples of how non-communicable diseases can be prevented. Can you think of any others?

Prevention of Non-communicable Diseases

Disease	Scientific knowledge	Prevention methods
Skin cancer	The major cause of skin cancer is over-exposure to the sun.	• Public health education campaigns to teach people the dangers of sun exposure. • Development of sunscreen lotions that block out the rays that cause skin cancer.
Heart disease	Risk factors for heart disease include high blood pressure, high cholesterol levels and obesity.	• Public health education campaigns to teach people the importance of a healthy diet and exercise. • Development of drugs that lower blood pressure and cholesterol levels.

FIGURE 8.29 How did learning about the causes of these diseases help us learn how they can be prevented?

Review and Apply

1. Explain how antibiotics help your immune system fight a disease.

2. In 1 or 2 sentences, explain why it is important to take antibiotics exactly the way your doctor prescribes.

3. Create a sequence of sketches that shows the 2 ways a bacteria cell can become antibiotic resistant.

4. Explain how knowledge of pathogens helped scientists find antibiotics that could be used to treat diseases.

5. In 1 or 2 sentences, explain how your personal hygiene habits can prevent the spread of disease.

6. Sometimes you might be concerned about the way food is stored or prepared in a public place, such as in a restaurant. Suggest a way to ensure that a place you are concerned about is operating in a safe manner, without having to confront the owner of the establishment.

7. Add the new concepts from this section to the graphic organizer you started in Section 8.1.

8. **Promoting Healthy Habits at Work**

Many of the non-communicable diseases that affect humans are caused by lifestyle choices. For example, smoking causes cancer. Employers can help both their companies and their employees by promoting healthy habits. Imagine you and a partner are the owners of a small business-services company. You have a staff of 20 people who produce business documents using a computer. Most of your employees spend the whole day sitting in an office chair using a keyboard. Even at lunchtime, most of the workers just go to the break room and sit again.

With your partner, make a list of at least 5 ways that you could help your employees lead more active, healthier lives. Remember that you are running a business, so your ideas should not cost your company too much money. Present the ideas in a chart. Indicate on the chart the idea that you think would be the most likely to be accepted by your employees.

Job Link

Nursing Attendant

Responsibilities of a Nursing Attendant

- providing basic patient care, such as serving meals, dressing and grooming patients, or accompanying patients on recreational activities
- taking patients' vital signs, recording and reporting on food and fluid intake, collecting patient specimens
- maintaining patients' rooms
- assisting with set-up and maintenance of medical equipment

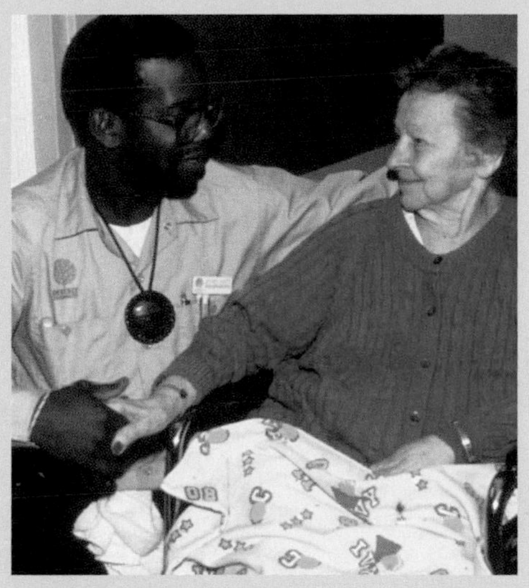

FIGURE 8.30 Nursing attendants assist nurses, hospital staff and doctors in caring for patients.

Where do they work?

- hospitals
- nursing homes
- patient's homes
- extended-care and hospice facilities

Skills for the Job

- patient, friendly and outgoing personality, because they must work directly with patients
- attention to detail, because there is no room for error when monitoring or caring for patients
- ability to follow instructions carefully, since most nursing attendants will receive many different orders for different patients on a daily basis
- clean and tidy work and personal habits
- good oral and written communication skills

Education

- some secondary school education and on-the-job training, at minimum
- some facilities require nursing attendants to have completed college courses and supervised practical training
- some facilities require other specialized courses in areas such as C.P.R., first aid, and food handling

LAB 8B The Effect of Household Cleaners on Bacteria

Be Safe!

- Do not eat or drink in the lab.
- Keep your hands away from your mouth and nose.
- Wash your hands with hot, soapy water before you leave the lab.
- Check the chemicals you are using for WHIMS symbols before you begin. You may review what these symbols mean by turning to Section 1.1.

The advertisements for many household cleaning products talk about how clean they can get your home. But does it really make a difference if you use a cleaner, or will plain old water work just as well?

Purpose

In this lab, you will compare the effects of several cleaning products on the growth of bacteria.

Materials

- tap water
- dilute dishwashing detergent
- household disinfectant cleaner
- dilute bleach
- filter paper discs
- masking tape
- yogourt with live bacteria
- 1 test tube with a cap, containing 5 mL of sterile water
- disposable transfer pipette
- forceps
- 1 Petri dish containing nutrient agar

Procedure

Part One: Predicting Results

1. In your notebook, create a data table using the headings in Figure 8.31.

Section	Chemical tested	Predicted results	Observed results

FIGURE 8.31

2. Predict which of the chemicals you are to use will be able to slow down or stop the growth of the bacteria that is in yogourt. Record your predictions in your data chart.

Part Two: Plating Bacteria

1. Using a waterproof marker, mark off 4 equal sections on the bottom of your Petri dish, as in Figure 8.32. Write your name on the dish.

2. Dip the sterile swab into the yogourt, then immediately remove it. Do not put the swab down!

3. Ask a classmate to remove the cap from the test tube, being careful not to touch the edge of the tube. Place the swab into the water and swirl it to wash off the bacterial cells. Dispose of the used swab as directed by your teacher.

4. Recap the tube and gently mix the contents. Try not to splash the liquid up against the cap of the tube.

5. Again ask your classmate to remove the cap from the test tube, being careful not to touch the edge of the tube. Squeeze the bulb of a disposable transfer pipette, and then lower the tip of the pipette into the liquid in your test-tube. Try not to touch the test tube with the pipette.

6. Release the bulb of the pipette and allow it to draw the liquid up until it reaches the 1-mL mark on the pipette. Remove the pipette from the tube, being careful not to touch the sides of the tube. Do not put the pipette down or squeeze the bulb.

7. Have a classmate remove the lid of the Petri dish. When a dish is opened, carefully release 1 mL of the liquid from the pipette onto the centre of the dish. Close the lid.

8. Rock the dish gently to spread out the liquid as much as you can, as shown in Figure 8.33. Leave the dishes sitting for at least 5 minutes, to allow the liquid to soak into the agar.

9. Store the dish in a dark place at room temperature for 1 to 2 days.

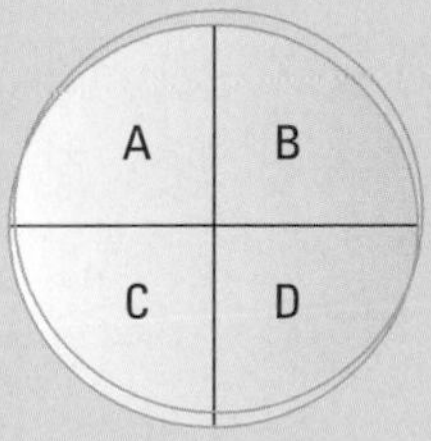

FIGURE 8.32 Divide your Petri plate in quarters, and label each quarter A,B, C, or D.

FIGURE 8.33 Rock the dish gently from side to side.

CONTINUED

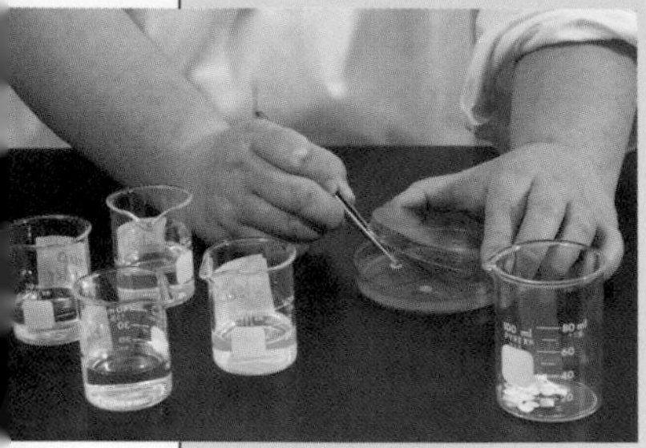

FIGURE 8.34 Press the discs against the agar surface, using the forceps.

Part Three: Testing the Chemicals

1. Using the forceps, pick up 1 filter paper disc and dip it into the tap water. Open the Petri dish and place the disc on the "A" quarter of the dish. Use the forceps to gently tap in the disc against the agar surface, as shown in Figure 8.34. Do not allow the forceps to touch the agar.
2. Repeat step 1 above for all the other chemicals, placing each disc on a different section of the Petri dish.
3. Close the lid and seal the edges of the Petri dish with tape. Store the dish in a dark place at room temperature for 1 to 2 days.

Part Four: Making and Recording Observations

1. Observe the bacteria on your dish. Do not open the dish.
2. Record your observations in your data table in a manner that will allow you to remember the important facts.
3. Discard your Petri dishes as directed by your teacher.

FIGURE 8.35 The clear area is where no bacteria were able to grow.

Analysis and Conclusion

1. If a chemical affected the growth of the bacteria, there will be a clear area around the disc, like in Figure 8.35. Which chemicals affected the growth of the bacteria in your experiment?
2. Did you get the results you predicted? Suggest reasons why your results might be different from the predicted results.

Extension and Connection

3. You are the supervisor of a busy restaurant. You notice that a staff member is wiping the tables with just tap water. What, if any, changes would you ask this person to make? Explain your answer.
4. Many cleaning products are labelled as antibacterial. These products often cost more than others. Based on your experimental results, do you think that people should buy antibacterial cleaning products? Give reasons for your answer.

8.4 Chapter Summary

Now You Can....

- Describe the components of the human immune system (8.1)
- Describe the role of blood components in controlling pathogens (8.1)
- Identify the causes, effects and treatments of common diseases associated with the immune system (8.2)
- Describe the use of antibiotics to prevent disease (8.3)
- Describe how overuse and improper use of antibiotics has caused bacteria to become antibiotic resistant (8.3)
- Describe how a better understanding of pathogens led to the development of antibiotics (8.3)
- Analyze and describe the relationship between the understanding of the causes of disease and new ways to treat and prevent disease (8.3)

Concept Connections

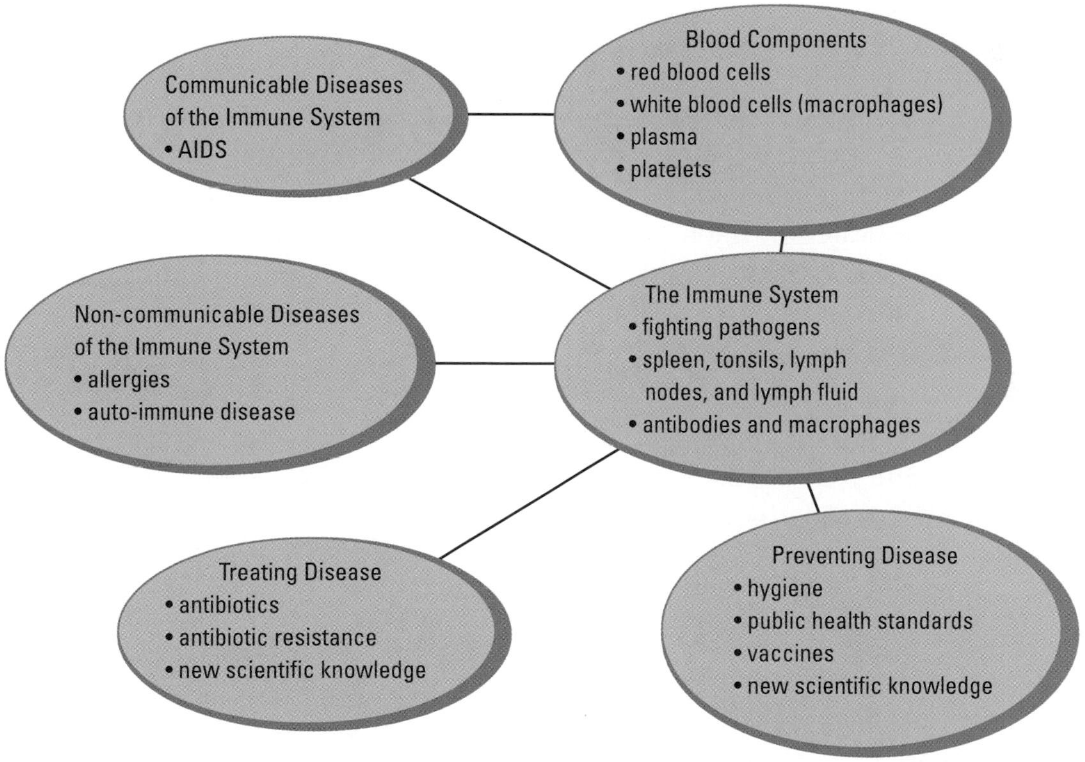

FIGURE 8.36 Compare your completed graphic organizer to the one on this page. How did you do? Can you add any new links to your organizer?

CHAPTER 8 *review*

Knowledge and Understanding

1. In your notebook, match each component of blood from Column A with its function in Column B.

Column A	Column B
a) Red blood cells	i) make blood clots to stop blood from leaving the body
b) Platelets	ii) destroy pathogens and make antibodies
c) Plasma	iii) carry oxygen to your cells and take away carbon dioxide
d) White blood cells	iv) take food and other chemicals to your cells and take away wastes

2. For each of the following, indicate whether the statement is true or false. Rewrite any false statements to make them true.
   - **a)** The immune system depends on cells that are in the blood.
   - **b)** Allergies are caused by the formation of antibodies to substances that are not normally dangerous.
   - **c)** Antibiotics can be used for any kind of pathogen infection.
   - **d)** When a person takes antibiotics, their immune system still works to destroy the bacteria in their body.
   - **e)** Non-communicable diseases cannot be treated or cured.
   - **f)** Scientists have found ways to prevent both communicable and non-communicable diseases.

3. Explain why you cannot use antibiotics to treat a disease caused by a virus.

4. Describe how laws and regulations can help prevent disease. Give an example in your answer.

5. Outline at least 5 roles that blood plays in the human body. At least 1 of the roles in your answer must relate to the human immune system.

Inquiry

6. You have just completed an experiment in which you plated bacteria from yogourt. Yogourt is a food that is made with bacteria that are not pathogens. Explain why you must still wash your hands before you leave the lab.

7. You are a laboratory technician at a major hospital. A doctor has provided you with a sample of bacteria from a patient and has asked you to test it to see if it is resistant to the antibiotic tetracycline. Outline an experiment you could carry out to determine if the bacteria is tetracycline-resistant.

Making Connections

8. Modern farming techniques often include feeding antibiotics to animals, such as cows and pigs, in order to keep them free from disease. These antibiotics are not present in the meat we buy. Do you think that this use of antibiotics is a safe practice? Explain your answer.

9. You and a friend run a small daycare business. One of the children in your care has asthma, a lung disease that has been related to allergies. When a parent drops off her child one morning, she also brings a little kitten. She asks if you could look after the kitten for just 1 day and offers to pay you. Would you allow the kitten to stay for the day? Give reasons to support your answer.

10. Imagine you are a restaurant inspector. You are responsible for making sure that restaurants do not have conditions that would allow pathogens to grow. Make a checklist of at least 6 different things that you would look for in a restaurant to successfully do your job.

Communication

11. You have a part-time job as a receptionist in a medical office. A patient in the waiting room has told you that the doctor has refused to give him a prescription for antibiotics. During the conversation, you find out that the doctor has diagnosed the patient with influenza, which is caused by a virus. Write a short description of what you might say to explain to this patient why he has not been prescribed an antibiotic.

12. The government in your city has decided that it does not need to hire people to inspect restaurants. Government policy makers reason that customers should be able to tell by a restaurant's appearance whether or not it is clean. Write a letter to your mayor that agrees or disagrees with the government's decision. Explain your reasons.

PUTTING IT ALL TOGETHER

Creating a Public Health Awareness Campaign

Public awareness is a very important part of fighting the spread of disease. In this unit, you learned about some of the ways that disease can be prevented. Think about what you learned. Could you use this information to convince other people to change their ideas and behaviour in order to prevent disease? In this activity, you will work in a group, and develop a public health awareness campaign to make people aware of behaviours that spread disease.

FIGURE 1D Who do you want to pay attention to your public health campaign?

Purpose

In your group, you will create a brochure or poster to communicate to a specific group of people, about a behaviour that contributes to the spread of disease. You will use the information in Chapters 7 and 8, as well as additional information that you obtain from other sources. Your brochure or poster must present the information in a clear and interesting way that will grab people's attention.

What You May Need

- access to the Internet and/or library resources
- coloured pens, markers, and pencils and/or a computer and colour printer
- heavy paper or Bristol board
- recent magazines or newspapers

What You Will Do

1. In your group, scan current magazines, newspapers, and Internet news sites for articles that involve communicable diseases in Canada. Read the articles to find out how the diseases are spread and how they can be prevented.

2. As a group, decide on one disease that interests you the most. You will create a public health campaign about this disease.

3. Answer the following questions for the disease you have chosen:

    - Who would be most at risk of getting this disease?
    - Of these people, whom do you wish to educate about the disease?

    The answers to these questions will tell you who will be the target of your public health campaign. You may need to conduct additional research to come up with answers.

4. Decide on a method of preventing the spread of this disease that you will present in your campaign.

CONTINUED

5. Brainstorm ways that you are most likely to get the information about disease prevention to your target audience. Are they people that like to read? Are they people who will be more likely to respond to pictures and slogans with only a small amount to read?

6. Create your brochure or poster.

Assessment

1. Post your brochure or poster in the place your teacher has prepared. Choose 1 group whose topic interests you. Ask a member of that group to explain how their campaign might improve the health of Canadians. Be prepared to discuss this question about your campaign.

2. Compare your work to that of the other groups in your class. What do you think they did well? What do you like the best about your public health campaign? If you were able to do this activity again, what changes would you make to your campaign? Why?

UNIT 5

Human Impact on the Environment

CHAPTER 9

Natural Relationships

We share Earth with millions of other living things. Many of us take nature for granted, never thinking about how we are all connected. We are learning that how we live can have a negative effect on the world around us. In future generations, the environment may not be able to support or sustain the lifestyles Canadians presently enjoy. This chapter will look at how natural systems work together and the various ways human actions can interfere with these natural systems. Look at Figure 9.1. What human activities might lead to or cause harm to the environment in the first photograph? What caused the harm you can see in the picture on the right? How do our lifestyle choices affect Earth's ability to support all life?

FIGURE 9.1

What You Will Learn

After completing this chapter, you will be able to:

- Describe the parts of ecosystems and how they interact with each other (9.1)
- Show and describe how energy and nutrients move through ecosystems (9.1)
- Describe how food energy is used within ecosystems (9.1)
- Explain how human population growth affects life on Earth (9.2, 9.3)
- Define carrying capacity and biodiversity (9.2)
- Explain the importance of biodiversity to life on Earth (9.2)
- Describe how factors such as competition can affect a species (9.2)
- Explain ways in which humans are destroying ecosystems (9.3)

What You Will Do

- Draw food chains and food webs to explain how living things obtain food (Lab 9A)
- Set up and monitor an ecosystem (Lab 9A)
- Explore loss of species and how lower biodiversity affects ecosystems (Activity 9B)
- Graph data to demonstrate how populations can change (Activity 9C)

Words to Know

abiotic
biodiversity
biosphere
biotic
carrying capacity
community
consumer
decomposer
ecological footprint
ecosystem
energy pyramid
extinct
food chain
food web
organism
population
producer
species
sustainability

A puzzle piece indicates knowledge or a skill that you will need for your project, Examining an Environmental Issue, at the end of Unit 5.

9.1 Understanding Ecosystems

Life can be found in many different places on Earth, from the deepest ocean floor to the tops of the highest mountains. All living things depend on their environment to provide them with everything they need to survive. What determines where a particular living thing can survive?

Ecosystems

An **organism** is a living thing. For example, 1 mule deer is an organism. A **species** is a group of similar organisms that are capable of breeding with one another and producing offspring. For example, a male and a female mule deer can reproduce to produce fawns. In contrast, a mule deer and a white-tailed deer could not produce fawns, because they are 2 different species.

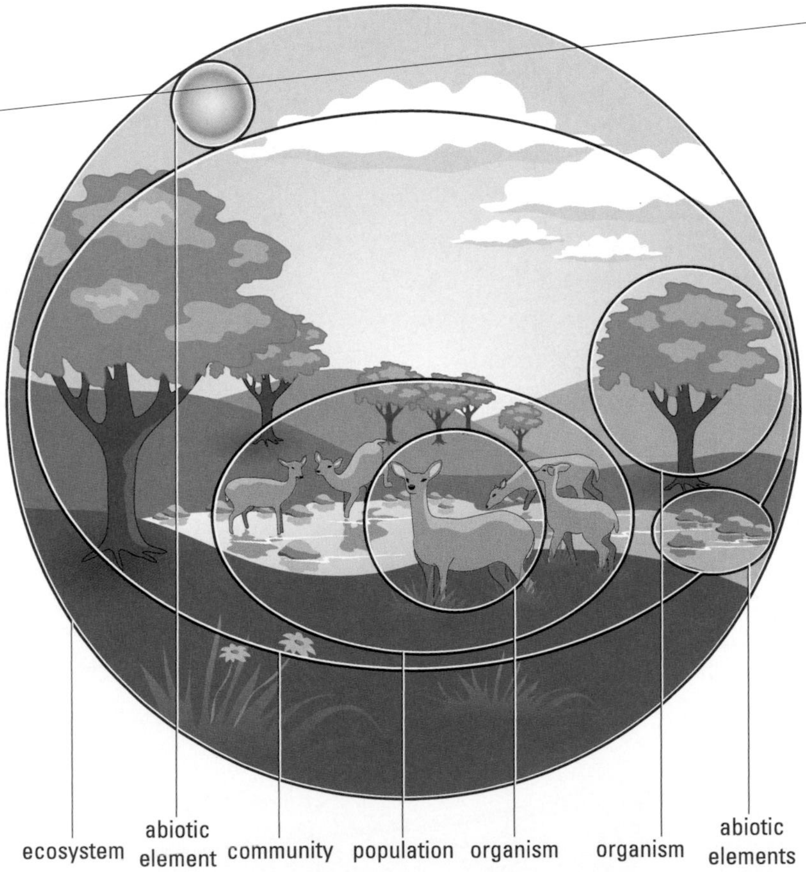

FIGURE 9.2 An ecosystem. Identify the biotic elements shown.

The organisms that share a particular area can be arranged into groups, according to their relationships. A **population** is a group of individuals of the same species. The 5 mule deer shown in Figure 9.2 form a population. A **community** is composed of all the different populations of species that share a particular area. The community in Figure 9.2 includes deer, species of trees, and species of grasses and flowers.

Any area that supports life contains both living and non-living elements. **Biotic elements** are the living things and **abiotic elements** are non-living things. In Figure 9.2, grass and deer are biotic elements, and rocks and air are abiotic elements. Communities, populations, species, and organisms all refer only to biotic factors. An **ecosystem** includes all the biotic factors plus the abiotic factors. The **biosphere** is made up of all the ecosystems on Earth. These relationships are summarized in Figure 9.3.

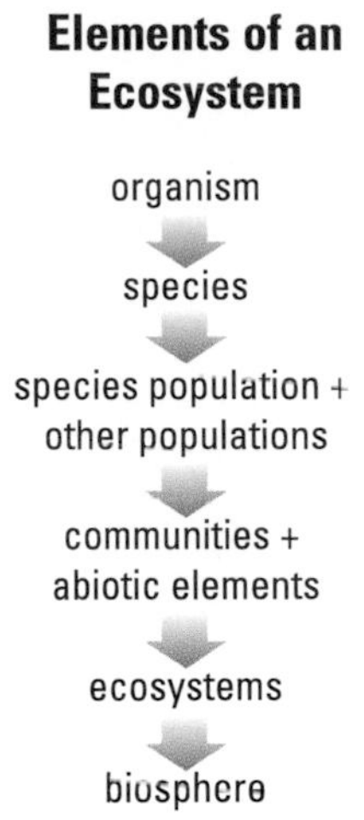

FIGURE 9.3 The elements of an ecosystem work together.

Food Chains and Food Webs

All organisms need a source of energy and nutrients to survive. The organisms in an ecosystem can also be organized according to how they meet this need. **Producers** are organisms that can make their own food. Plants are producers. Plants make food in the form of sugars through the process of photosynthesis. **Consumers** are organisms that get food from eating other organisms. Consumers such as deer, that eat only plants, are herbivores. Consumers that eat only animals, such as coyotes, are carnivores. Omnivores are consumers that eat both animals and plants. Bears, for example, are omnivores. **Decomposers** are organisms that use dead plants and animals as food. Many fungi and bacteria are decomposers. You can learn more about fungi and bacteria in Section 5.1.

Whenever a producer makes its food, or a consumer or decomposer eats something, energy is transferred, as shown in Figure 9.4. The organisms within an ecosystem are dependent on these transfers of energy for their survival.

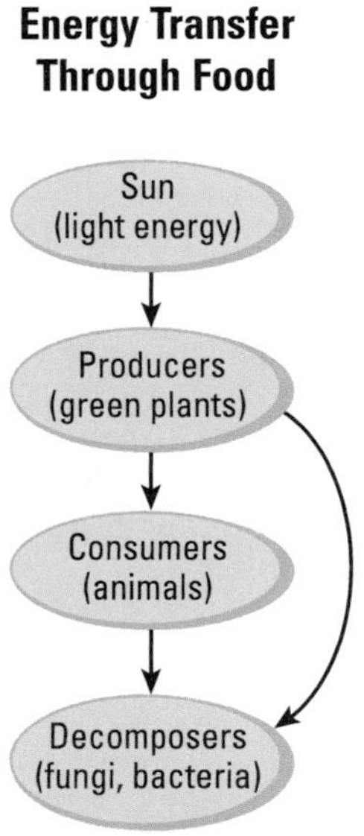

FIGURE 9.4 Identify the abiotic element in the cycle.

Two Food Chains

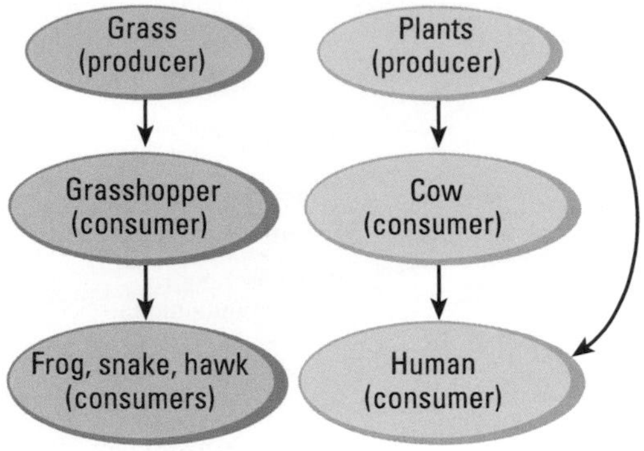

FIGURE 9.5 The grasshopper eats the grass and the frog eats the grasshopper. Each part of the food chain gives energy and nutrients to the next.

You may need to know about how natural systems work together for your project, Examining an Environmental Issue.

A **food chain** refers to the sequence through which energy transfers from organism to organism. Food chains always begin with producers, then show what eats what for food. Figure 9.5 shows 2 examples of food chains.

However, the line from sunlight to dinner is rarely as straight as in these examples. You are a consumer: think of how many different foods you eat. Consumers and decomposers rarely eat only 1 type of organism. A **food web** shows how all the species in a community or ecosystem are related in the search for food. Figure 9.6 shows 2 examples of food webs. What are some of the food chains within these food webs?

Food Webs

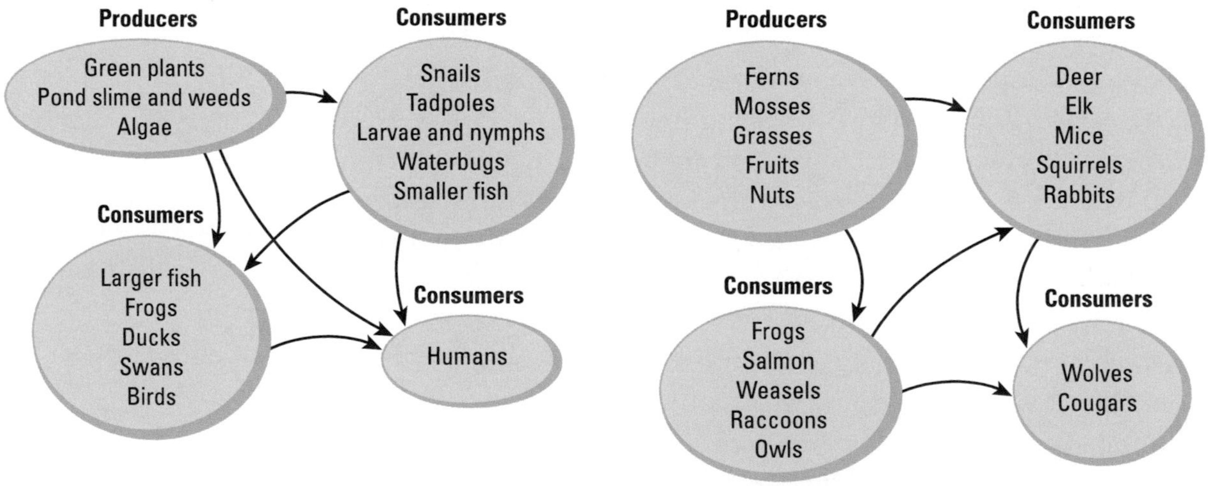

FIGURE 9.6 Although you may not want to eat everything an omnivore can eat, you could get the energy and nutrients you need from all the above. Where in North America do you think you would find each food web?

Energy Pyramids

When energy that began as food or sunlight moves through a food chain, organisms use some of that energy for motion, growing, producing body heat and other activities. Because energy is used for these activities at each stage of the food chain, the amount of available energy is less for each population higher up in the food chain. A food or **energy pyramid** shows the use and loss of energy at each point in a food chain. At the base of the pyramid are the producer populations, as shown in the example in Figure 9.7. At the top of the pyramid are the final carnivores which, when they die, get broken down by the decomposers and their nutrients returned to the food chain. There are always fewer carnivores than herbivores in an ecosystem, because the environment cannot provide enough energy to support a large number of carnivores.

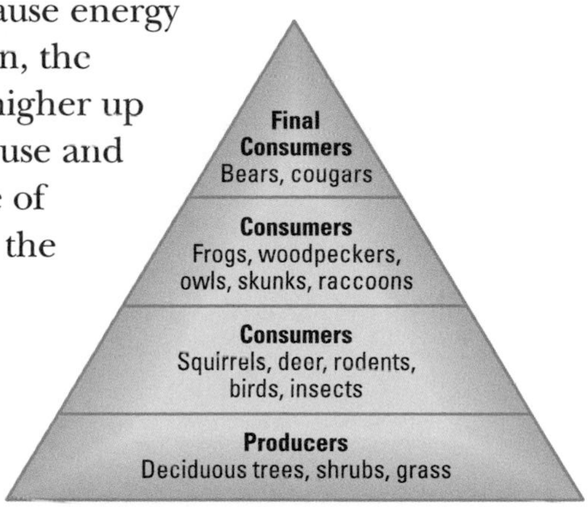

FIGURE 9.7 An energy pyramid. Where would you fit into an energy pyramid?

Agricultural Energy Pyramids

An agricultural energy pyramid shows the flow of energy through a food chain that includes foods produced by agriculture. In an agricultural energy pyramid, humans control the flow of energy. There is energy input from the sun, but we also add energy from oil, electricity and human labour. We use this energy to add nutrients and water to the soil, to sow and harvest crops, and to care for livestock. Figure 9.8 shows an example of an agricultural energy pyramid. What are some differences between this pyramid and the pyramid in Figure 9.7?

This addition of energy and nutrients helps farmers to grow all of our plant food, such as grains, fruits and vegetables. Some of the plants produced are fed to animals, such as chickens and pigs, which are then consumed by humans. Just as in natural energy pyramids, this move up the food chain results in an energy loss. In agricultural food pyramids, energy is also used in the manufacture of fertilizer and pesticides, in the care and shelter of livestock, and in the processing and transportation of crops and livestock.

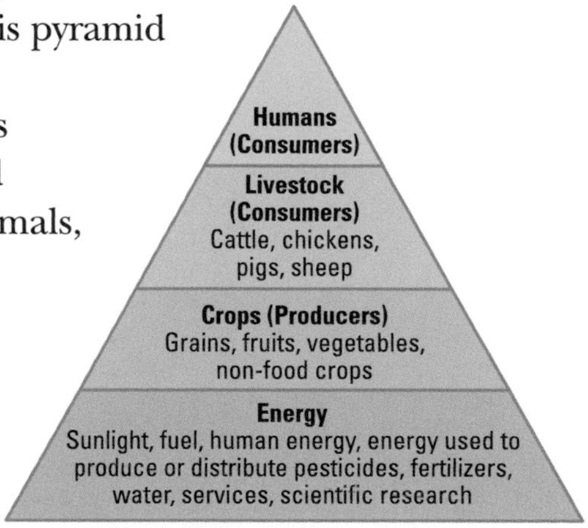

FIGURE 9.8 Would a vegetarian diet alter this food pyramid? Why?

Review and Apply

1. Draw a diagram of the ecosystem in which you live, showing all the elements in Figure 9.2.

2. What are the main parts of a food chain? What would happen if there were no producers? No decomposers?

3. Draw an energy pyramid using these organisms: owls, crickets, grass, mice, trees, frogs, hawks, shrubs, cougars, snakes and deer. Draw an agricultural food pyramid using these organisms: hay, chickens, corn, cows, sheep, tomatoes, apples, humans and wheat.
   a) Identify the producers and consumers in each pyramid.
   b) Identify the food choices for humans in the agricultural food pyramid that use the least energy. Explain your choice.

4. Look at the energy pyramid in Figure 9.9 and respond to the following, using pictures, words, or both.
   a) Not all the sun's energy taken in by the grass becomes energy available to the mice. How does the grass use up this energy?
   b) Not all the grass energy eaten by the mice becomes energy available to the snakes. How do the mice use up this energy?
   c) Why must there be many more mice than snakes in this pyramid? What would happen if there were no snakes? What would happen if there was no grass?

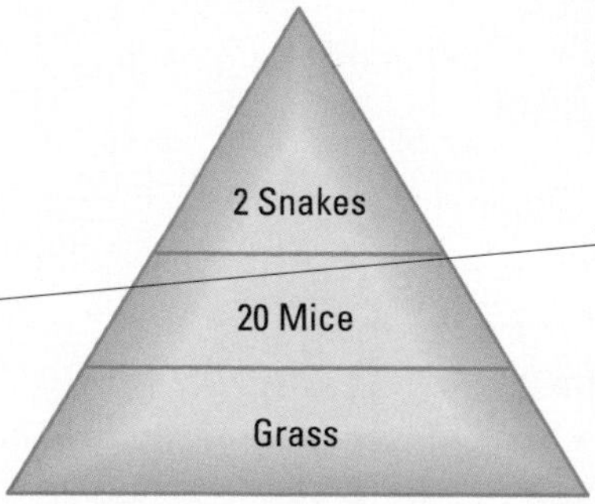

FIGURE 9.9

5. Organize the concepts you have learned in this section in a graphic organizer.

6. **Are you what you eat?**

   Humans can survive on an incredible variety of foods, leaving us with many options for our diets. Some people are omnivores and others are herbivores, or vegetarians. With a partner, brainstorm and research arguments for and against either lifestyle. Be sure to analyze the risks and benefits of the lifestyle to both the individual and to society.

Job Link

Parks Worker

Canada's national and provincial parks protect and preserve ecosystems, while allowing people to enjoy the natural world. Parks workers must understand the interactions of the organisms in the park ecosystems, and the impact humans can have.

Responsibilities of a Parks Worker

- protect and maintain ecosystems
- spread top soil, lay sod, plant flowers, grass, shrubs and trees and perform other landscaping activities in areas reserved for human use, such as picnic and camping areas
- maintain and repair buildings, roadways, walkways, and equipment
- operate and maintain heavy equipment used for park maintenance, such as snow plows and backhoes
- may help park naturalists to track numbers of particular species of plants or animals, especially endangered species
- may assist in presenting information on the park and its inhabitants to the public by giving talks or leading nature walks
- preventing and/or responding to emergencies, such as forest fires or floods
- police and assist park visitors

Where do they work?

- in provincial, national, and municipal parks and conservation areas

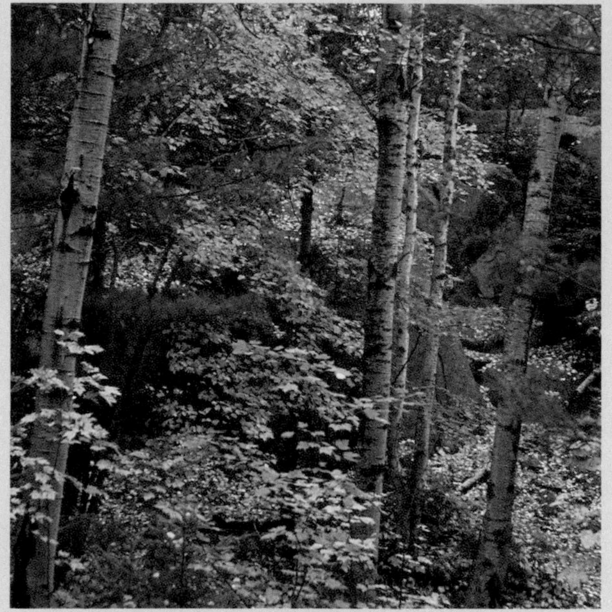

FIGURE 9.10 A parks worker helps to protect natural ecosystems.

Skills for the Job

- knowledge of organisms in the ecosystem and the interactions between them
- ability to work independently and as a member of a team
- a friendly, out-going personality
- may require some computer skills for parks that reserve camping spaces

Education

- a secondary school diploma may be required
- a driver's license is needed in most parks
- may require licenses to operate other machinery
- many positions require a diploma in natural resource management or a related area

LAB 9A

Building a Mini-ecosystem

Be Safe!

- Do not spill any water. Wet floors can lead to accidents.
- Wash your hands after handling soil, snails, or your mini-ecosystem.

Most natural ecosystems include some carnivores. What happens to an ecosystem when carnivores are absent?

Purpose

In this lab, you will set up and observe the changes that take place in an ecosystem composed of only producers and herbivores, and observe the changes that take place over time.

Materials

- 2-L clear plastic bottle, empty
- water that has been aged 3 to 4 days, to allow the chlorine to escape
- 20 g to 40 g of garden soil, not sterilized
- 200 mL pond water (make sure the water contains algae)
- 2 snails

Procedure

1. Rinse the bottle clean. Do not use soap.
2. Pour 1500 mL of aged water into the bottle. Let it stand for a few minutes.
3. Add 200 mL of pond water. Be sure that your pond water has some algae.
4. Add the soil.
5. Put the cap loosely on the top of the bottle. Place the bottle in a source of direct light.
6. In your notebook, create a data table like the one in Figure 9.12.

FIGURE 9.11 Your mini-ecosystem.

Day	Observations	Drawings
1		
2		
3		
4	Addition of 2 snails	

FIGURE 9.12

7. Observe your ecosystem daily for the next 3 days. Watch for any changes in the growth of the algae, the colour of the water, or in the soil. Record your observations in your data table.
8. On the fourth day, carefully add 2 living snails to your ecosystem. Continue to observe your ecosystem every class day for about the next 3 weeks. Record your observations in your data table. If necessary, use additional sheets of paper to make sketches of the changes you observe. Make note of changes in the number of snails, as well as changes in the amount of algae, water colour, and in the soil.
9. At the end of your experiment, clean up the components of your ecosystem as directed by your teacher.

Analysis and Conclusion

1. What was the source of energy for your ecosystem?
2. Construct a food chain showing the transfer of energy in your ecosystem.

Extension and Connection

3. What do you think would happen if you placed your ecosystem in a closet?
4. What happened to the snail population? What do you think would have happened if 50 snails were added instead of 2?
5. What would happen if no algae were present? Explain your answer.
6. In a pond ecosystem, birds and fish would be predators of snails. Would snails be able to survive for longer in your ecosystem, where there are no predators, or in the pond ecosystem, with predators? Explain your answer.
7. If you have a video camera available, videotape your ecosystem over the course of this lab to show changes over time. If you have a digital camera available, create a series of computer images based on the changes in your ecosystem.

9.2 Ecosystems in Action

Ecosystems are dynamic. There are many interactions between the abiotic and biotic factors. This results in constant changes to an ecosystem. Weather changes and seasons change. Organisms live, reproduce, and die, and populations increase and decrease. But what happens when a species disappears completely from an area? What if humans flood an area to build a hydroelectric dam or a manufacturing plant is built in the area? How do you think these changes affect ecosystems?

Population Growth

In an ecosystem, the number and variety of species can change for many reasons. Population numbers can change based on how many of a species are born and how many of the same species die over a given time. Usually, organisms have more young than is needed to replace themselves when they die. In this case, the birth rate is higher than the death rate. When there is nothing to control this growth, such as predators or limited food resources, a population can increase very quickly. Figure 9.13 shows an example of the world's human population growth. The Population Division of the United Nations estimates that the world population will be about 9 billion by the year 2050.

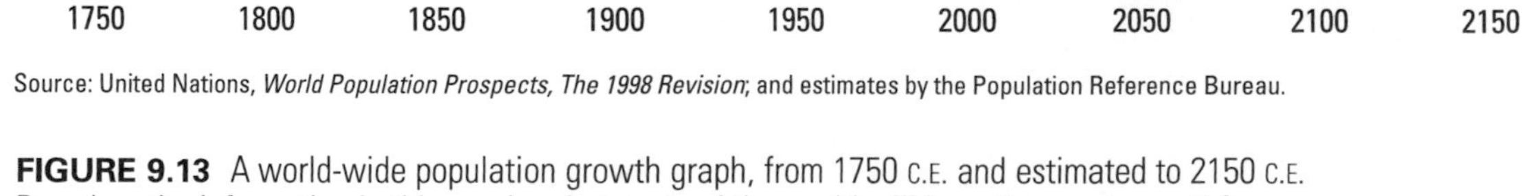

Source: United Nations, *World Population Prospects, The 1998 Revision*; and estimates by the Population Reference Bureau.

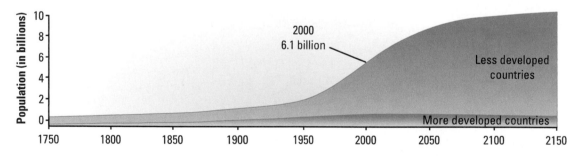

FIGURE 9.13 A world-wide population growth graph, from 1750 C.E. and estimated to 2150 C.E. Based on the information in this graph, what parts of the world will have the most growth?

Without population controls, a population will use up all of its resources and die. The availability of food at each level can have a big effect on population numbers. If a population of birds becomes much larger than its food supply, the birds will run out of food and eventually die. Fortunately, there are many natural factors that control population growth in ecosystems. Competition over resources can limit growth. Populations can move in and out of ecosystems, if they can adapt to a different ecosystem. Disease and natural disasters, such as fires or floods, can also quickly destroy entire communities. Humans can also be a factor in ecosystems. Populations move as we expand our cities and farms. Humans can affect whole populations by killing off predators or destroying a food source.

You will need to know about the impact humans have on their environment for your project, Examining an Environmental Issue.

Carrying Capacity

Carrying capacity describes or determines the population numbers that can be supported by the resources in an area, without ruining the environment for present and future generations. The natural factors mentioned above work together to keep populations balanced over time (Figure 9.14). In this way, organisms can make maximum use of the energy and nutrients available, without using them up. This balanced level is called the steady state. It is usually below the carrying capacity. Growing beyond the carrying capacity can cause the collapse of an ecosystem.

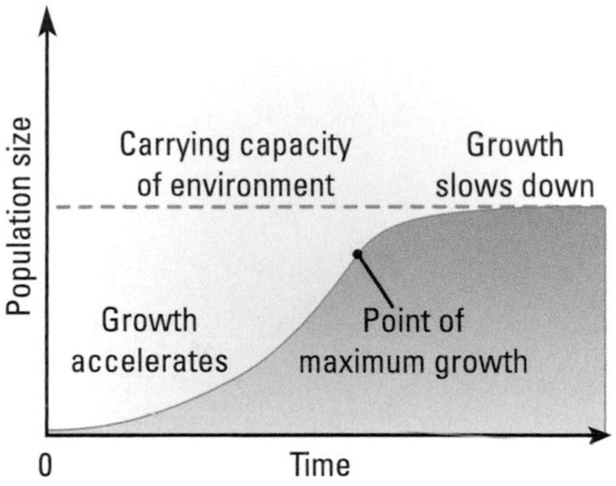

FIGURE 9.14 A carrying capacity graph. What happens in a natural ecosystem once a population exceeds the carrying capacity of its ecosystem?

Think of a school cafeteria. Sometimes it runs smoothly. Other times it can get overcrowded, with long lines and nowhere to sit. When that happens, you could say that the cafeteria's population is beyond its carrying capacity.

Figure 9.13 shows human population growth. When we consider how humans use Earth's resources, we must think about the carrying capacity of the planet. There are now over 6 billion people on Earth. What will happen if our population doubles in the next 50 years? Will we grow beyond the Earth's capacity to sustain us?

Earth's carrying capacity for the human population is very difficult to measure. Scientists have proposed comparing our use of resources to the Earth's ability to sustain us by using what is called an **ecological footprint**. This involves calculating the number of hectares of land that is needed to support an individual's lifestyle, including that person's food, clothing, housing, energy

FIGURE 9.15 Non-natural systems also have a carrying capacity. Would you say that capacity has been reached on the street pictured here?

consumption and other uses of resources. You have seen from examining an agricultural energy pyramid that it takes a lot of energy to raise food for our consumption. Driving a car and manufacturing consumer goods also uses energy that comes from Earth's resources. The more resources you use, the greater your footprint.

The ecological footprint, or number of hectares of land, needed to support the average Canadian is 7 hectares. In China, the average is 1 hectare per person. The number of hectares of land available over the whole planet that can be used to supply resources is 2 hectares per person. If every person in the world used resources at the same rate as Canadians do, we would need 3.5 Earths to sustain the world's population. Since Canada is a large country with a small population, we are living below the carrying capacity of Canada, but far above the carrying capacity of the Earth.

ScienceWise Fact

One hectare is approximately the size of a soccer field.

Surf the Web

Visit **www.science.nelson.com**, and follow the links for ScienceWise Grade 11, Chapter 9, Section 9.2. Find the link "ecological footprint." You will find a website that asks a series of questions about your food choices, shelter, travel and other habits, and then calculates your ecological footprint. If the number is given in acres, you can convert these to hectares by dividing the number of acres by 2.5. How does your ecological footprint compare with the average Canadian's? List some things you could change that would reduce your ecological footprint. Imagining you have made these changes, enter the information again and see how small you can make your ecological footprint.

Biodiversity

The energy and nutrients available in each ecosystem directly determine the variety of organisms that can live there. More energy and nutrients available to each organism means that an ecosystem can sustain a greater variety of species and greater population sizes. **Biodiversity**, a short form for biological diversity, describes the variety of living things found in ecosystems and in the world in general. For example, tropical rain forest ecosystems have many thousands of species of plants, mammals, birds, reptiles, insects, micro-organisms and other living things. Tropical rain forest ecosystems have very high biodiversity. The tundra ecosystems in the Arctic have only a relatively few species, leading to relatively low biodiversity.

FIGURE 9.16 The swamp contains many kinds of living things in large numbers. Variety and numbers are much smaller in the snowy Canadian tundra. Draw food webs for these 2 ecosystems.

Imagine that you are a very fussy consumer. In fact, you only like carrots. What would happen to you if a strange plague wiped out carrots? Would you starve to death? Clearly, it is an advantage to not only like a wide range of foods, but also to have a variety of food available to you. The situation is similar in the tundra. In some cases, consumers rely on 1 or 2 food sources for survival. For example, the main food source for wolves in the Artic is mice. If a disease or genetic defect wiped out the mouse population, what would happen to the population of wolves? Unless the wolves found another source of food, their ecosystem would no longer be able to sustain them. **Sustainability** refers to an ecosystem's ability to support life and maintain resources for future generations. Wolves living in an ecosystem with higher biodiversity have a greater choice of alternative foods, and so a better chance at survival.

The carrot example from the previous page may seem unlikely, but it is close to the truth. We are relying on fewer and fewer species of plants and animals as our food sources. As human populations grow and raise fewer and fewer species for food, we are in more danger of starvation if a disease or a pest were to wipe out crops or livestock.

FIGURE 9.17 We have a wide variety of food choices. Some developing countries have fewer choices, and all food crops and livestock are vulnerable to disease, pests, changes in weather and natural disasters. What does this mean for sustainability?

The Importance of Biodiversity

Earth's biodiversity provides for large, complex food webs that have many links between many producers, consumers and decomposers. Less biodiversity means fewer links, less complex webs and more serious consequences if a species disappears.

Scientists have identified 1.6 million species of living things. In fact, some scientists believe there are more species still to be discovered or identified, than have been discovered or identified so far. We depend on many living species for food, medicines and other products. Figure 9.18 shows the foxglove plant and the willow tree. Foxglove provides Digoxin, a heart medicine, and the fever- and pain-relieving powers of willow bark were the basis for the pain-reliever acetylsalicylic acid. New sources of foods and medicines might come from species that have not yet been discovered or properly studied. Earth's biosphere depends on all species, identified and unidentified, for natural functions such as cleaning the air and water, and making soil.

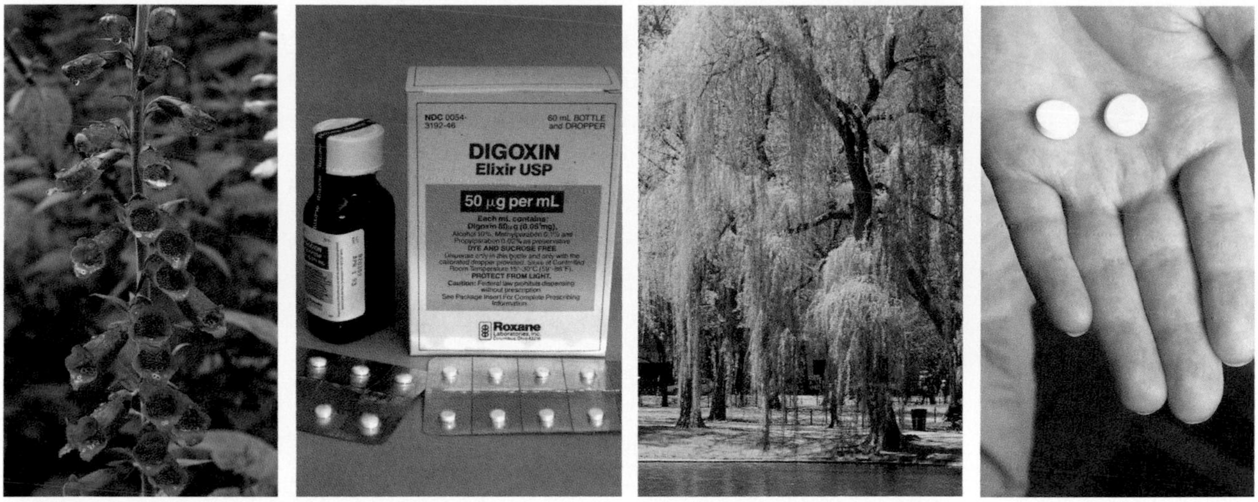

FIGURE 9.18 Foxglove, Digoxin, willow bark and acetylsalicylic acid. What and who would have been harmed if the plant species had disappeared before the medicines had been discovered?

Biological diversity can be observed in 3 ways.

- Ecosystem diversity — the wide range of ecosystems found around the world from the poles to the equator. Deciduous forest, prairie and tundra are all examples of Canadian ecosystems.
- Species diversity — the different kinds of living things found in ecosystems. Many species are too small to be noticed by most people, but they are very important in food chains and food webs.
- Genetic diversity — the genetic variety found within a species, which allows species to adapt to changes in the environment. The various breeds of dogs or the dozens of varieties of rice grown in Asia are examples of genetic diversity. Humans are also genetically diverse.

There is concern in Canada and worldwide that the range of biodiversity on the Earth is decreasing. As our population increases, we eliminate some ecosystems, such as wetlands, through the expansion of cities and agriculture. Overconsumption of resources, such as northern cod, and forms of pollution such as acid precipitation, result in species loss and therefore loss of Earth's biodiversity.

FIGURE 9.19 The grizzly bear is 1 example of a species at risk of extinction.

The changes we make put living things at risk of becoming extinct. A species is **extinct** when it no longer exists anywhere in the world. This can happen if organisms have no place to live, are unable to adapt to change, or are hunted to such a level they can no longer sustain their numbers through reproduction. This leads to fewer species and less species diversity. In Canada at present, there are about 350 endangered species (Figure 9.19).

How much biodiversity can we lose and still sustain life on Earth? We are only beginning to understand ecosystems and how all things are interconnected, both living and non-living. Imagine a huge structure made of pop cans. You carefully pull out a can near the bottom. Nothing happens. Then you pull out another can from a different place. Nothing happens. It looks like you can pull out a lot of cans and the structure will keep standing. Is this true? Or, after pulling out the fifth, or the twelfth, or the twentieth can, will the whole structure fall apart?

If the Earth loses 1 species, life will continue. If an alien species displaces a native species, life will continue. We do not know how many species the Earth can lose before the sustainability of life here becomes threatened. We can all do our part by being more aware of nature around us. Take time to appreciate it. Try not to destroy it or pollute it. Take care not to destroy native plants and animals. Do not use products made from endangered species.

ScienceWise Fact

The human population carries in its genes an enormous amount of genetic diversity. This diversity may explain why some people live longer than others or why some seem to be more likely to catch or develop certain diseases. Sickle-cell anemia is a genetic disease found mostly in people of African descent. When a sickle-cell gene is inherited from 2 parents, it can cause death because the body is unable to get enough oxygen. When the sickle-cell gene is inherited from only 1 parent it provides a person with immunity to malaria, a deadly disease found in central Africa, as well as Asia and parts of South America. Genetic diversity can have both advantages and disadvantages.

ACTIVITY 9B

Investigating Biodiversity

As human consumption and our use of resources grow, we are affecting species and their ecosystems. Are Canadian ecosystems in good shape? Are there areas of concern? What can be done?

What You Will Need

- paper, pen, pencil, drawing materials
- access to the Internet

What You Will Do

1. Your teacher will divide you into small groups of about 4 or 5. Each group will be assigned a type of ecosystem found in Canada from the list below:
   - arctic
   - boreal forest
   - deciduous forest
   - tundra
   - prairie
   - mountains
2. Using resources supplied by both your teacher and the websites suggested at **www.science.nelson.com**, (follow the links for ScienceWise Grade 11, Chapter 9, Activity 9B), select a plant or an animal species that lives in your assigned ecosystem and is considered to be endangered. Find out the following about your choice:
   - physical description
   - life cycle
   - habitat
   - food sources and predators
   - population statistics
   - present status
   - sustainability in its ecosystem
   - future prospects
   - agencies, organizations and groups that are working to protect your plant or animal and its ecosystem
3. Based on your research, report on your findings. Divide the work equally among your group members. Include charts, diagrams and pictures. You may choose to make a poster, a small booklet, or a computer presentation. Include in your report responses to the questions below.

What Did You Find Out?

1. How is your species important to its ecosystem? What effect would its loss have on the ecosystem?
2. What were the reasons for loss of diversity and habitat in the ecosystem you researched?
3. What are people doing to help protect your species? Is there anything you, your group, your class, or your community can do to help their efforts?

Making Connections

4. What human influences did you find present in your species' ecosystem? If human activity caused a loss of biodiversity, what did humans gain from the activity? What did the Earth lose from the activity? Consider social, economic, and technological gains and losses.

Science around Us

Zebra Mussels: Ecosystem Invaders

Zebra mussels are an excellent example of how a new species can quickly spread and take over an ecosystem. These mussels are small, freshwater molluscs similar to clams. It is believed they were unknowingly brought to Canada in a ship from Europe and released into the Canadian water system.

FIGURE 9.20 Zebra mussels can grow on any underwater surface and cause damage. Zebra mussels have no natural predators in Canada. How does this fact relate to the rapid increase in Zebra mussel populations?

They were first discovered in Lake St. Clair in 1988. Since that time, they have spread throughout the Great Lakes and the St. Lawrence River, as well as through some southern Ontario waterways.

Zebra mussels reproduce very quickly. A female can lay about 1 million eggs a year. The eggs hatch into free-swimming larvae that spread rapidly. In 2 to 3 weeks they attach themselves to any underwater surface. They grow shells that are usually about 3 cm long.

Zebra mussels can grow into large colonies. They have been found clogging water intake pipes for towns and industries. They have covered the bottoms of boats, as shown in Figure 9.20, and their sharp-edged shells will cut the unprotected feet of swimmers.

Surf the Web

Visit **www.science.nelson.com** and follow the links for ScienceWise Grade 11, Chapter 9, Section 9.2, to find out how Zebra mussels can affect the biodiversity of the Great Lakes. Present your findings on a poster.

Review and Apply

1. What factors can affect the size of populations and the variety of species in an ecosystem?

2. How does the increasing human population and our use of natural resources affect Earth's carrying capacity?

3. An early spring drought has dried up a number of ponds. In what ways might this affect the frog population? What other populations might be affected?

4. Discuss how the ecological footprint of someone living in a refugee camp would differ from your ecological footprint.

5. Suppose you were learning about motors by taking one apart, and there were 300 pieces. To be cautious, you probably would not throw away any of the parts, no matter how unimportant it looked. Explain why this is a good way to think of Earth's ecosystems and biodiversity.

6. What can happen to an ecosystem when it loses a number of species or abiotic elements, whether through natural means or through human intervention? In what ways can this loss of biodiversity threaten life on Earth?

7. Add the new concepts in this section to the graphic organizer you started in Section 9.1.

8. **Our Planet, Our Choice**

   With a partner, explore how your daily dietary choices affect your ecological footprint and your demands on natural resources, such as land use, pollution and energy. Keep a list of your food choices for one day and then explore some options for more environmentally friendly choices. How do your choices affect Earth's ability to support human life?

ACTIVITY 9C

Examining Population Change

We know that populations can change naturally, due to birth and death rates and the movement of animals. Hunting, or predation, is another factor that affects animal populations. Humans hunt many things, including whales. In this activity, you will see how hunting by humans caused a dramatic change in the populations of many whale species around the world.

What You Will Need

- graph paper
- pencils

What You Will Do

1. Figure 9.22 shows estimated population numbers for certain whale species before they were hunted by humans and at present.
2. Graph the data in Figure 9.22 using a bar graph. Try using graphing or spreadsheet software to create your bargraph.
3. Calculate the percentage of whales lost for each whale species. Use the following formula, with the Northern Right Whale as the example.

Northern Right Whales lost
= 10 000 − 350 = 9650

Percentage loss
= 9650/10 000 × 100 = 96.50%

What was the percentage loss of all populations combined?

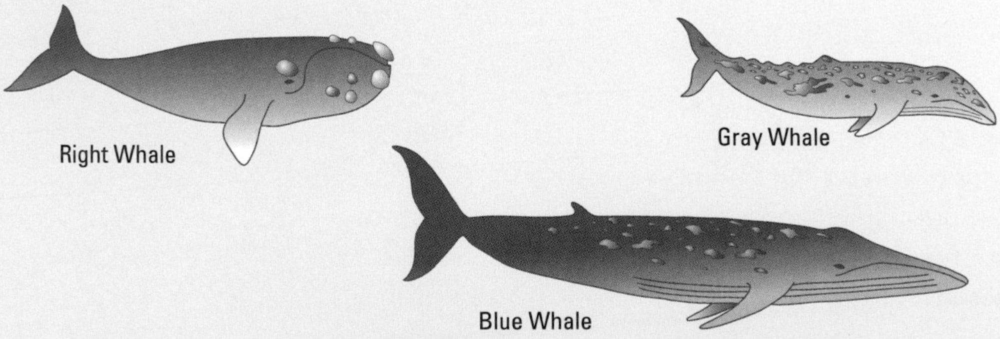

FIGURE 9.21 Use your school library or the Internet to find out where these whale species live.

Estimated Whale Population

Whale species	Population before hunting	Population at present
Northern Right Whale	10 000	350
Blue Whale	228 000	14 000
Sei Whale	256 000	54 000
Humpback Whale	115 000	10 000
Bowhead Whale	30 000	7 800
Gray Whale	20 000	21 000

FIGURE 9.22 Whaling data.

What Did You Find Out?

1. What is unusual about the Gray Whale population?
2. Which whale species do you think could most easily become extinct? Why?
3. In the 1800s, both the Northern Right Whale and the Gray Whale were hunted almost to extinction. What would you have predicted would have happened to the 2 populations? What actually did happen?

Making Connections

4. Whales are used for human and animal food. Whale oil is used for fuel and cosmetics. Explore the types of jobs linked to the whaling industry.
5. Except for some Aboriginal hunting, Canada has not had much of a whaling industry. This means fewer jobs for people. Is that good or bad? Explain your answer.
6. How do you think the extinction of whale species occurs? How could it be prevented?
7. Consider a whale's ecosystem. What would the loss of a whale species mean to the decomposers in its ecosystem? To the producers? How could this affect the biodiversity of the area?

9.3 Human Destruction of Ecosystems

Both by accident and on purpose, we are damaging ecosystems around the world. As our population increases, so does our use of resources and the problems caused by human consumption and over-consumption, such as the environmental problems caused by energy resource use that you learned about in Section 4.2.

Using Natural Resources

In the past 500 years, the human population has increased rapidly. It has followed the same pattern as the growth curve in Figure 9.13. Our large numbers are causing problems in ecosystems around the world.

We have become the world's largest consumer. Like all other living things, the human population needs energy and food for survival. However, unlike other consumers, human society has developed industry and technology to satisfy human wants, not just our needs. As the human footprint on the planet grows, we use up more and more resources. Some of the natural resources we use are:

- Energy
- Mineral
- Forest
- Marine
- Wildlife
- Water

Many scientists are predicting that we will soon run out of many of these resources and our use of natural resources can cause problems such as pollution, deforestation, habitat damage and species extinction. Following are a few examples of some types of human resource use and the problems they can cause.

Mineral Resource Use

The International Nickel Company (INCO) in Sudbury is one of the largest producers of nickel in the world. Pollution from nickel smelters killed all the plant life for many kilometres around Sudbury. To help solve the problem, a very large smokestack was built, like the one in Figure 9.23. Unfortunately, this just spread the gases over a much wider area. Filters were put in the stack to remove pollutants. Sudbury is now becoming green again with the help of volunteer planters.

FIGURE 9.23 Humans can both harm and help the environment. How is this demonstrated in these 2 pictures?

Energy Resources Use

The bird on the left in Figure 9.24 is covered with crude oil. Crude oil is the raw form of oil, before it is converted by oil refineries into gasoline and other products. Large ocean tankers transport millions of litres of crude oil from sources around the world to refineries found mostly in Europe and North America. Bad weather or human error can cause these tankers to have accidents and spill their contents into the ocean. Oil spills that reach the shore damage ecosystems and kill many plants and animals. The bird will die if not cleaned with human help.

FIGURE 9.24 How can taking public transportation, rather than driving alone in a big car, help prevent future instances of oil-covered birds and beaches like the ones shown here?

Forest Resource Use

The Amazon rain forest of South America has the greatest amount of biodiversity in the world. Every year, scientists are discovering new plants and animals in the Amazon. More and more of this diverse habitat is lost each year as the forest is chopped, burned and cleared to make room for farmland. The forest soil is low in nutrients. After 2 or 3 years of growing food, farmers must clear more land to continue farming. It is possible that the forest could be destroyed entirely, and this could lead to climate changes around the world. As you learned in Section 4.2, carbon dioxide is a greenhouse gas that contributes to global

FIGURE 9.25 Do you think it is worth losing large portions of the Amazon rain forest in order to have more room for cattle to graze? What can you do to prevent rain forest destruction?

warming. Trees in the rain forest use a lot of the carbon dioxide that is produced by the burning of fossil fuels, replacing carbon dioxide with oxygen. The rain forest also acts like a giant sponge. Without the trees to hold the water, the water will move to other parts of the planet, changing wind and rain patterns.

Marine Resource Use

Fishing has provided an important food resource for thousands of years. When early explorers visited Canada's east coast and the Grand Banks of Newfoundland, they reported the amount of cod to be so thick in the water that their boats had trouble sailing through them. Now, these fish are almost gone. In the mid-1990s, Canada banned fishing for cod and has since imposed strict limits on how many can be caught. This action has resulted in job losses and economic hardship for many people (Figure 9.26).

Surf the Web

Go to **www.science.nelson.com** and follow the links for ScienceWise Grade 11, Chapter 9, Section 9.3 to find out why there are limits to the number of fish and other animals that can be killed. Make a collage to explain your answer.

FIGURE 9.26 The fishers on strike show how environmental protection can conflict with the economy. What other industries might have the same conflict?

Review and Apply

1. Choose 3 of the natural resources listed on page 304.
   - **a)** List 2 jobs related to each resource chosen.
   - **b)** List 2 environmental hazards related to either the people working with these resources or to the environment through the use of these resources.
   - **c)** If cost, technological limitations and government regulations were not an issue, how would you make the use of these resources more environmentally friendly? Be creative. Use words, diagrams, charts, or whatever else you may need to make your innovation understood by others.
2. What types of industry or agriculture are in your area? In what ways might this industry or agriculture be affecting your local ecosystem?
3. Working with a partner, discuss the resources being used in the photographs you have seen in this section. What do you think we could do to use less of these resources? Explore different ways we can all contribute to help solve the problems discussed in this section.
4. Add the new concepts in this section to the graphic organizer you started in Section 9.1.
5. **Your Government at Work**

Over the years our governments have made many laws that may help minimize environmental damage. Both federal and provincial governments in Canada have environment ministries that make and enforce environmental laws.

Visit **www.science.nelson.com** and follow the links for ScienceWise Grade 11, Chapter 9, Section 9.3 for government environment websites. What types of laws have been passed? What laws do you think we need? Write a letter to an environment minister. Tell him or her about your concern, what you think of the existing laws, and what laws should be added or changed.

Do not think that letters to the government, to industries, or to newspapers are not effective in bringing about change. All of these groups are very interested in what the public thinks.

Companies that survey public opinion say that every letter written really represents 1000 people who have the same view but did not write a letter. Do your part as a concerned citizen. Always ask for a reply. You will receive one. Share it with the class.

CASE STUDY

The Oak Ridges Moraine and Urban Sprawl

Everyone needs a place to live. People also need jobs to pay for housing and food. Once you have finished school you will be looking for a full-time job and a place of your own to rent or buy. You will not be alone. Your schoolmates and students across the country will be in the same position. More housing will be built to meet these needs, which is good as it creates jobs in the construction and service industries. Unfortunately, there is also an environmental price to pay.

You could choose urban sprawl as the topic of your project, Examining an Environmental Issue.

Canada has many natural resources. However, there is one resource that is in short supply, high-quality farmland. Less than 1 percent of Canada's land area is considered high-quality farmland. The majority of this farmland is located within 160 km of our biggest cities. Guess where 75 percent of Canada's population lives? That's right, in those same cities. As the need for housing increases, cities expand outward and use more and more land. This expansion has been called "urban sprawl."

Urban sprawl is now causing a major problem in southern Ontario. The Greater Toronto Area (often called the GTA) is the fastest growing region in Canada. Development, such as building houses and roads, is expanding north from the city into an area called the Oak Ridges Moraine. Many concerned groups are asking that growth on the moraine be stopped and that other ways to solve the need for housing be found.

The Formation of the Moraine

Just what is the Oak Ridges Moraine and why is it so important? During the last ice age, glaciers covered much of Canada. These glaciers were huge sheets of ice more than a kilometre thick. About 12 000 years ago the ice melted, leaving behind big piles of sand and gravel. These big hills of sand and gravel are called moraines. The Oak Ridges Moraine is located north of Lake Ontario and stretches east to west about 160 km (Figure 9.27).

The layers of sand and gravel that make up the moraine act like a big sponge. They soak up rain water and melted snow. This water is then released to the 65 streams and rivers that start in the Oak Ridges Moraine. There are many kettle lakes and bogs

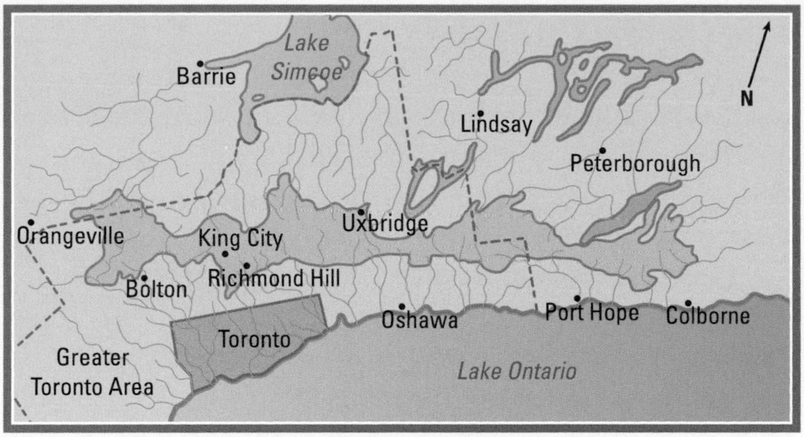

FIGURE 9.27 The Oak Ridges Moraine is indicated in purple.

or swamps on the moraine. Kettle lakes were formed when large chunks of ice melted and left holes in the ground. They have no inlets or outlets. Their water comes from crystal-clear springs. Most have steep, sandy banks and some are as deep as 30 metres.

Biodiversity on the Moraine

Close to 30 percent of the moraine is covered by forests. Many different species of plants and animals live on the moraine. Some of these are considered vulnerable, threatened, or endangered. They include:

- American Ginseng
- Red-shouldered Hawk
- Southern Flying Squirrel
- Jefferson's Salamander

FIGURE 9.28 Humans, plants and animals need places to live. What do you think we can do to make sure they all have proper living environments?

Much of the land cleared on the moraine is high-quality farmland. It is a source of food for many people in the GTA. Communities use the moraine as a source of clean groundwater. Many people use the Oak Ridges Moraine for recreation. There are hiking trails, parks and conservation areas in which to enjoy nature. There are already about 250 000 people living on the Oak Ridges Moraine. Real estate developers have plans to build housing for hundreds of thousands more people.

CONTINUED

FIGURE 9.29 Do we have to choose between one or the other? How do you think we can meet in the middle?

What Should Be Done?

People against this growth say that more housing and roads will damage the moraine. Wildlife habitat will be lost. Valuable farmland will disappear. There will be fewer places for recreation. The moraine's ability to hold water may be destroyed.

People who support the development say that by using the ideas of "sustainable development," there will be less environmental damage. Sustainable development for the moraine means that green space is planned into the design of new communities. Natural passageways will be left for wildlife and very sensitive areas will be left alone. Development on the moraine will also create thousands of jobs in the construction industry. Once there are new communities there will be many more jobs in the retail and service industries.

Local and provincial governments are working with both sides, trying to find a solution to this difficult environmental problem. It will not be easy.

Analysis and Communication

1. How would building on the moraine affect biodiversity? Explain.
2. Visit **www.science.nelson.com** for some links to sites about the Oak Ridges Moraine. Make sure to visit sites both for and against development of the moraine. After doing some research, decide what you think should be done. Work with a partner to defend your position.

Making Connections

3. What types of recreational activities happen on the moraine? What kinds of jobs are linked to the activities?
4. List some jobs connected to the construction industry. Do you think the construction industry supports development of the moraine? Support your answer.

9.4 Chapter Summary

Now you can...

- Describe ecosystems and how they work (9.1)
- Describe energy pyramids and agricultural food pyramids (9.1)
- Define population growth and explain how human population growth affects life on Earth (9.2)
- Define carrying capacity and biodiversity (9.2)
- Demonstrate why biodiversity is important to life on Earth (9.2)
- Explain ways that human activity destroys ecosystems (9.3)
- Describe how human activities affect the environment (9.3)

Concept Connections

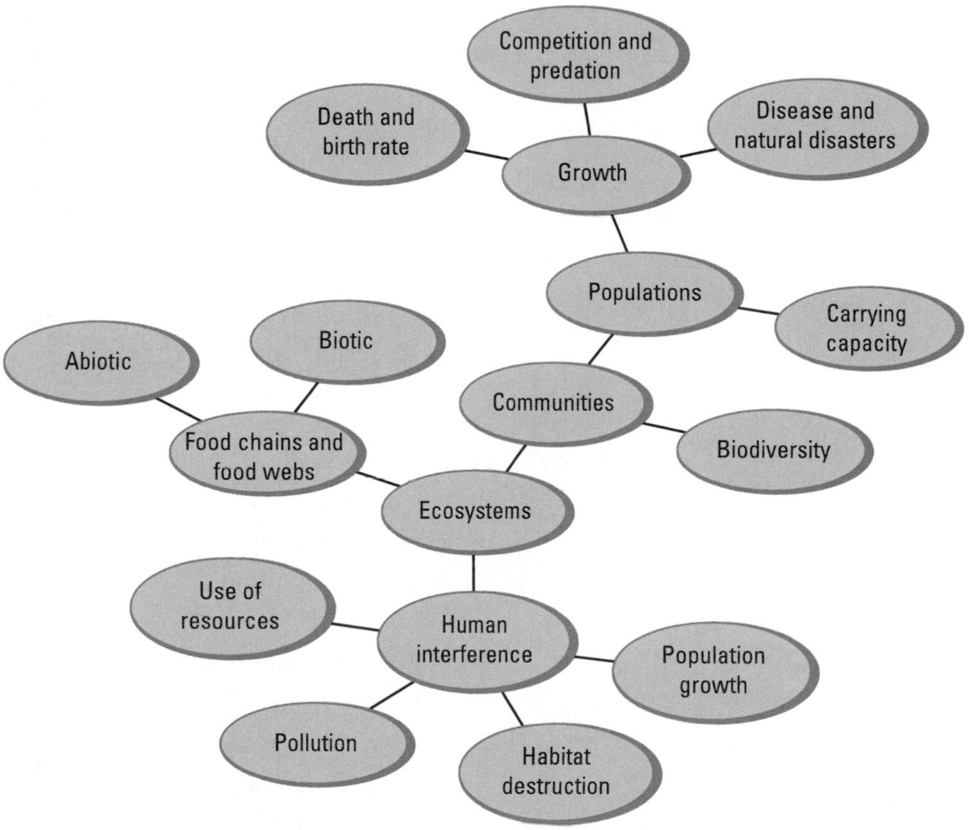

FIGURE 9.30 Compare your completed graphic organizer to the one on this page. How did you do? Can you add any new links to your organizer?

CHAPTER 9 *review*

Knowledge and Understanding

1. Match the words to their definitions:

a) eats meat
b) shows what eats what
c) a group of one type of plant or animal living in an area
d) shows energy being released in food chains
e) bacteria and fungi
f) makes food
g) describes the variety and numbers of living things
h) eats plants

i) energy pyramid
ii) decomposers
iii) food web
iv) producer
v) carnivore
vi) biodiversity
vii) herbivore
viii) population

2. Describe the natural ways that changes can occur in an ecosystem. Describe the ways that human intervention can change an ecosystem.

3. Think of the food you ate today. Draw a food web with you in it.

Inquiry

4. How could you use your mini-ecosystem to show the effects of pollution on the environment?

5. In 1901, Canada's population was 5 371 000. In 1951, it was 14 009 000. By 2001, the population had reached 30 007 094. Explain how this growth changes Canada's demands on natural resources. What lifestyle factors can change our demand on natural resources? How would these changes affect Earth's carrying capacity?

6. Many homes have compost bins. These bins help return important nutrients to the soil. Find out what foods go into a compost bin. Make a plan explaining why your school should have a compost bin. Explain how you would get people in the school to participate.

Making Connections

7. Canada's proposed Species at Risk Act, known as SARA, will be our legislation to protect endangered and threatened species. Using the Internet, research information about this legislation. How does it intend to protect species at risk? Do you think it will be effective? How would you improve SARA?

8. Why do elevators have signs listing the number of people that can be in them at one time? How does this relate to what you have studied in this chapter?

9 Do you have a part-time job or have you had a summer job? What tasks did you perform that may have affected the environment? If you have not had a part-time or summer job, think about what job you would like to do and how that may affect the environment.

10 Jobs in forestry, pipeline construction, or housing development could affect northern ecosystems. Explore the positive and negative impact that these jobs can have on the environment, economy and society in a small northern community.

Communication

11 Why should we be concerned about saving an endangered species such as the whooping crane or some plant in the tropical rain forest? Following are 5 reasons that we could consider:

a) Compassion — We feel sorry for species that may soon cease to exist or exist only in zoos.

b) Aesthetics — We see the beauty in the appearance, form and function of a species.

c) Economic worth — We understand the value of the food, medicines, or materials the species provides.

d) Life-support system — We appreciate the services provided by the species, such as oxygen production, carbon dioxide removal, filtering of pollutants, replenishing of soil, or pollination.

e) Ethical — We believe that each species is unique and irreplaceable, and has a right to exist.

The 5 reasons given for saving endangered species are in no particular order, and there are other reasons we could consider as well. In small groups, discuss these 5 reasons and decide what reasons you think are more important and which are less important? Write a report on what your group decided and why.

12 What do you think about the statement below? How does it relate to what you have learned in this chapter?

"The Earth does not belong to man, Man belongs to the Earth."

– Chief Seattle

CHAPTER 10

What Can I Do?

As we go through our everyday activities, our actions have an impact on the world around us. The activities we choose and how we choose to do them determines the amount of natural resources that we use. For example, you might choose to spend a day riding a bicycle, or you might take a drive to the shopping mall. Each of these activities uses different amounts of resources. Look at the pictures of Figure 10.1. What resources are used when laundry is dried outdoors in the sun and wind? How does this change when we choose to use a dryer? How much fuel would you use up if you choose to use mass transit? Would the amount of fuel change if you used a single passenger vehicle?

FIGURE 10.1

What You Will Learn

After completing this chapter, you will be able to:

- Analyze interactions between the environment and human activities (10.1, 10.2, 10.3)
- Describe the historical development and improvement of farming methods (10.1)
- Describe how and why a technology has developed and improved over time (10.1)
- Identify and explain various methods of waste management (10.2, 10.3)
- Explain the process of water treatment (10.3)
- Analyze specific technologies and their advantages and disadvantages to society, the economy and the environment (10.1, 10.2, 10.3)
- Describe the impact of humans on the environment (10.1, 10.2, 10.3)

Words to Know

agriculture
domesticated
fertilizer
genetically modified organisms
incineration
leachate
leaching bed
pesticides
pests
potable
resistant
sanitary landfill
septic system
sewage treatment plant
sludge
wastewater
wet mount

What You Will Do

- Analyze why and how fertilizer use has increased in Canada (Activity 10A)
- Analyze how much garbage your school produces (Activity 10B)
- Investigate the effects of pollutants on aquatic life (Lab 10C)
- Ask scientific questions and plan procedures that investigate damage to aquatic life (Lab 10C)
- Identify the factors that influence a decision on a science-related issue (Case Study)
- Compare various points of view on an environmental issue (Case Study)

A puzzle piece indicates knowledge or a skill that you will need for your project, Examining an Environmental Issue, at the end of Unit 5.

10.1 Food Production

Humans once lived in hunter-gatherer societies. They roamed from place to place in small tribes, eating whatever food they could find. They ate mostly plant material, such as roots, nuts, berries and seeds, and hunted game. Everything they ate, produced, and threw away was natural.

Early Farming

The amount of food that can be obtained by hunting and gathering is limited. When plants or animals cannot be found, hunter-gatherers may go hungry. Over time people found ways to produce their food, by growing plants and keeping animals. **Agriculture** is the use of land for growing plants (crops) and raising animals (livestock). Agriculture first developed about 12 000 years ago, in the area known as the Fertile Crescent (Figure 10.2).

Domestication

What is the difference between a crop plant and a wild plant? The main difference is that crops are plants that we humans grow to meet our needs. For example, we grow wheat because we can use the wheat grain for food. Similarly, a wild animal is one that does not normally live with humans. How would you define a tame animal?

All of our crops and livestock began as wild species. As human society developed, we found that some species were particularly useful to us. Over time, these species were **domesticated**, or made to live with humans.

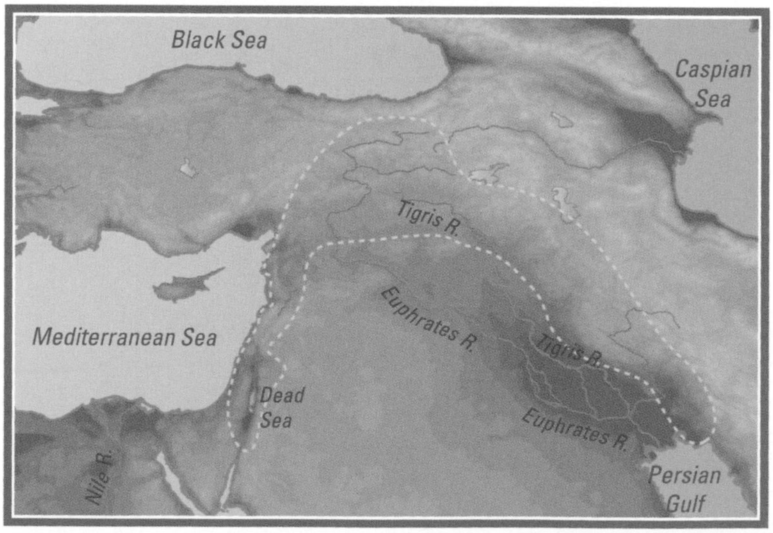

FIGURE 10.2 This map shows an area called the Fertile Crescent, the site of some of the earliest farming villages. Find this area on a world map.

The first animal to be domesticated was the sheep, about 10 000 years ago. Domestication of dogs soon followed. Over the next 3000 or 4000 years, many other animals were domesticated. Not all these animals were used as food. Some were put to work in the fields, helping to make farming easier for humans. They also provided companionship.

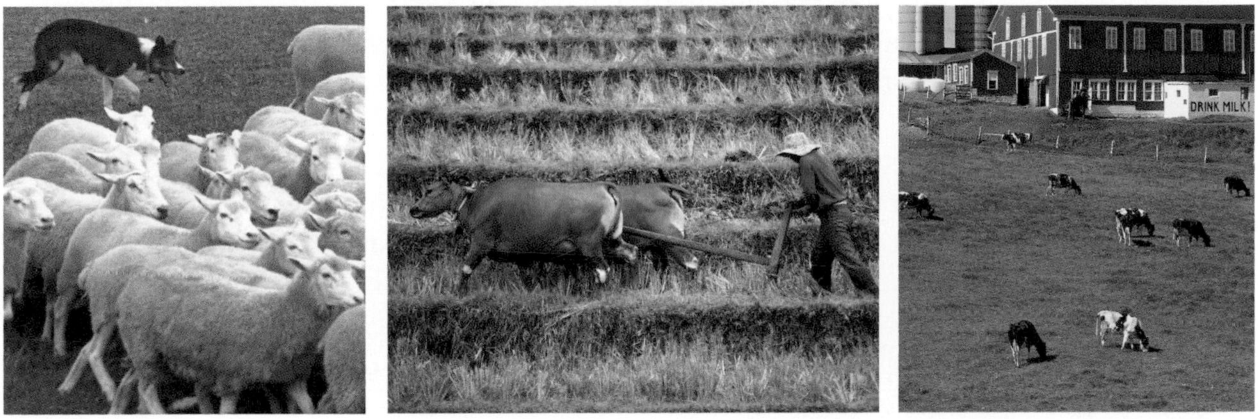

FIGURE 10.3 What animals do you see here? Why did humans choose these animals to domesticate?

Farming allowed people to stay in one place. Surpluses of food were grown and herds of animals increased. Secure food sources led to an increase in the human population, which led to the establishment of small villages and then towns. Trade developed, new occupations arose, and technological inventions were created.

Humans have also domesticated some insects, such as the honeybee. The honeybee was domesticated about 5000 years ago, in the Nile Valley of Egypt. Honeybees provide us with food, in the form of honey. They also pass pollen from plant to plant, which is essential for many plants to produce fruits or seeds (Figure 10.4). By keeping hives close to their fields, early farmers were able to provide food for humans and pollinators for their crops. Many farmers keep bees for these same reasons today.

FIGURE 10.4 Bees pollinate plants and make honey.

Modern Farming

You may need to know about the basics of agriculture for your project, Examining an Environmental Issue.

As our society developed, people learned more about the needs of the plants and animals they had domesticated. By providing crops and livestock with conditions to keep them healthy, farmers were able to increase the amount and quality of food they produced. Modern farmers continue to look for better ways to produce our food. We have also learned that some farming practices have a negative effect on ecosystems, and are working to reduce these effects.

Machinery

Throughout history, new technologies have been developed to produce more food of higher quality. At one time, all the work involved in food production relied solely on human labour. Farmers then used domesticated animals to help in their work, such as for pulling plows. The invention of the internal combustion engine revolutionized the farm workplace. Today, machinery has taken over much of the work previously performed by people and animals (Figure 10.5). Machinery allows us to produce more food, and more quickly and easily than previously. As a result, it takes far fewer people to run a farming operation.

Using machinery also requires energy, however. You saw in Section 9.1 that the agricultural energy pyramid takes into account all the energy used to produce foods. The earliest agriculture relied only on the energy from sunlight and the energy supplied by human labour. Today, much higher amounts of fuel are needed to run the machinery required to produce our food. The next challenge is to reduce the amount of energy used to produce our food. New engines that use less energy are being developed. New farming practices that require less use of machinery are also being adopted. These advances help our environment and can also save farmers money.

FIGURE 10.5 Modern agriculture is a big and expensive business. From what you see here, how has mechanization reduced the number of people needed to work on a single farm?

Pest Control

Every plant or animal that we use for food can also be food for other organisms. For example, corn is also food for many insects. Other organisms may also use the water and nutrients that we provide. For example, weeds use up the water and nutrients we provide to our crops. Since these unwanted organisms, or **pests**, reduce the amount and quality of food that farmers produce, controlling pests is an important part of successful agriculture.

FIGURE 10.6 A crop duster spraying a field with pesticides. Mechanization made the application of pesticides much more widespread.

Pesticides are chemicals that kill pests (Figure 10.6). There are three classes of pesticides commonly used in agriculture: insecticides that kill insects, herbicides that kill weeds, and fungicides that kill fungi. Most pesticides are human-made chemicals, but some are naturally occurring chemicals that we have learned to use for our benefit. For example, Bt toxin is a chemical produced by soil bacteria, which is used to control insects. You can find more information about the use of Bt toxin in Section 6.2.

Pesticide use can also cause problems. Some pesticides are toxic to many other organisms, including humans (Figure 10.7). Pests can also become **resistant** to the chemicals used to control them. When this happens, the pesticide is no longer useful, and new chemicals must be developed. When we control pests, we also affect the food chain that includes that organism. Insects, for example, are an important food source for many birds. By reducing the number of insects, we also reduce the number of these birds, which in turn affects the organisms that feed on the birds.

FIGURE 10.7 What should you do when you see this warning?

Surf the Web

Go to **www.science.nelson.com.** Follow the links for ScienceWise Grade 11, Chapter 10, Section 10.1, for more information on chemical-free pest control. ■

Today, scientists and farmers are working to find ways to reduce the harm caused by pest control. They have found that including the predators of pests in the agricultural environment can reduce the need for pesticides. Pesticides that are not as toxic or affect fewer species are being developed. Crops that are naturally resistant to pests are also being produced.

Fertilizer

Crops need nutrients from the soil to grow and produce our food. When they are in nutrient-poor soil, crops grow slowly, are smaller or become unhealthy. **Fertilizer** is any substance that is used to provide nutrients to plants. The earliest fertilizers were substances found naturally in the environment, such as manure. Manure adds nutrients to the soil through the action of decomposers. Today, nutrients are usually supplied by human-made chemical fertilizers. The use of fertilizer dramatically increases the amount of food that can be produced on a hectare of land.

Fertilizer use can also have negative environmental consequences. If manure is used as fertilizer, it is difficult to know the amounts of nutrients that are being added. If too many nutrients are added to soil, the unused nutrients wash into streams and lakes and cause algal blooms. Manure can also contain harmful micro-organisms that may pollute the water supply. You can find more information about these problems in Section 6.1. Because they are prepared with specific amounts of nutrients (Figure 10.8), it is easier to control the levels of nutrients added by chemical fertilizers. However, much more energy and resources are needed to make chemical fertilizers. Many chemical fertilizers are made from fossil fuels, which are in limited supply. Once all the fossil fuel supplies are used up, we will also run out of these fertilizers.

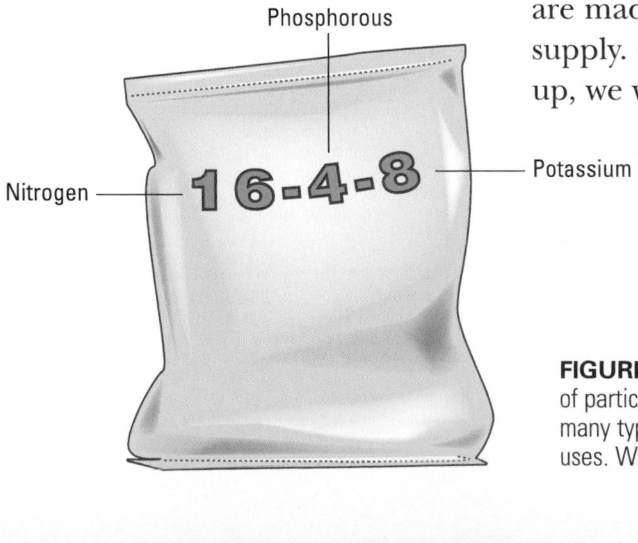

FIGURE 10.8 The numbers indicate the percentage of particular nutrients in the fertilizer mix. There are many types of fertilizers available for a wide range of uses. What is the advantage of this?

Changes in Crops and Livestock

Using machines and adding fertilizer has helped us to provide more food more easily. Equally important, however, is the changes we have made to the plants and animals that we use in agriculture.

From the first days of agriculture, farmers chose particular individuals of plants and animals to include on their farms. These plants and animals had characteristics that were valuable, such as producing large amounts of milk, or grain that could be made into good flour. Eventually, farmers began to breed particular plants and animals, so they could be sure that their offspring would have at least some of these characteristics. The species we use as crops and livestock today are the result of this selection process. Wild species of plants and animals have characteristics (traits) that help them to survive in their environment. Crop and livestock species have characteristics that are useful to us. This process has produced plants and animals that barely resemble their ancestors (Figure 10.9).

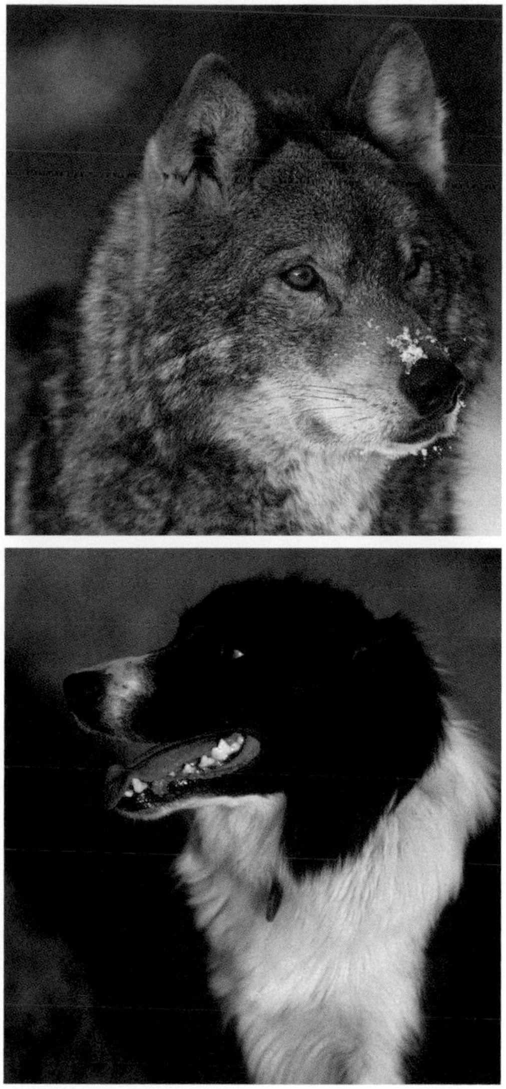

FIGURE 10.9 The border collie still has many traits in common with its wild relative, the wolf. What characteristics did humans select to develop this type of dog?

As we have learned more about how characteristics are passed from generation to generation, we have found ways of getting the traits we want at a much faster rate. The traits of an organism are determined by genes, which are part of the genetic material of a cell. Genes are passed on from one generation to the next. Scientists have found ways to change genes and even to move genes from one organism to another. **Genetically modified organisms** are organisms with changes in their genes. Scientists can now take desirable traits from one species and introduce it into a completely different species by moving particular genes.

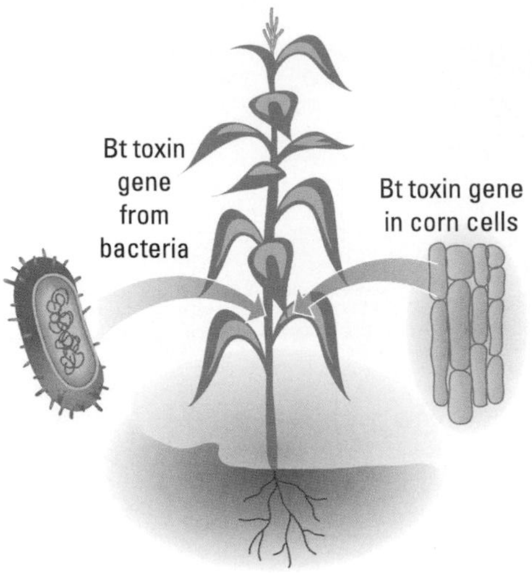

FIGURE 10.10 Scientists have produced a corn plant with its own built-in defences against insects.

For example, scientists have been able to produce corn plants that can make Bt toxin themselves (Figure 10.10). These plants do not need to be sprayed with the micro-organism that produces Bt toxin, so farmers have to use less energy and resources to control pests on this type of corn. Genetically modified organisms will also pass their human-added characteristics on to their offspring.

Many people have concerns about genetically modified crops and livestock. Moving characteristics between different species may have unforeseen consequences. For example, many crop plants can still breed with their wild relatives. If genetically modified crops that are resistant to a herbicide cross with their wild relatives, we might find that we are less able to control these plants. Our ability to produce food could suffer as a result. Other people are concerned that introducing characteristics from other species into our food could cause health problems. Producing genetically modified plants and animals also requires a lot more energy and resources than traditional breeding.

ScienceWise Fact

Scientists at the University of Guelph have developed a genetically modified pig that produces manure with 75% less of a particular plant nutrient. Widespread use of these pigs could help to reduce the problem of nutrient run-off from manure.

Biodiversity and Agriculture

As you learned in Chapter 9, the greater the biodiversity in an ecosystem, the healthier it is. For example, a diverse ecosystem can better withstand climate change or pollution than one with less diversity. In our agricultural systems, we are relying on fewer and fewer species of plants and animals, or lower and lower biodiversity, to supply our food. Today, less than 20 species of plants feed the majority of our population, and many of the traditional varieties or breeds of livestock, such as chickens, pigs and cattle, are on the verge of extinction. There are fewer varieties of wheat, corn, and rice grown as large seed companies persuade farmers, especially in developing countries, to abandon their traditional varieties in favour of a few particular varieties.

This lack of biodiversity is risky. For example, if a disease arose that wiped out any 1 of the plants or animals that we rely on, our entire food supply would be affected. In order to preserve the diversity of plants that supply food, the United Nations Food and Agriculture Organization is storing over a million seed samples, and efforts are being made to preserve traditional breeds of livestock.

ACTIVITY 10A

Fertilizer Use in Canada

Fertilizer was introduced in the 1920s, but not used until the early 1930s. It did not take farmers long to learn the value of fertilizing their fields. By graphing its use in Canada, you will see how fertilizer use grew during the last century.

What You Will Need

- graph paper
- pencils

What You Will Do

1. The table below (Figure 10.11) shows the number of thousands of tonnes of fertilizer applied each year in Canada at 10-year intervals (1996 is the last year for which data is available).
2. Make a line graph using the data provided.
3. Compare your results with your classmates.

Fertilizer Use in Canada

Year	Thousands of tonnes (000) per year
1921	0
1931	254
1941	289
1951	688
1961	961
1971	1885
1981	3501
1991	3811
1996	4378

Statistics Canada: *Human Activity and the Environment, 2000.*

FIGURE 10.11

What Did You Find Out?

1. Which 10-year time period had the biggest increase in fertilizer use?
2. What was the percentage increase in fertilizer use from 1931 to 1996?
3. From your graph, estimate how much fertilizer was used in 2001. How much fertilizer do you think will be used in 2011? Why?

Making Connections

4. Suggest several reasons for the increase in fertilizer use from 1931 to 1996.
5. How do you think a farmer would decide if it is worth the extra cost to use more fertilizer?
6. What types of jobs do you think were created by the increase in fertilizer use? Include jobs created by:
   a) the manufacturing of fertilizer
   b) the increase in food production
   c) the concern with excess fertilizer use

ScienceWise Fact

The food processing industry is the second largest manufacturing industry in Canada. In 1996, it employed 228 000 people and accounted for 11% of total manufacturing employment.

Job Link

Dairy Farm Worker

Dairy farm workers assist in the management and operation of farms that raise livestock for milk production.

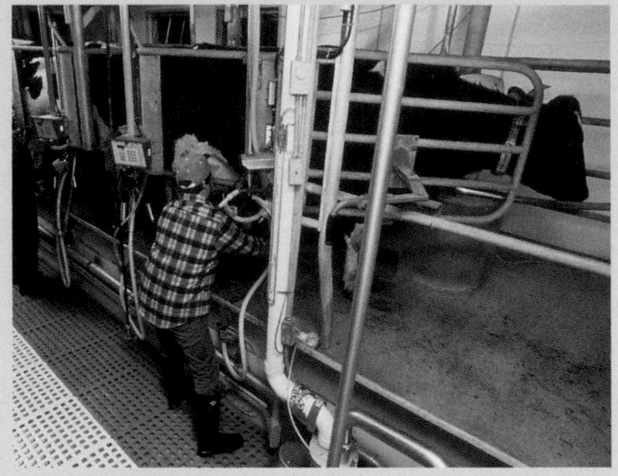

FIGURE 10.12 Dairy farm workers need to know about all aspects of farming.

Responsibilities of a Dairy Farm Worker

- feed and care for dairy cattle according to prepared schedules
- operate and maintain milking equipment
- maintain other related farm machinery, equipment and buildings
- may develop or keep financial and production records

Where do they work?

- privately-owned farms; many dairy farm workers are self-employed
- farms owned by corporate dairy producers

Skills for the Job

- good task planning and organizational skills
- ability to work as a member of a team
- may require good physical stamina

Education

- experience working with animals in a farm environment is generally required and is usually obtained on-the-job
- high school diploma is usually required
- specialized diploma in agricultural science may be needed in some workplaces

Review and Apply

1. Give 2 examples of species that were domesticated for agriculture. Explain why these examples were useful to humans.
2. What are the advantages of using machinery in agriculture? What are the disadvantages?
3. Explain why pesticides were developed.
4. Create a food web that shows how pesticides can have a negative effect on an ecosystem.
5. In a chart or table, compare the advantages and disadvantages of manure versus chemical fertilizers.
6. Describe the 2 general ways that humans produce plants and animals with the traits we desire.
7. Biodiversity is important to natural ecosystems. Is biodiversity important to agriculture? Explain your answer.
8. Organize the concepts you have learned in this section in a graphic organizer.

Try This at Home

Your Diet and Biodiversity

One reason why there is low biodiversity in agricultural plants and animals is that most of us only buy a limited range of foods. For example, maybe you only like apples, and so only buy that type of fruit. But how many other types of fruit have you actually tried? How much variety is there in the foods you eat?

1. For a week, keep a journal of all the different types of foods you eat. Include the ingredients listed on any prepared foods, such as breakfast cereals or frozen dinners.
2. At the end of the week, sort your list into species. For example, you might have eaten corn in the form of breakfast cereal, taco shells, and as corn-on-the-cob. Maybe you ate chicken in canned soup, as a take-out meal, and as luncheon meat.
3. Most of our food today comes from fewer than 20 species of plants and animals. Count up the number of species of plants and animals that were in your diet. How does your tally compare with the global average?

10.2 Where Does the Waste Go?

"Don't forget to take out the garbage!" A household chore right up there with "Clean up your mess!" There is no question that we live in a throwaway society. We produce. We consume. We create waste. Unlike natural ecosystems, most of our waste does not decompose and get reused in the food chain. In Chapter 9, you investigated ways in which we consume resources, and in Section 10.1 you investigated ways in which we produce food. Much of what we consume and produce either creates waste or becomes waste. As our population grows, we are making more and more waste. What do we do with it?

Waste Disposal

In Ontario, local governments are responsible for the disposal of household waste. Homeowners and renters pay taxes to the municipality for this service. If you are a renter, your taxes are included in your monthly payments. In most urban areas, garbage is picked up on a regular basis. Whether you drop it down a chute or take it to the roadside, your garbage disappears. But it does not just go away.

Landfill Sites

The most common way people dispose of garbage is to bury it in sanitary landfills. **Sanitary landfills** are large holes in the ground that we fill with the things we throw away. Figure 10.13 shows the parts of a sanitary landfill. Sanitary landfills are lined with layers of sealer to stop leakage into the ground. Pipes are placed along the bottom to collect liquid **leachate**, the liquid from garbage that drains to the bottom of the landfill site. Vertical pipes are used to vent the gas that is produced by the decomposition of garbage by bacteria. Some landfill sites collect this gas for later use or to generate electricity. All garbage delivered to the landfill is compacted and buried in layers by huge earth-moving machines.

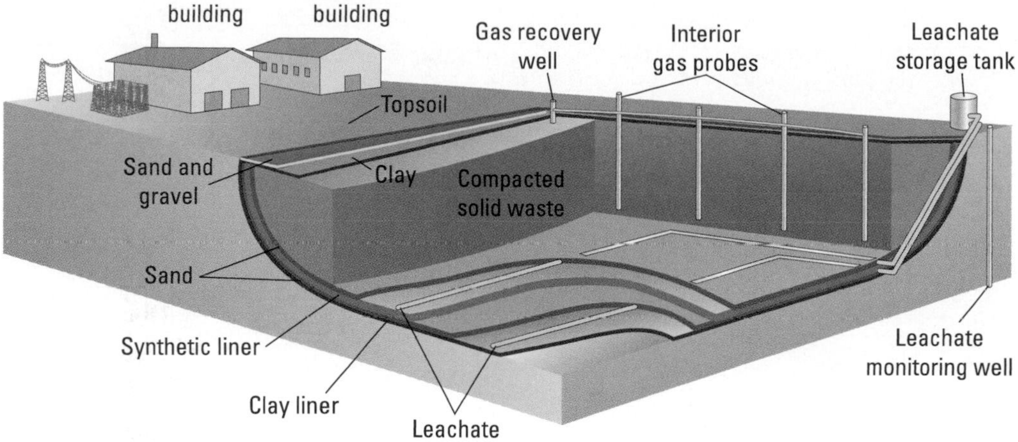

FIGURE 10.13 Parts of a sanitary landfill site. What does each part do?

New landfill sites must be made as older ones fill up. It takes years of research and planning to build a new site. Although we need to have landfill sites, no one wants to live close to one. This is often called the "Not In My Back Yard" or the NIMBY attitude.

You may need to know about waste disposal for your project, Examining an Environmental Issue.

Other Methods of Waste Disposal

There are 2 other main methods of getting rid of waste. They are burning, or **incineration**, and dumping in the ocean. These methods are rarely used in Canada, as they cause air and water pollution. But as landfill sites close and new ones become harder to find, some areas are considering using incineration again. New incineration technologies may be able to remove pollutants before they get into the air. The energy released from burning waste could also be converted to electricity.

Trucking Toronto's Trash

Toronto, Ontario is Canada's largest city. It also produces the most waste. Toronto sends its waste to sanitary landfill sites. Toronto has used the Keele Valley landfill site in York Region for many years. This site is now full and can no longer be used. The city has already begun to send garbage to new landfill sites in the state of Michigan, USA (Figure 10.14). Where does the garbage go in your municipality?

FIGURE 10.14 The garbage route. What environmental problems may be involved in trucking Ontario's garbage to Michigan?

FIGURE 10.15 Find out what qualifications are needed to drive a garbage truck.

Toronto's garbage goes on quite a journey. It starts at someone's home and is loaded into a city garbage truck. From there it is taken to a garbage transfer station. There are 7 transfer stations in Toronto. The garbage is then dumped into a 2-storey compactor, which stuffs as much garbage as possible into specially designed trucks and trailers.

These special trucks weigh almost 25 tonnes. They have 34 wheels instead of the usual 18, in order to support a 33-tonne load of garbage.

In 2001, up to 100 of these trucks travelled from Toronto to Michigan and back daily. This was planned to double after 2002, unless Toronto could find other sites.

Many people are concerned about road safety with the addition of this many trucks to the already crowded highways. Trucking officials say it is not that important an issue since there are already 15 000 trucks travelling Highway 401 every day. The trucking industry also provides a wide variety of employment opportunities for many people. Drivers are needed, and there are many jobs in manufacturing, maintenance, repair, inspection and shipping and receiving.

Surf the Web

Go to **www.science.nelson.com.** Follow the links for ScienceWise Grade 11, Chapter 10, Section 10.2, for links to the trucking and waste removal industries.

Reduce, Reuse, Recycle

The best way to increase the lifetime of a landfill site is to stop garbage from getting to it in the first place. Most communities have programs in place to encourage residents to do just that. If each one of us does our part, we can make a difference.

Reduce

Many municipalities now limit the amount of garbage a household can put out on collection day. Depending on where you live, it could be 2, 3 or 4 bags. In some areas, you must pay for each bag you put out.

Much of today's garbage is leftover packaging from products we buy. Following are some things you can do to reduce the amount of garbage you create.

- Buy products with little or no packaging.
- Say "No bag please" if you buy 1 or 2 items.
- At fast-food restaurants, do not take more straws, napkins, or packages of condiments than you need.
- Avoid using disposable plates, cups, and plastic cutlery.

FIGURE 10.16 What could you do instead of using disposable items? What else can you do to reduce the amount of waste going to landfill sites?

Reuse

Another way to keep things out of the garbage is to use them more than once. Here are some ways you can do this.

- Take a reusable cloth bag when shopping. Some stores charge for new bags.
- Reuse boxes and packaging.
- Use both sides of a sheet of paper when writing or copying.
- Use waste paper from computer labs for rough work.
- Buy products made from recycled material.
- Use rechargeable batteries.

FIGURE 10.17 There are ways to help the environment while shopping. Suggest 2 or 3 of these ways.

Recycle

In parts of Ontario, the blue box is now a familiar sight. By using these boxes, large amounts of garbage stay out of landfill sites and instead become a valuable resource. In 1997 alone, the Ontario Blue Box Program recycled 429 000 tonnes of paper, 102 000 tonnes of glass, 44 000 tonnes of metals and 27 000 tonnes of plastic. You can help make recycling run more smoothly by:

- separating recyclables into paper, glass, plastic and metals
- returning bottles and cans to collect on deposits
- taking hazardous wastes to safe disposal sites
- composting kitchen and yard waste in backyard or neighbourhood composters.

FIGURE 10.18 The blue box is everywhere. What items does your municipality recycle?

ACTIVITY 10B

How Much Garbage Does Your School Make?

Think about a typical day at school. What do you throw out? Where do you put it? It may not seem like much to you, but it adds up. In this activity, you will measure the amount of garbage your school makes in a day.

Be Safe!

- Wear protective gloves.
- Use caution when lifting bags.

What You Will Need

- bags of school garbage from the cafeteria, classrooms, offices, and hallways
- blue boxes of recyclable waste, if your school recycles
- bathroom scale
- notebook and pen or pencil

What You Will Do

1. For this activity, you will need the help of your school's custodial staff. Your teacher will arrange for the custodians to save all the garbage bags and blue boxes collected in the school the day before the activity. Ask if the custodians would separate the bags into piles from the cafeteria, classrooms, offices, and hallways.
2. Create a data table or spreadsheet to record your results. You will need columns for each of the garbage bag locations and for the blue boxes. You will also need to record the mass of the garbage and the kinds of garbage that were collected.
3. Visit the garbage storage area. Bring the scale, your notebook, and a pen or pencil.
4. Step on the scale and read your body mass. Record the number.
5. Weigh yourself again holding a bag of garbage. Record this number.
6. Calculate the mass of the garbage using the following formula:

   Mass of self with garbage − mass of self = mass of garbage

   Record the result.
7. Carefully open the bag and record the kinds of garbage in the bag: organic, paper, metals, plastics, glass, and so on. Note roughly how much of the garbage is recyclable waste. Close the bag when you are finished.
8. Record the information.
9. Repeat steps 4 to 8 until all the bags and boxes have been measured and analyzed.

10 How many bags were measured? Enter the mass of each garbage bag in your data table or spreadsheet.

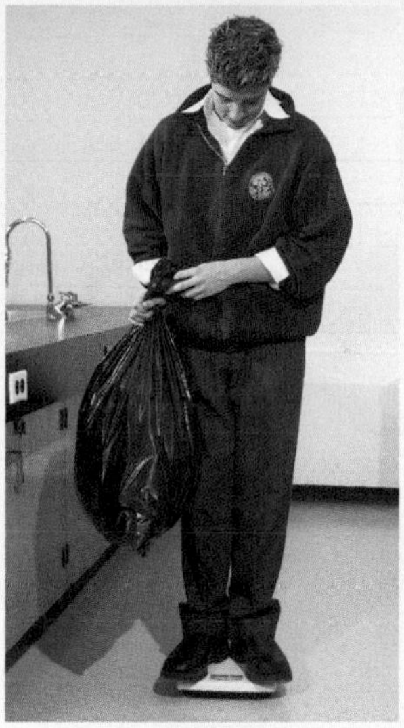

FIGURE 10.19 Weighing in.

What Did You Find Out?

1 Calculate the total amount of garbage measured from the cafeteria, classrooms, hallways, offices and blue boxes. What was the total mass? What was the average mass of each bag?

2 What percentage of the total mass of garbage was in blue boxes and was to be recycled? Did you find recyclable waste in the garbage bags? Estimate how much of the waste in the garbage bags could have been recycled if it had been placed in blue boxes.

FIGURE 10.20 What was your result?

3 Assuming you measured a typical day's garbage, how much would your school produce in a week? In a year? How much would each student produce? Did the results surprise you? Why or why not?

Making Connections

4 How can your school reduce the amount of garbage it produces? You may want to ask the school custodians for some ideas. Based on your assessment of the contents of the garbage bags, make lists similar to those on page 329 for your classroom to help encourage your classmates to reduce the amount of garbage they produce. Make another list of suggestions for the cafeteria. Distribute your suggestions in class and in the cafeteria. Set an example by using recycled or scrap paper and include a request to recycle the paper.

5 How has this activity helped you to understand 1 of the jobs done by your school's custodian? Besides co-ordinating garbage collection in your school, custodians work in many other areas. What else do they do to help your school run smoothly and efficiently?

6 What qualifications would you need to become a custodian? How do you apply?

7 Perform the same activity at home. Present your family with the results and discuss how you can reduce the amount of waste at home.

CASE STUDY

Who Wants a Landfill Site?

Welcome to Anytown, Ontario

Anytown, Ontario is fictional, but it is a lot like many towns. Anytown is not too big and not too small. It has municipal services, nice shops, good schools, parks and recreation, and some light industry. However, some of the young people have to look elsewhere for work. The town council could use more tax dollars, and some business people would like more business, but overall, Anytown is a good place to live.

FIGURE 10.21 Anytown is a friendly, welcoming town. Will it also welcome a new sanitary landfill site?

The town council of Anytown has just announced a proposal to build a sanitary landfill on the edge of town. This landfill will use up some farmland and about half of a hardwood forest, and new roads will be needed. The sanitary landfill will also provide employment and more tax dollars. Because building a sanitary landfill has both benefits and costs, the town council has called a town hall meeting for the residents of Anytown to share their views. After the meeting, the town residents will hold a vote to accept or reject the proposed new sanitary landfill.

Before the Town Hall Meeting

You and your classmates each have a role to play in the town meeting. You will be role-playing 1 of the following town residents: the mayor, a town councillor, a farmer, an unemployed person, a member of the local environmental club, a homeowner, a restaurant owner, a real-estate agent, a parent, a construction worker, a doctor, or a truck driver.

Meet with all other classmates who will be playing the same role as you. For example, if you are to play a construction worker, meet with all the others playing construction workers. Discuss the advantages and disadvantages of the proposed sanitary landfill from the perspective of the person you are playing. For example, would a construction worker be likely to get more business from this project? Use print and electronic resources to find additional information on sanitary landfills and their effects on communities.

All Come to Order!

The mayor has called the meeting to order. Everyone will now get a turn to describe his or her position on whether the sanitary landfill should be built. Be prepared to give convincing reasons for your position. Listen and take notes on the positions of the other town members. When everyone has finished his or her presentation, take a class vote on whether to accept or reject the proposed sanitary landfill.

Analysis and Communication

1. Write a short essay summarizing your position on the landfill. Compare your position to the positions taken by 1 person who agreed with you and 1 person who disagreed with you.

Making Connections

2. Based on your experience during this activity, why is it important for community members to participate in making decisions about environmental issues? How does hearing different viewpoints benefit a community?

3. Before it can be constructed, government specialists analyze all possible environmental, economic, and social impacts of a sanitary landfill. The government then approves or rejects the sanitary landfill based on this analysis. From the presentations in the town hall meeting, make a list of all the possible impacts of the sanitary landfill that the government should consider.

Review and Apply

1. **a)** Describe the actions you currently take to reduce, reuse and recycle. Provide examples for each.
   b) Describe 3 additional actions you could take in each area.
2. What safety features are built into sanitary landfill sites to protect the environment?
3. What types of jobs are related to waste management? What types of jobs and industries have been created by recycling programs?
4. Investigate recycling in your community. Is your community exploring new ways to reduce garbage? What are the options? Phone or visit your municipal office and find out.
5. Add the new concepts in this section to the graphic organizer you started in Section 10.1.
6. **The Life of a Newspaper**

   Working with a partner, put "reduce, reuse, recycle" into action. To make a poster, draw all the stages you know in the useful life of a newspaper, beginning as a tree. Show how your newspaper goes through the various processes: reduce, reuse and recycle.

10.3 Down the Drain

As well as producing solid waste that is taken to landfills or recycled, we produce liquid **wastewater** or sewage every time we use the toilet, take a shower or do laundry. This water must be treated to remove harmful chemicals and micro-organisms before it can be returned to rivers or lakes.

Sewage Treatment

When the human population was small, waste was simply dumped or buried. As the population grew, dumping waste into the streets was no longer a solution. As you have already learned, this can cause the outbreak of many diseases. To control the disposal of waste, underground pipes are built connecting the various buildings in towns and cities. Wastewater is collected in them and channelled to a central location for disposal. These pipes are called sewers. Today most sewers are connected to a **sewage treatment plant**, which is a facility where sewage is treated and water purified before it is returned to the environment. In addition to household sewage, sewers also carry sewage from industrial and commercial activity.

FIGURE 10.22 Where are the water-using areas in your home? Where do you think the water goes?

There are 3 levels of treatment in modern sewage treatment plants.

Primary Treatment
Insoluble garbage, such as sticks and cloth, are removed by filters and sent to landfill sites.

Secondary Treatment
Solid matter, or **sludge**, is separated from liquid in sedimentation tanks. The sludge settles to the bottom of the tanks and is then removed and sent to digestion tanks, where bacteria break it down. Some sludge is dried and incinerated to reduce volume, but most is directly spread on fields as fertilizer. The liquid is sent to aeration tanks where more bacteria break down any remaining sludge. It then goes to a final sedimentation tank for removal of any remaining sludge. Finally, the water is disinfected with chlorine and discharged into a river or lake.

FIGURE 10.23
A sewage treatment plant. Find out where the water is discharged in your community.

You will need to know about human impact on the environment for your project, Examining an Environmental Issue.

Tertiary Treatment

In some cases, a third level of treatment is used to remove contaminants left over from secondary treatment. These contaminants are chemicals that should not be released into our environment, such as heavy metals like lead.

As our cities grow, the demand for sewage treatment and sewage workers will also increase.

Septic Systems

Most urban areas have a sewage system of some type. Rural areas are more likely to use **septic systems**. These are systems designed to treat the sewage of a single house.

Wastewater from the house enters the septic tank, which is usually buried at the side or in the backyard. Heavy matter settles to the bottom of the tank, where it is decomposed by bacteria. Liquids leave the tank and flow out through a distribution box to a **leaching bed**. The leaching bed is a network of perforated pipes. The liquid then filters into the ground, where bacteria decompose the waste.

People who have septic systems must be careful about what they put down the drain. Grease, garbage and toxic chemicals can affect the operation of the system. Also, the tank must be pumped out every 2 or 3 years to prevent sludge buildup. Septic systems can be a source of pollution if they are too close to a lake, stream or well.

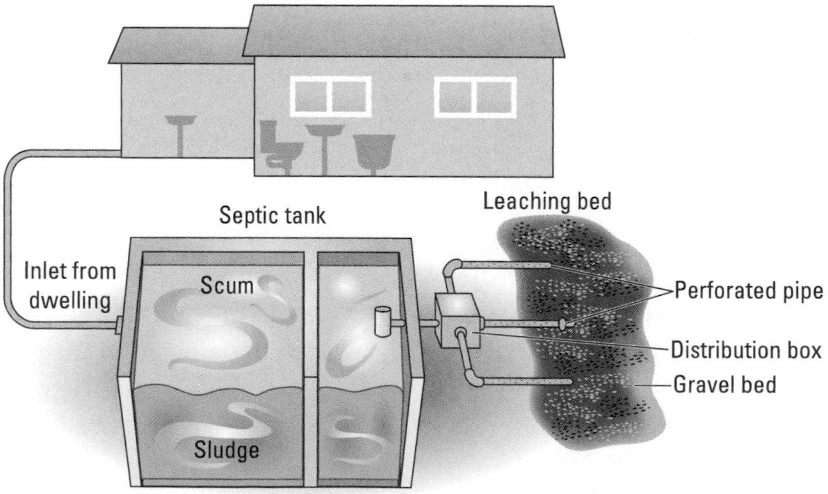

FIGURE 10.24 A septic system. How could it be overloaded?

Where Does the Water Go?

When it rains or when snow melts, the water not absorbed by the ground flows downhill into streams, rivers, and lakes. This water is called runoff. Roads, towns, and cities can block runoff water, which can then collect in hollow areas and cause flooding. When trees and other vegetation are removed from the land surface for farming or building, water can move more quickly, carrying away soil and leaving cuts in the ground. This is erosion. Properly channelling runoff can help prevent erosion.

We have developed systems to deal with the problems of erosion and flooding. In rural areas, ditches and culverts are used to direct runoff. A culvert is used when ditches go underneath roads. In towns and cities, storm sewer systems are built to collect runoff and send it underground to streams, rivers, or lakes. This water is not treated in the sanitary sewer system, but goes directly into the river or lake.

Wetlands such as marshes, bogs, and swamps are nature's system of holding back water. This helps prevent flooding. The wetlands and the plants in the wetlands are also very effective filters. The plants remove many chemicals and organic matter from the water as it flows through the wetland.

FIG 10.25 What happens if you dump toxic chemicals into a storm sewer?

ScienceWise Fact

Some small communities have used lagoons or ponds to process sewage. The filtered water is then released into a wetland. Tests show that when the wastewater reaches nearby streams and rivers, it is cleaner than water treated in regular sewage treatment systems. Unfortunately, the lagoon system cannot process large amounts of sewage from a large city.

Turning on the Tap

Sometimes we forget that all the wastewater we send to sewage treatment plants today will be the same water we bring into our homes in the near future. In Ontario, our water comes from the Great Lakes, rivers, or groundwater. Groundwater is water that is stored deep underground in soil and gravel deposits. It is precipitation and runoff that has taken many years to filter downward and is usually very clean. It is critically important that these water sources are protected from pollution by agricultural runoff of fertilizers and manure, industries, landfill sites, and careless dumping.

Communities have water treatment plants for treating water before it comes into your home. This makes the water safe to drink, or **potable**. Water treatment plants remove debris, cloudiness from tiny soil particles, and micro-organisms by using sand and gravel filters, and disinfect the water you use by adding chlorine or ozone. Some communities add fluoride to help prevent tooth decay.

LAB 10C Assessing Harm

In Unit 1, you learned about the safe handling of chemicals. Some people choose to ignore these rules and dump unsafe material down the drain. What can happen to ecosystems if unsafe materials are released into the environment?

Be Safe!

- Wear eye protection and protective gloves.
- Handle all liquids carefully. Avoid spilling. Return materials to your teacher as soon as you have finished with them.
- Clean up thoroughly.
- Note any HHPS symbols on the chemicals and handle then accordingly.

Purpose

In this lab, you will examine the effects of a chemical on an aquatic ecosystem.

Materials

- safety goggles, lab coats and gloves
- mini-ecosystem from Lab 9A, with the snails removed and returned to a safe environment
- test chemicals, such as dish detergent or bleach
- graduated cylinder
- microscope
- microscope slides

Procedure

1. You will be testing the effect of a common chemical pollutant on the growth of algae in the mini-ecosystem you constructed in Lab 9A. Be sure all snails are removed from your mini-ecosystem before you begin. Read through the entire procedure. In your notebook, create a data table to record your observations.

2. Using the dropper, add 1 drop of the water in the ecosystem to a microscope slide. Carefully lower a cover slip onto the drop, being careful to avoid making air bubbles. This method of preparing a sample for viewing is called a **wet mount**.

3. View the wet mount with the 10× objective lens on your microscope. In your data table, describe the number and kinds of organisms you observe.

4. Choose 1 chemical to test. Measure and add 25 mL of the chemical to the ecosystem.
5. Record any changes that you can observe without the microscope.
6. Repeat steps 2 to 3. Record any changes you observe with the aid of the microscope.
7. After 30 minutes, repeat steps 5 and 6, and record any changes that have occurred.
8. Repeat steps 5 and 6 after 24 hours, and again after 1 week.
9. Dispose of your mini-ecosystem as directed.

Analysis and Conclusion

1. Create a chart or other presentation that summarizes the effects of the chemical on your mini-ecosystem. Did the chemical damage the ecosystem? What evidence did you use to decide if there was damage?
2. Exchange summaries with a group that tested a different chemical. Compare the effects of the chemicals.

Extension and Connection

3. Have you ever put any of the chemicals tested in this lab down the drain? Based on the results of this lab, will you continue to put these chemicals down the drain? Justify your answer.
4. A cottager accidentally releases a large volume of the chemical you tested into a lake.
   a) How would this chemical affect the algae in the lake?
   b) How would this chemical affect other micro-organisms in the lake?
   c) What effect would the changes to the algae and other micro-organisms have on the food web of the lake ecosystem?

Review and Apply

1. Summarize the stages of sewage treatment.
2. What potential environmental problems do septic systems pose?
3. What are the risks to our water supply that result from population growth? Consider all the parts of our water supply: sources such as lakes, rivers, and groundwater; community and rural water treatment; and the disposal and treatment of wastewater.
4. In communities with a municipal water supply, the cost of sewage treatment is often linked to the amount of water used. Do you think this is fair or unfair? Why?
5. Add the new concepts in this section to the graphic organizer you started in Section 10.1.
6. **Groundwater Contamination**

   The groundwater sources of a small town are found to be contaminated from various chemicals that, for many years, were carelessly stored by the paint manufacturing company in the town. Safe water has to be piped from a nearby city.

   Townspeople are worried about their health and the health of their children. The paint factory is the major employer in the town. Describe:

   a) the problems this situation poses
   b) the steps needed to solve the problem
   c) various solutions to the problem
   d) who should be involved in the decision-making process
   e) what additional information is needed
   f) how to get all parties to participate.

10.4 Chapter Summary

Now you can...

- Describe how human activity affects the environment (10.1, 10.2, 10.3)
- Explain how new technology increased world food production (10.1)
- Explain the importance of biodiversity in agriculture (10.1)
- Identify and describe the methods of waste management (10.2, 10.3)
- Describe how we treat sewage before releasing it back into the environment (10.3)
- Identify the advantages and disadvantages of various technologies (10.1, 10.2, 10.3)

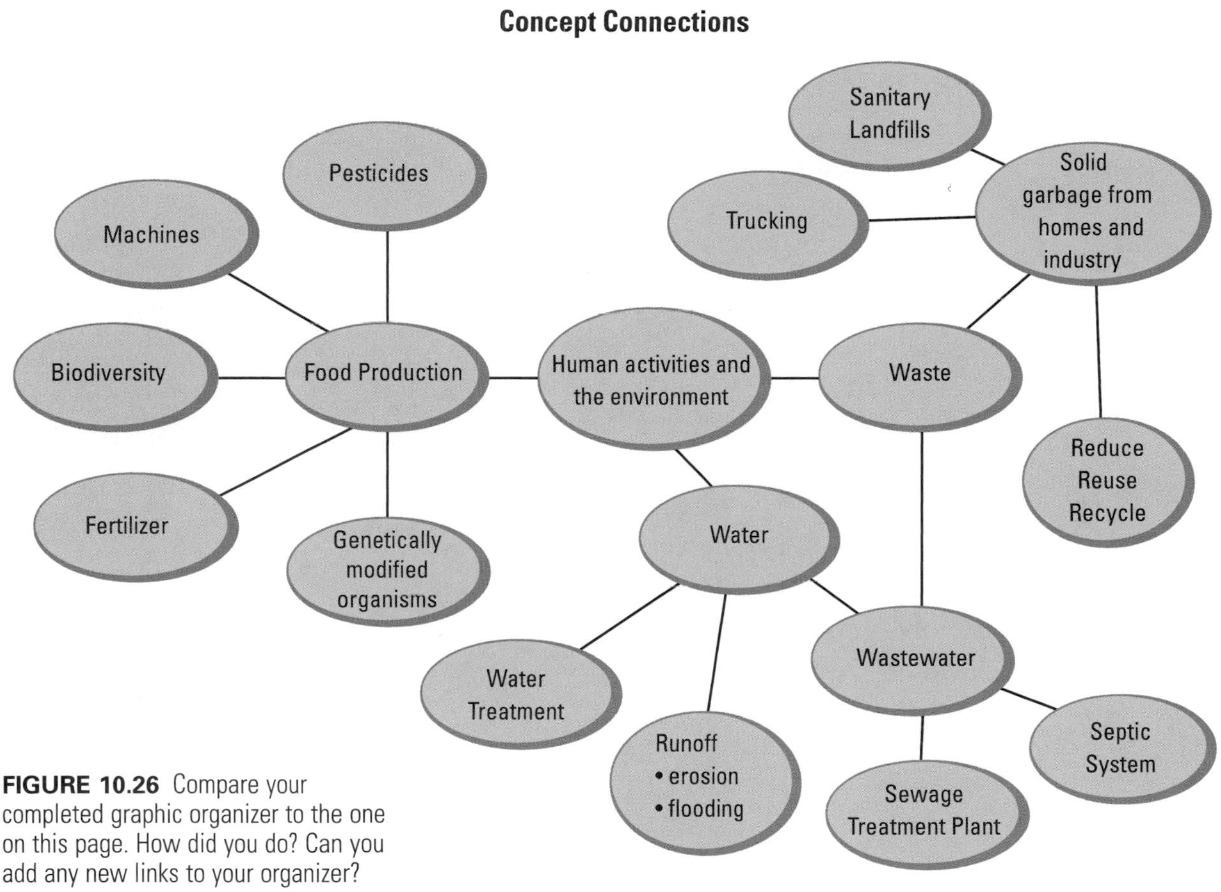

FIGURE 10.26 Compare your completed graphic organizer to the one on this page. How did you do? Can you add any new links to your organizer?

CHAPTER 10 *review*

Knowledge and Understanding

1. Briefly define 6 key words from the Words to Know list on page 315.
2. Using words or pictures, trace how a single cup of water comes into your home, how it is used and how it is then released back into the water system.
3. Why have communities introduced recycling programs?
4. What does the bacteria do in a sewage treatment plant?

Inquiry

5. What do you think would happen if you put some fertilizer in your mini-ecosystem?
6. Some toilets use 6 to 8 litres of water per flush, while others use up to 20 litres. One load of laundry can use as much as 200 litres. A 10-minute shower can use 100 litres. Find out how much water your toilet, washing machine and shower use. Then calculate how much water these 3 appliances use in your home in 1 week. Suggest ways your household could reduce its water usage.
7. The food industry employs many people in Canada. What kind of work do they do?

Making Connections

8. In the past, most agricultural work was manual labour in the fields and stockyards. Now workers must have much more knowledge and many skills. Why?
9. Select 1 of the following scenarios. Use what you have learned throughout this text about chemicals, electricity, micro-organisms, human health and the environment to determine how your chosen scenario will affect the community, the economy and the environment.
   a) A developer wants to build a golf course on undeveloped land.
   b) A large farm decides to become "organic" and use only environmentally friendly practices.
   c) A rainstorm overloads the sewage processing facility of a small community.
   d) A company that manufactures herbicides proposes to build a factory near a town that is surrounded by both vegetable farms and wetlands.
   e) Ontario Power Generation agrees to build an experimental wind turbine electrical generator to supply a small isolated community with electrical energy.

10 More herbicide and insecticide is used in Saskatchewan than any other province. Why?

11 As you know, a lot of the garbage that ends up in waste disposal sites is packaging. In 1988, about 5.4 million tonnes of it was sent to landfill sites. In 1996, about 2.6 million tonnes ended up in landfill sites. Why do you think this reduction happened?

Communication

12 Make a poster to advertise a recycling program. Your poster must show people what to recycle, how to recycle, and when to recycle. Get your information for the poster from the recycling program in your municipality.

13 Suppose a landfill site was to be built near where you live. How would you feel about it? Write your ideas in your notes and share them with some of your classmates.

PUTTING IT ALL TOGETHER

Examining an Environmental Issue

Canada and U.S. reach new agreement on emissions
Smog levels highest ever

FIGURE E1

There is no question—the environment is big news. In newspapers, magazines, and on TV, we are constantly hearing about some environmental event, whether it is local, national, or international in scale. It is important for all of us to learn about environmental issues. After all, the Earth is the only planet we have. We live here and we need to take care of our home.

The Plan

With this project, you will have the opportunity to explore an environmental issue or problem. You will look for causes and effects and suggest possible solutions to the problem.

What You May Need

- paper and pen
- recent newspapers, news magazines, or newsletters, and/or Internet access

What You Will Do

1. As a group, look through recent newspapers, magazines or Web sites for articles dealing with environmental issues. Find articles on at least 3 different issues.

2. From the articles you found, as a group choose 1 issue to investigate further.

3. Collect additional articles and information related to the issue you chose. You can find information from many sources. For example, you might find additional newspaper articles, write to an expert on the issue, or interview someone whose workplace is affected by the issue. For each source you find, prepare a point-form summary of the additional information. Note the source of the information (e.g., the title of the publication or the name of the person), and the date of the publication or conversation.

4. Meet the other members of your group, and discuss the information you have collected. As a group, prepare a summary of the issue. You can complete an effective summary by answering the following questions:
   - Who?
   - What?
   - Where?
   - When?
   - Why?

5. Decide as a group on an effective way to present the information you have collected. Your presentation must clearly address the following points:
   a) the problem or issue you investigated
   b) the reasons you chose this problem
   c) the solutions that have been or are being tried
   d) alternative solutions to the problem, suggested by either other people or by you
   e) the strengths and weaknesses of each solution
   f) the solution you think would be the most effective, and your reasons for choosing that solution

6. Share your learning with your classmates.

Assessment

1. What issues did you and your classmates investigate?
2. Of the issues that were presented, which were local issues? Which were national issues? Which were international?
3. What did you learn about environmental issues?
4. Consider the issues raised. What are some additional questions you would like to ask about these issues? What issues would you like to get more involved with?
5. Based on what you learned from your classmate's projects, how have your views about the future of our planet changed? Give reasons for your answer.
6. In a paragraph, comment on what you think was done well in other groups' presentations. Did any projects go beyond the guidelines? If so, what was the end project like? How could you improve your project if you had the opportunity?

Glossary

A

abiotic: the non-living things in an ecosystem, such as air, rocks and water

absorption: process of chemical substances entering the body through the skin and eyes

acid cabinet: a well-ventilated, sealed cabinet where acids are stored

acid precipitation: rain, snow, or hail that is much more acidic than it is supposed to be, causing damage to forests, crops and buildings

activity series: list of how well a metal gives up electrons

acute: having a quick effect after a short exposure

agriculture: the use of land for growing plants (crops) and raising animals (livestock)

algal bloom: a very high concentration of algae cells that are harmful to the environment

allergen: anything that causes an allergy

allergy: an immune response by the body to something that is not usually harmful

alternating current (AC): the back and forth movement of electrons through a wire

ammeter: device used to measure current (i.e. it measures how many coulombs of charge pass a certain point in a circuit every second)

ampere: unit of electric current

anatomy: refers to the structure of organisms

antibiotic: chemical that kills or slows down (inhibits) the reproduction of micro-organisms

antibiotic resistant: the ability to withstand an antibiotic that should kill or inhibit the growth of a micro-organism

antibiotic susceptible: micro-organisms that are killed or stop reproducing in the presence of an antibiotic

antibody: a chemical that can determine if something in your body is foreign or non-self (i.e. it is not really a part of you)

antigen: anything in your body that an antibody has determined to be foreign or non-self

antiseptic: a chemical that slows down the growth of micro-organisms and can be applied to the skin (e.g. when you cut yourself)

aqueous solution: dry chemicals that have been dissolved in water

asexual reproduction: reproduction without exchange of genetic material

atom: the smallest particle of a chemical element; it is made of a positive nucleus (containing protons and neutrons) surrounded by electrons

auto-ignition temperature: the temperature at or above which a material will spontaneously ignite without an external spark or flame

auto-immune disease: disease in which the immune system attacks cells in a person's own body

B

bacteria: micro-organisms that cannot make their own food; they have a cell wall but no nucleus; they come in different shapes: either rod or stick-shaped, circular, or spiral

binary fission: division of a cell into two equal halves; sometimes the process can take as little as 20 seconds

biodiversity: the variety of living things found in ecosystems and in the world in general; short for biological diversity

biosphere: all the ecosystems on Earth

biotic: the living things in an ecosystem, such as plants, animals and micro-organisms

blue-green algae: monera containing no cell nucleus and living in water only; they can make their own food

budding: division of a cell to form two new cells, in which the new cell is always much smaller

Building Code: laws ensuring the safe construction of buildings

C

Canadian Hazardous Products Act: safety law requiring all consumer products containing chemicals to be identified properly

Canadian Standards Association (CSA): a not-for-profit organization made up of members from many different occupations and backgrounds who develop a set of standards that address issues like improving public safety and health

carbon: a chemical that is used to make substances that provide energy for many organisms, including humans

carbon cycle: the process by which carbon is used again and again by organisms

carrier: an organism that is infected by a pathogen but is not sick (*see* vector)

carrying capacity: the population numbers that can be supported by the resources in an area, without ruining the environment for future generations

cellular membrane: the thin layer that surrounds a cell and keeps the jelly-like cell contents together

chemical change: process of forming a new chemical substance; it usually occurs when a gas is formed, heat or light are given off or a precipitate is formed

chemical reaction: process in which reactants are converted into products

chlorophyll: a chemical that is required in the process of photosynthesis and gives organisms like blue-green algae their characteristic colour

chloroplast: a cell structure that carries out the process of photosynthesis

chronic: having an effect that requires repeated exposure and that involves a delay between the time of exposure and any health symptoms

circuit breaker: an automatic device that is designed to open when too much current flows through it

closed circuit: an unbroken electrical path through which electrons are moving

combustion reaction: a chemical reaction in which a substance combines with oxygen to produce heat and light

communicable disease: a disease that can spread from person to person (*see also* infectious and contagious disease)

community: composed of all the different populations that share a particular area

compost: soil that is high in nutrients (made from kitchen, garden and animal waste)

composting: the process of turning kitchen and garden waste into nutrient-rich soil

conductor: a device that allows electricity to pass easily through it

consumer: an organism that gets its food by eating other organisms

contagious disease: a disease that can spread from person to person (*see also* infectious and communicable disease)

corrosion: the process of corroding; of a metal being chemically eaten away

coulomb: unit of electric charge

current: the flow of electrons around an electric circuit

cytoplasm: a jelly-like substance found in all types of cells containing the genetic material

D

decomposer: an organism that uses dead plants and animals as food

decomposition: process by which substances are broken down, or decomposed

direct current (DC): the movement of electrons through a conductor from a negatively charged area to a positively charged area

disease: a change in the normal way a body functions that causes harm to the body

disinfectant: a chemical that can kill micro-organisms on surfaces

domesticated: made to live with humans, especially agricultural plants and animals

dry chemicals: chemicals that are found in crystal or powder form and are stored on shelves according to their group name

E

ecological footprint: the number of hectares of land needed to support an individual's lifestyle, including that person's food, clothing, housing, energy consumption and other resources

ecosystem: all the biotic factors plus the abiotic factors that interact in an environment

electric circuit: path through which electricity flows

electric power: energy per unit time measured in watts or kilowatts

electron: a negatively charged, sub-atomic particle

energy pyramid: a pyramid-shaped graphic showing the use and loss of energy at each point in a food chain

energy source: source that gives the circuit its energy

exposure: the process of being in contact with a chemical; depends on both the concentration of the chemical and the length of time of contact with it

extinct: the state of a species when it no longer exists anywhere in the world

F

fertilizer: any substance that is used to provide nutrients to plants

filamentous: term meaning long thread-like; can refer to the shapes of micro-organisms such as fungi

Fire Code: laws containing fire safety standards to reduce the risk of fires

flammable cabinet: a sealed cabinet where chemicals that are easily set on fire are stored

flashpoint: the minimum temperature that can cause a chemical to give off a vapour that will combine with the air and burst into flames

food chain: the sequence through which energy transfers from organism to organism

food poisoning: disease caused by eating food that contains harmful micro-organisms

food web: a graphic that shows how all the species in a community or ecosystem are related in the search for food

fragmentation: formation of small pieces, by spore formation, or by sexual reproduction

fume hood: a well-ventilated, closed area that allows one to work or do experiments without breathing in excess fumes

fungi: micro-organisms that are composed of at least one cell and contain a cell nucleus; most fungi undergo both asexual and sexual reproduction

fuse: excess-current protection device (*see* resistor)

G

galvanizing: process in which a less reactive material is coated with a more reactive material

general defence: a defence that acts against any pathogen (e.g. your skin and your macrophages)

genetically modified organisms: organisms with changes in its genes, especially human-made changes

global warming: increase in the average temperature of Earth's atmosphere

greenhouse gases: gases that absorb infrared radiation, heating up the atmosphere

ground fault circuit interrupter (GFCI): device that detects and shuts-off unwanted current flow that may produce shock or fire hazard

H

HHPS (Household Hazardous Product Symbols): symbols identifying consumer products containing chemicals

hydrocarbons: chemical compounds made of hydrogen and carbon atoms

I

immune: the state your body is in when it can resist infection by the pathogen that causes a disease

immune response: the human body's response to an antigen it recognizes

immune system: network that carries white blood cells and antibodies to where they are needed; made up of lymph fluid, lymph vessels and nodes, the thymus, the spleen, and the tonsils

incineration: burning, especially of garbage or other waste

incomplete combustion: combustion reaction in which products like carbon monoxide and carbon are formed because there is not enough oxygen present to convert the hydrocarbon into carbon dioxide and water

infected: the state your body is in after being exposed to a pathogen

infectious disease: a disease that can spread from person to person (*see also* contagious and communicable disease)

ingestion: the process of eating and swallowing; provides a way for chemical substances to enter the body

inhalation: process of breathing in; provides a way for chemical substances to enter the body

ion: an atom that has gained or lost an electron

irradiated: exposed to high energy beams (e.g. to control harmful micro-organisms)

J

joule (J): SI unit for energy

K

kilowatt (kW): unit of electric power

kilowatt hour (kWh): gives how much electricity is used over a certain time; one kilowatt hour is 1000 joules of energy each hour

L

leachate: the liquid from garbage that drains to the bottom of a sanitary landfill

leaching bed: a network of perforated pipe in a septic system

life cycle: refers to all the stages that occur from the time an organism is first formed to when it first reproduces

lightning arrester: safely guides a lightning strike to the ground without damaging the equipment

load: a device or appliance that uses energy

lymph: a watery fluid similar to blood plasma that is used by the immune system to carry white blood cells and antibodies to where they are needed

lymph node: part of the immune system that filters out pathogens and harmful chemicals and that produces white blood cells

M

macrophage: cells in the blood that fight infection

micro-organism: any living thing that is too small to see with the naked eye; it can be helpful or harmful

monera: micro-organisms composed of one cell that does not contain a cell nucleus

mould: fungi that usually are filamentous

MSDS (Material Safety Data Sheets): sheets providing detailed information about the chemical product

mucus: a thick, sticky fluid that is expelled when you sneeze

mutation: change in the genetic material of an organism

N

neutral wire: path back to the service panel

nitrogen: a chemical that is used to make protein

nitrogen cycle: the process that allows nitrogen to be reused again and again

nitrogen fixation: the process of converting nitrogen gas in the air into other nitrogen-containing substances

non-communicable disease: any disease that cannot be spread from one person to another (e.g. diabetes)

nuclear waste: highly radioactive products of nuclear reactions of power plants

nucleus: a special structure in some cell types that contains the genetic material

O

Occupational Health and Safety Act: laws ensuring safety in the workplace

ohm: unit for the resistance

ohmmeter: device used to measure the resistance

open circuit: an electrical path having a break in it; electrons do not flow through

organic matter: any matter derived from living organisms (e.g. excrement or bodies of dead plants and animals)

organism: an organism is a living thing

oxidation: the process in which a substance loses one or more electrons

oxidizing agent: a substance that gains one or more electrons

P

parallel circuit: a circuit providing many paths for electrons to flow

parasite: an organism that lives on or inside another living organism and gets its food from that organism

parts per million (ppm): units for exposure concentration; one ppm is one gram of solute in a million grams of solution

pathogen: something (generally micro-organisms) that enters your body, reproduces (makes more copies of itself), and causes you to become ill

pesticides: chemicals that kill pests, such as weeds or insects

pests: an insect which destroys crops or plants

photosynthesis: the process in which the sun's energy is used to change carbon dioxide, a gas in the air, to carbon-containing sugars

physiology: refers to the way the body of an organism works

plasma: a yellowish liquid made of water and dissolved chemicals in which all cells of the blood float

platelets: cells that form blood clots to seal a wound

population: a group of individuals of the same species

potable: drinkable

potential difference: measure of the energy per coulomb

potential energy: energy that is stored or energy that is not actually in use at the present moment

preservatives: chemicals that are added to food to control the growth of micro-organisms

producer: an organism that can make its own food

products: the substances you end up with after chemical reactions take place

protein: an important building block for the cells of most living things

protist: a micro-organism that is usually composed of only one cell with a cell nucleus; most protists undergo only asexual reproduction

protist algae: protists that are plant like

protozoa: protists that are animal like; usually have only one cell with a nucleus but no cell wall

public health standards: guidelines and laws that are prepared by government groups at the federal, provincial, and municipal level to ensure the safety of the public

R

rate of reaction: the speed at which a new substance is formed

reactants: the substances you start out with at the beginning of chemical reactions

red blood cells: the cells of the blood that carry oxygen to cells and take carbon dioxide away

redox reaction: a chemical reaction in which oxidation and reduction occur together involving an electron transfer

reducing agent: the substance that loses electrons

reduction: the process in which a substance gains one or more electrons

resistance: the measure of how easily current can flow through a material

resistant: to be able to withstand (e.g. a certain type of wheat is resistant to the fungus that causes wheat rust)

resistor: a material that is difficult for electrons to flow through

respiration: process in which carbon-containing substances such as sugars are broken down to release energy and carbon dioxide gas

S

sanitary landfill: large holes in the ground that we fill up with the things we throw away; garbage dumps

schematic diagram: a diagram that uses symbols to represent a set-up like a circuit

septic system: systems designed to treat the sewage of a single home

series circuit: a circuit that provides only one path for electrons to flow

service drops: conductors from the transformer that step down the voltage to 120/240 V service for your home, school, or workplace

service panel: the link between the main electrical service in your building and the electrical outlets in your house or apartment

sewage treatment plant: a facility in which sewage is treated and water purified before it is returned to the environment

sexual reproduction: reproduction that involves the exchange of genetic material

short circuit: occurs when electrons can get from the negative terminal of an energy source to the positive terminal, without flowing through a load or resistor

sludge: muddy or slimy sediment

species: a group of similar organisms that are capable of breeding with one another and producing offspring

specific defence: a defence that acts against only one pathogen (e.g. antibodies)

spleen: part of the immune system that produces and stores white blood cells and destroys foreign particles

spore: a special structure, similar to seeds, which allows the mould to spread to a new area

surge protectors: protect the devices connected to them from sudden increases in current

sustainability: an ecosystem's ability to support life and maintain resources for future generations

symptom: a change in our bodies that happens when we get a disease (e.g. some symptoms of a cold may be sneezing, runny nose, coughing, and aching)

T

tap changing under load (TCUL): method used by power companies in which taps automatically adjust the output voltage of the transformer to match a predetermined voltage

tonsils: part of the immune system that filters out pathogens and harmful chemicals and that produces white blood cells

toxicity: the ability of a substance to cause harmful effects

transformer: a device that transfers electric energy from one place to another using induction instead of conduction

turbine: the device that turns the generator, which produces the electricity

V

vaccination: an injection that protects you from getting a particular disease (e.g. many children receive a vaccination to protect them from getting measles)

vaccine: the substance that is injected into your body during a vaccination

vector: an organism that is infected by a pathogen but is not sick (*see* carrier)

virus: a micro-organism made up of only genetic material wrapped in protein molecules

volt: unit of the potential difference

voltmeter: a device used to measure the potential difference

W

wastewater: sewage

watt (W): unit of electric power

wet mount: the method of preparing a live sample for viewing with a microscope

white blood cells: a group of cells that perform different functions in the body (e.g. macrophages are a type of white blood cells)

WHMIS (Workplace Hazardous Materials Information System): Canada's standard method of communicating information about hazardous, or potentially harmful, chemicals

Y

yeast: fungi that are usually single round or oval cells

Index

Photograph Credits

Every effort has been made to find and to acknowledge correctly the sources of the material reproduced in this book. The publisher welcomes any information that will enable it to rectify, in subsequent editions, any errors or omissions.

COVER: From Left: Peter Beck/Firstlight.ca; Michael Newman/Photo Edit; Stephen Stickler/Stone/Getty Images.

Unit One Opener: Cindy Wilson/CP Photo Archive; Chapter One: 1.1 Left to right: Myrleen Ferguson Cate/PhotoEdit, MaXx Images/Ken Wardius, Michael Rosenfeld/Stone/Getty Images; 1.4 Courtesy of WHMIS; 1.5 Courtesy of WHMIS; 1.6 Courtesy of The Workers' Compensation Board of British Columbia; 1.7 Left to right: David Young-Wolff/PhotoEdit, Northern Light Images/Firstlight.ca, Andy Sacks/Stone/Getty Images; 1.8 Barry Cohen; 1.9 Courtesy of The Workers' Compensation Board of British Columbia and Praxair; 1.11 Courtesy of WSIB; 1.14 Ken Gigliotti/CP Photo Archive; 1.17 MaXx Images/Inga Spence; 1.18 Dupuis/Greenpeace; 1.19 Valastro/Greenpeace; 1.23 From Top left: MaXx Images/Omni Photography, Eyewire, MaXx Images, Gary Conner/PhotoEdit, Doug Scott/Firstlight.ca.; Chapter Two: 2.1 Left to right: Lester Lefkowitz/Firstlight.ca, Michael Newman/PhotoEdit, PhotoDisc; 2.4 Top to bottom: Barry Cohen, David Young-Wolff/PhotoEdit, David Young-Wolff/PhotoEdit, Barry Cohen; 2.6 Ken Doubleday/CP Photo Archive; 2.8 & 2.9 Patti McConville/The Image Bank/Getty Images; 2.13 Rudy Von Briel/PhotoEdit; 2.17 silver and tin images courtesy Al Léger; 2.20 Michael Newman/PhotoEdit; 2.21 Chuck Stoody/CP Picture Archive; 2.22 Courtesy of Compes Inernational; 2.29 Top to bottom: Liane Cary/Firstlight.ca, Tony Freeman/PhotoEdit; 2.31 Courtesy of Senco Sensors Inc.; 2.32 Left to right: Tony Bock/CP Photo Archive, Richard Kellaway/PCServices; 2.33 MaXx Images/NASA; 2.34 Jonathan Hayward/CP Photo Archive; 2.35 CP Photo Archive; 2.40 Top to bottom: Spencer Grant/ PhotoEdit, Spencer Grant/PhotoEdit, MaXx Images/ Erik Kamp, Spencer Grant/PhotoEdit, Spencer Grant/ PhotoEdit; 1A, Enrico Morelli, Barry Cohen; Chapter Three: 3.1 Left to right: Courtesy of OPG, Tony Freeman/Photo Edit; 3.10 Left to right: Bonnie Kamin/PhotoEdit; 3.19 © (1990 Richard Megna) Fundamental Photographs NYC; 3.21 Courtesy of OPG; 3.22 Courtesy of OCAA-Clean Living; 3.23 Courtesy of OPG; 3.30 Courtesy of Tracy Poole; 3.35 Barry Cohen; Chapter Four: 4.1 Clockwise: Mugshots/Firstlight.ca, Barry Cohen, MaXx Images/ZEFA Visual Media; 4.4 © The EnerGuide label and text is reproduced with permission of the Minister of Natural Resources, Canada 2001; 4.5 Left to right: Courtesy of UL Canada, Courtesy of CSA Group, Courtesy of UL Canada, Courtesy of Entela; 4.6 Michael Newman/PhotoEdit; 4.7B Don Smetzer/Getty Images; 4.9 Courtesy of Bill Shewan; 4.11 Courtesy of OPG; 4.12 Courtesy of Richard Dubois; 4.13 Eclipse Photography/Firstlight.ca; 4.14 Courtesy of Utopia; 4.15 MaXx Images/Craig Witkowski; 4.19 J.A. Wilkinson/VALAN PHOTOS; 4.28 MaXx Images/Rob Bartee; 4.30 Courtesy of Kevin McCormick/ Hydro One; 4.31 Courtesy of Kevin McCormick/Hydro One; 4.32 Jacques Boissinot/CP Photo Archive; 4.33 Ryan Remiorz/CP Photo Archive; 4.34 Courtesy of Emergency Preparedness Canada; 4.35 Courtesy of Kerry Chalmers; Unit Three Opener: Left to right: Michael Rosenfeld/Stone/Getty Images, Alfred Pasieka/Science Photo Library; Chapter Five: 5.1 Left to right: MaXx Images/John Burke, Mel Yates/FPG International/Getty Images, Peter Beck/Firstlight.ca; 5.2 MaXx Images; 5.3 Bruce Ayres/Stone/Getty Images; 5.4A) S. Lowry/Univ. Ulster/Stone/Getty Images; 5.4B) Professor David Hall/Science Photo Library; 5.5A) M. Peres/Custom Medical Stock Photo; 5.5B) J.L. Carson/Custom Medical Stock Photo; 5.6A) Custom Medical Stock Photo; 5.6B) Andrew Syred/Science Photo Library; 5.9 Chuck Savage/Firstlight.ca; 5.10 Left to right: Imagestate/Firstlight.ca, Chuck Stoody/CP Photo Archive, MaXx Images/Bonnie Lange; 5.19 David Atkinson/Stone/Getty Images; 5.20A) Andrew Syred/Science Photo Library; 5.20B) Dr. David Patterson/Science Photo Library; 5.22 Top to bottom: Eric Grave/Science Photo Library, R. Becker/Custom Medical Stock Photo; 5.26 Kevin Udahl/CP Photo Archive; 5.27 Top to bottom: Andrew Syred/Science Photo Library, Dr. Jeremy Burgess/Science Photo Library, Andrew Syred/Science Photo Library; 5.36 Food & Drug Administration/Science Photo Library; 5.38 Food & Drug Administration/Science Photo Library; 5.40 MaXx Images/Carol Guenzi Agents; 5.41 MaXx Images/Rudi Van Briel; 5.43A) J. Forsdyke/Gene Cox/Science Photo Library;

5.43C) S. Lowry/Univ. Ulster/Stone/Getty Images; 5.43D) Eric Grave/Science Photo Library; Chapter Six: 6.1 Clockwise: Imagestate/Firstlight.ca, Dick Luria/FPG International/Getty Images, Scott Spiker/Firstlight.ca; 6.4 Bill Van Aken/CSIRO/Science Photo Library; 6.6 David Woodfall/Stone/Getty Images; 6.7 David Young-Wolff/PhotoEdit; 6.8 Robert Lankinen/Firstlight.ca; 6.9 Bill Stormont/Firstlight.ca; 6.10 Adam Hart-Davis/Science Photo Library; 6.11 Esbin-Anderson/Firstlight.ca; 6.12A) Astrid & Harris – Frieder Michler/Science Photo Library; 6.12B) Dr. Jeremy Burgess/Science Photo Library; 6.12C) Astrid & Harris – Frieder Michler/Science Photo Library; 6.13 Max Nash/CP Photo Archive; 6.15 U-AT/Firstlight.ca; 6.16 Martin Rogers/Stone/Getty Images; 6.22 B & D Productions/Firstlight.ca; 6.23 Top to bottom: MaXx Images/Great American Stock, Joaquim Vila/Firstlight.ca; 6.24 Clockwise: MaXx Images/Sylvia Bissonnette, MaXx Images/Tom Vano, Mugshots/Firstlight.ca, MaXx Images/Omni Photo Communications; 6.25 Michael Newman/PhotoEdit; 6.26 John Millar/Stone/Getty Images; 6.27 MaXx Images/Peter Ardito; 6.28 Top to bottom: David Young-Wolff/PhotoEdit, Michael Newman/PhotoEdit; 6.29 Premium Stock/Firstlight.ca; 6.33 Courtesy of Colin Francis; 6.34 Chronis Jons/Stone/Getty Images; 6.36 Custom Medical Stock Photo; 6.37 Ken Chernus/FPG International/Getty Images; 6.39 David Kelly Crow/PhotoEdit; C1 M.J. Cardenas Productions/ The Image Bank/Getty Images.Unit Four Opener: MaXx Images/Alan Bolesta; Chapter Seven: 7.1 Clockwise: Color Day Production/The Image Bank/ Getty Images, Michael Newman/PhotoEdit, Roger Wright/Stone/Getty Images; 7.3A) Custom Medical Stock Photo; 7.3B) Science Photo Library; 7.4 NMSB/Custom Medical Stock Photo; 7.5 PhotoDisc; 7.7 Bettman/CORBIS/MAGMA; 7.8 MaXx Images/ Michael Howell; 7.9 Top to bottom: Science Photo Library/Custom Medical Stock Photo, Creasource/ Firstlight.ca, PhotoDisc; 7.10 Top to bottom: Mad Cow Studio/Firstlight.ca, Mark Clarke/Science Photo Library, Reggie Parker/FPG International/Getty Images; 7.19 Charles Gupton/Firstlight.ca; 7.22 Dr. P. Marazzi/Science Photo Library; 7.27 Ross Whitaker/ FPG International/Getty Images; 7.29 Dr. P. Marazzi/Science Photo Library; 7.30 Custom Medical Stock Photo; 7.31 Left to right: Bettman/CORBIS/MAGMA, Archivo Iconografico, S.A./CORBIS/MAGMA, Bettman/CORBIS/MAGMA; Chapter Eight: 8.1 Clockwise: Michael Newman/PhotoEdit, Michael Newman/PhotoEdit; Stephen Stickler/Stone/Getty Images; 8.5 Imagestate/Firstlight.ca; 8.7 Eric Grave/Science Photo Library; 8.9 Fitzharris/Firstlight.ca; 8.10 Left to right: Premium Stock/Firstlight.ca, Iwago/Firstlight.ca; 8.12 Logical Images/Custom Medical Stock Photography; 8.14 Eyewire; 8.15 Top to bottom: MaXx Images/Peter Ardito, Premium Stock/Firstlight.ca; 8.16 St. Mary's Hospital Medical School/Science Photo Library; 8.17 John Durham/Science Photo Library; 8.19 Josa Luis Pelaez/Firstlight.ca; 8.23 It Stock/Firstlight.ca; 8.24 Imagestate/Firstlight.ca; 8.25 MaXx Images/Chip Henderson; 8.26 Mark Richards/PhotoEdit; 8.30 Steve Skjold/PhotoEdit; 8.35 John Durham/Science Photo Library; 1D Clockwise: Rob Allen/Firstlight.ca, Imagestate/Firstlight.ca, Imagestate/Firstlight.ca, Roger Ball/Firstlight.ca.; Unit Five Opener: MaXx Images/ Jeff Bray; Chapter Nine: 9.1 Left to right: Yokohama/Firstlight.ca, Werner Otto/Stone/Getty Images; 9.12 MaXx Images/Frank Staub; 9.14 Massimo Mastrorillo/Firstlight.ca; 9.15 Left to right: David Nunuk/Firstlight.ca; MaXx Images/Roger Leo; 9.16 MaXx Images/Jim McNee; 9.17 Left to right: PhotoDisc, Custom Medical Stock Photo, MaXx Images/Walter Biikow; 9.18 MaXx Images/Robert Franz; 9.19 Peter Yates/Science Photo Library; 9.22 Left to right: Eyewire, Dennis Bueckart/CP Photo Archive; 9.23 Left to right: Jack Smith/CP Photo Archive, Ben Osborne/Stone/Getty Images; 9.24 Left to right: Bonnie Kamin/Photo Edit, Jacques Janqoux/Stone/Getty Images; 9.25 Left to right: Joe Gibbons/CP Photo Archive, B & C Alexander/Firstlight.ca; 9.28 Top to bottom: Brian Milne/Firstlight.ca, MaXx Images/Phil Cantor; Chapter Ten: 10.1 Left to right: J. DeVisser/IVY IMAGES, MaXx Images/Pat Canova; 10.3 Left to right: Michael Lea/CP Photo Archive, Jordi Cami/Firstlight.ca; David Forbert/Superstock; 10.4 Left to right: Minden Pictures/Firstlight.ca, Minden Pictures/Firstlight.ca; 10.5 Tom Bean/Firstlight.ca; 10.6 MaXx Images/Kevin Beebe; 10.9 Left to right: MaXx Images/James Prout, MaXx Images/Peggy Koyle; 10.12 MaXx Images/Grant Heilman Photography; 10.15 MaXx Images/Elfie Kluck; 10.17 Mugshots/Firstlight.ca; 10.18 Alan Davis; 10.21 MaXx Images/Eric Figge; 10.22 MaXx Images/ Chris Lowe; 10.23 John Edwards/Stone/Getty Images; 10.25 Henry Diltz/CORBIS/MAGMA.